UNDERSTAND
YOUR BRAIN:
For A Change

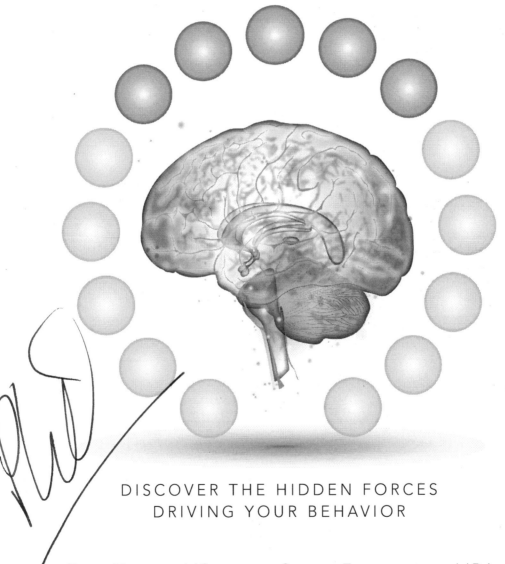

DISCOVER THE HIDDEN FORCES
DRIVING YOUR BEHAVIOR

Phil Dixon, MSc with Scott Fitzgerald, MBA

OBI PRESS

OBI Press
Oxford, North Carolina, USA

ISBN-13: 978-1-7338307-1-3

Second edition 10 9 8 7 6 5 4 3 2 1 1

Understand Your Brain: For a Change
Part of a Series

This book, *Understand Your Brain: For a Change*, is the first in a multi-part series.

This book is mostly background theory. The others in the series address the application of that theory in day-to-day life.

The first part of the book addresses the fundamentals of the brain and how it works; the second part looks at the Self, i.e., you.

So this contains the basic understandings required for reading the rest of the series.

The specific contents of this volume are listed in the Table of Contents

The working titles for the next two books in the series are:

> *A Field Guide to Using Your Brain at Work*
> *A Field Guide to Using Your Brain at Home*

These books will take what you have learned in this book and apply it at four levels, namely:

1. When you are on your own.

2. When you are with another person, e.g., a work peer or significant other.

3. When you are with a small group of people, e.g., a work team or your family.

4. When you are with a large group of people, e.g., your organization or your community.

The fourth book in the series will be:

> *A Field Guide to Using Your Brain as a Coach*

Scott and I plan to have these next three books published late 2019 or early 2020.

Happy reading!

Heads up! Warning! Watch out! Do not try this at home!

This book is based on research and the opinions of me, Phil Dixon, its primary author. It is intended to provide interesting and helpful information about the brain and the self as it relates to generating positive change.

To the best of my research abilities, the information is accurate at the time of publication.

Table of Contents

Some Strategies for Reading this Book

Our brains like choices or options. So, here's your first choice. There are a couple of ways you can read this book.

Option 1: The obvious approach is to read from front to back, starting here. I have written it so that it flows best that way.

Option 2: Option 1 means that you will read about background topics that I think are important like why I wrote it, the state of leadership development, neuroscience, scientific discoveries, acknowledgments, dedications – things like that. I think they will add to the enjoyment of your read, but I would also fully understand if this is not your cup of tea. If that is the case, jump ahead and go to page 23 where the meat of the book starts. So, Option 2 is to leap ahead.

Option 3: Options 1 and 2 rely on a sequential approach. Option 3 is a more ad-hoc approach. Go back to the Table of Contents and select topics that intrigue you and jump straight to those topics. For some people's brains, this is the most exciting way to read a book. For others, this drives them crazy.

Just some options for you to choose from. If you want a recommendation then I, of course, would recommend Option 1.

This page intentionally left blank

Section A.
A Few Notes Up Front to Set the Stage

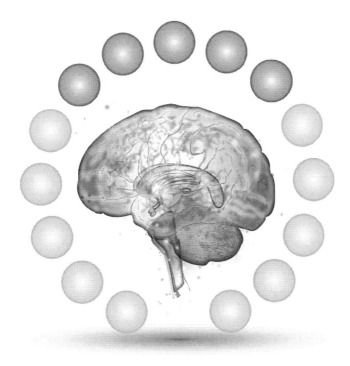

This is what is in Section A.

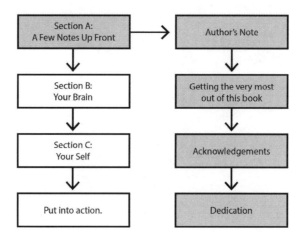

Section A Part 1: Introduction

In this book, you will learn some amazing things about you and your brain. Things that will change how you deal with the world on a day-to-day basis. For example, and you may have a tough time believing this right now, the majority of the decisions that you make are done by your brain without you being consciously aware of them. Who knew? This is just one example of many things that will come as a surprise to you as you *Understand Your Brain*.

Before we jump in, however, a couple of words about me and why I felt compelled to write a book about the brain, change, and leadership. Starting at Apple in the early days of the 1980s, I have been teaching leadership, doing executive coaching, and helping people and teams go through change for over thirty years. About ten years ago, as part of a Master's program at Oxford Said Business School and HEC Paris, I was exposed to the neuroscience of the brain. And learning about the brain caused me to change the way I helped people at a fundamental level. Over the next year or so, I changed all of my programs, classes, and lectures so that they included the latest research on the brain. I co-authored a paper on the neuroscience of giving feedback. And I founded a company that focuses solely on teaching people to understand their brains so that they can become better leaders, team members, and citizens.

Then I had requests for a book that covered exactly what I was teaching and talking about. This is it.

The next twenty pages or so address some of my comments on change, why I felt I needed to write the book, why this book, some overall context, how you might go about reading it, some thoughts on leadership, some thoughts on neuroscience, some disclaimers, and some general advice. Some brains really like knowing what is going to get covered and why. They want the background detail. For other people, that background detail is not nearly as important.

Now, personally speaking, I think that the notes here are thought-provoking, useful, and, in some cases, reasonably witty. ☺ But if your brain doesn't like or need that background detail, then please jump to Section B (**page 23**) where we get down to business and start to talk about the brain. On the other hand, you will never know what you missed!!

<u>Some Comments on the Brain's Struggles</u>

You probably think that you are in control of your thoughts, decisions, and actions. Well, sorry to shatter your illusions, but you are not. Your brain is. You can blame it for pretty much everything. It does your thinking for you, your feeling for you, it controls your actions and reactions … and everything in between. You are even aware of some of the things it does but not many!

Internally, however, it is engaging in a number of constant struggles. Here are some of them:

> ➢ the struggle between reacting quickly out of fear and controlling that fear reaction
> ➢ the struggle between your conscious thoughts and your nonconscious thoughts
> ➢ the struggle between your rational thinking and your emotions and feelings

> ➢ the struggle between how you react when you are alert and awake and how you react when you are tired and sleepy
> ➢ the struggle between your innate biases and socially acceptable behavior
> ➢ the struggle between different parts of your personality
> ➢ the struggle between your old habits and the new ones that you are trying to put into place as part of a change

You will meet and learn about all of these struggles as we journey through this book.

Some Fundamental Premises

I know that it is almost a cliché to say that we're all different. "Well," you say, "of course we are."

But that is the first fundamental premise of the book. We are all different. But that difference comes roaring to the forefront when we start to look at the brain. We all have the same components and structures in our brain (well, most of us do, but that's a different story and a different book), and yet what happens to our brain as it absorbs life's experiences makes us all unique. Advice columns, self-help books, and how-to guides rarely, if ever, take those differences into account. Yet, understanding the differences in and uniqueness of your brain and making you into an expert on your brain are what will increase the chance of you changing and possibly increasing your effectiveness, happiness, and health.

I have always had a mistrust of books that preach, "… this is how to … *[fill in the blank]."* Whether it be how to manage time, how to write a book, how to get rich, or how to get divorced, the advice always seems to be slanted towards what worked for the advice-giver with the underlying assumption that what worked for them will work for you. In my case, that has always proven to be wrong. Very wrong in the case of the four topics I mentioned. I have tried many time management systems, and none of them worked until I developed my own. We all think, work, and change differently. Some writers suggest that in order to write a book like the one you are currently reading, then you have to start early in the day and produce at least four pages a day. Get a regime. Start at the same time every day. On one occasion, this worked for me. On this occasion, it didn't. So, not only are we different from other people, but we are different than who we were last year, last month, last week, yesterday, and, even possibly, a few hours ago.

So, in these two volumes I am going to say out loud to you that YOU are different – and all I can do is offer you a number of ingredients to help you understand yourself, ingredients that you may be able to select and blend into something that works for you. I offer you some models, tools, and techniques that have worked for many other people. There's a good chance that they will work for you.

The second fundamental premise of this book is that you are operating exactly the way you are designed to operate and the results you are getting are often perfectly aligned with that of your behaviors. Many of our clients work with an assumption that there is something wrong with them because they tend react to a threat in an emotional manner. If we can sway the "inner critic" from *being judgmental* to *being inquisitive,* it opens the door to a more creative journey to effectively understand your brain – for a change! ☺

I am a very serious Pink Floyd fan. Now that's a statement that I bet you never thought you would read in the first pages of a serious book about the brain and change. Nor did I until I was reading a bookazine (yes, that is now a word) on the 45th anniversary celebration of the release of "Dark Side of the Moon." Hang in there with me, now. There is a point to this. In an interview with Roger Waters, Carol Clerk asks a question about the song "Time"* to which Roger answers:

> *"... (the point of the song) is actually about understanding your own autonomy."*

He follows this with a couple of poignant sentences:

> *"I suddenly realized at 29 that I had been fulfilling someone else's prophecy. I was programmed by my childhood and education into believing that I was preparing for a life that was going to start later. It was never explained to me as a child that I was actually, moment by moment, in it."*

So, that's the third fundamental premises of this book. It is your life, and it is happening now!

And the results of these three fundamental premises are that when you realize that you are different, that you decide to take control of this life, and that you want to understand and become an expert on yourself, then it will probably result in some degree of change. Oh, yes. Back to that word "change" again.

Why I Wrote This Book

My interest in the application of neuroscience to leadership, management, teams, and change started many years ago although I wasn't aware of it at the time. My initial studies at university were theoretical chemistry and computer science, but I always had a keen interest in the management and leadership side of my profession.

After university, I attended my first management training program at the ripe old age of 21 and have been on at least one training session every year since then. Yet, with all that learning, one thing has always puzzled me. There were so many things that a manager and/or a leader was supposed to know and do. How was it possible for any one person to be capable of correctly doing them all?

Later, I attended a leadership training program and realized that in addition, people had to distinguish between being a manager and a leader with supposedly two overlapping but different sets of skills to master. Later in my career, I came across the Lominger competencies and was totally shocked. Sixty-seven of them! And that was just the start! How could I remember all of these? As a manager/leader it seemed that I needed to study for a degree in order to even be a manager, let alone a leader. It was overwhelming. So much so that at one time I developed a program entitled "So You Want to be a Manager?" It was deliberately aimed at turning people away from the idea of becoming a manager and a leader. My observation was that it was too hard, and most people were not that good at it.

Then, in the early 80s, I started to question why some teams worked well and other teams didn't. What was the difference between the two? I went to HR, and they didn't know. I kept looking for something that was more foundational than the theories of leadership and teams that were being taught at the time. I was searching for something that lay beneath all of these skills, attributes, requirements, and competencies. I reasoned, to myself and anyone who would listen, that there had to be something more

---

*For those of you who may not know the song, you can find the lyrics by doing a simple Google search.

fundamental than all of these competencies and attributes. What was the "secret sauce" or "connective tissue" that lay underneath everything? If we cracked that, then maybe we could better understand management and leadership. I started my quest for what I dubbed "The Leadership Genome."

In addition, I was amazed and disappointed that the fields of leadership, management, training & development, coaching, organization development – and there are many more areas of study that are applicable – produced thousands of theories, books, and papers every year, but there seemed to have been little improvement in the overall quality of leaders and managers that we were producing. If anything, I think the quality has gone down rather than up over the past several decades. Now, I know that some people, especially those in the leadership industry, will dispute that statement. I soon discovered that this was not just my own observations and opinions; there were other people out there who agreed. Let me cite just one: Jeffrey Pfeffer, one of the leading experts on leadership development.[1] Pfeffer opines:

"How can this be – all this failure (of leadership) – after the thousands of leadership books, talks, blogs, classes, and leadership-development programs seeking to make leaders more effective? How can this be, after more than a century of research seeking to figure out how to select better leaders?" (p 2).

He continues by saying:

" … I lay out evidence demonstrating four things: (1) the leadership industry is large and prominent, but, notwithstanding its magnitude and reach, (2) workplaces in the United States and around the world are, for the most part (as there are obviously exceptional places on "best places to work" lists), filled with dissatisfied, disengaged employees who do not trust their leaders; (3) leaders at all levels lost their jobs at an increasingly fast pace, in part because they are unprepared for the realities of organizational life, and thus (4) the leadership industry has failed and continues to fail in its task of producing leaders who are effective and successful, and it has even failed to produce sufficient talent to fill leadership vacancies."

Jeffrey cites Barbara Kellerman, a published author on leadership and lecturer on leadership at Harvard Kennedy School:

"… the leadership industry has failed over its roughly forty-year history to, in any major, meaningful, measurable way, improve the human condition."

and

"… the rise of leadership as an object of our collective fascination has coincided precisely with the decline of leadership in our collective estimation."

I felt somewhat better that I was in good company, but that discovery just confirmed my conclusions that we must be doing something very wrong. There's an old adage that says that the definition of insanity is doing the same thing again and again and expecting a different result. That was my experience in the leadership development field. We just kept doing the same old thing, or slight variants of it, and expecting different results.

I was looking for something completely different. In 2009 and 2010, I was studying for my Master's degree and, for the first time, was exposed to the neuroscience of the brain. I was immediately fascinated and realized that, just maybe, this was the

"Leadership Genome" that I had been looking for. The brain! The organ that underlies it all.

During that introduction to the neuroscience of the brain, I decided that I would use a brain-based approach to all of the work that I did with regard to leadership development, team building, coaching, etc. I re-wrote all of my material and was lucky enough to spend a lot of time during the following years with some of the leading thinkers in the field of neuroscience.

I have become convinced that a possible solution to the frustration that Jeffrey Pfeffer and many others, including myself, have voiced about the failure of the leadership development industry may lie in the failure (or absence) of teaching leaders about the neuroscience of the brain.

Since those early days, I have spoken to many audiences and teams using the brain as the basis for discussions. Many times, people would come up after the session and ask for the name of a book that covers the material that I had presented. While I could (and did) give them many references, there were no books that I could find that fully aligned with my approach. Some had too much detail and others not quite enough. None blended the neuroscience with practical application to day-to-day situations.

So, this is another reason that I decided to write my own. In this book, I hope to have redressed that balance between not enough detail and too much.

There's an additional reason why the brain is the focus of the book. Everything we do, everything we think, every action we take, every reaction we have...they all start in the brain. Every act in humankind's history, for good or bad, has started in someone's brain. Every act you take as an individual, as a partner in a relationship, as a peer at work, as a boss, as a subordinate, as a member of a team, or as a leader of an organization...they all started in your brain.

So, what about the change aspect of the book? Why not just write a book about the brain? I have been fascinated with what makes people change for many decades. My research and thesis in my Master's degree were about the factors that cause managers to change after they have received feedback. In addition to that long desire to understand change, there was a recent set of articles in *Harper's Magazine* [2] that caught my attention and summarized a predicament that we face today in our world. I will cite the first few sentences of the article:

> "'Progress is impossible without change,' George Bernard Shaw wrote in 1944, 'and those who cannot change their minds cannot change anything. But progress through persuasion has never seemed harder to achieve. Political segregation has made many Americans inaccessible, even unimaginable, to those on the other side of the political divide. On the rare occasions when we do come face-to-face, it is not clear what we could say to change each other's minds or reach a worthwhile compromise. Psychological research has shown that humans fail to process facts that conflict with our preexisting world views. The stakes are simply too high: our self-worth and identity are entangled with our beliefs – and with those who share them. The weakness of logic as a tool of persuasion, combined with the urgency of the political moment, can be paralyzing.'"

The series of articles then goes on to examine what activities might bring about a change of mind. Violence? Protest? Reason? Money? Music? Loved ones? Data? These were the eye-catching headlines on the front cover.

The thoughts expressed in that introductory paragraph frightened me …

> *"… persuasion has never been harder to achieve."*

and

> *"… it is not clear what we could say to change each other's minds or reach a worthwhile compromise."*

I hope that I might do my little bit by writing about what goes on when we are faced with a change and, just maybe, increase the chance of you changing your own mind or finding what to say to help change someone else's mind.

And it's not going to get any easier. In the 1920s, Max Born, a scientist of the same standing (but less well-known) as Einstein, predicted that "we had reached the end of certainty." [3] His thinking and predictions proved to be amazingly prescient.

In addition, I think that we are going to need to face change at an increasingly rapid rate. In his book, [4] Bob Johansen, the CEO of the Institute for the Future, states it very clearly:

> *"The VUCA World of volatility, uncertainty, complexity, and ambiguity will get worse in the future."*

As you will come to see, the brain hates those conditions. It wants predictability not uncertainty. It doesn't like ambiguity. It likes simplicity. Maybe if we can understand a little more about why the brain has these needs and the impact of a VUCA world on the brain, we might be better equipped to face our individual and collective futures.

An Objective for You, the Reader

I have one main objective for you as a result of reading this book:

> ➢ *By getting to know your brain, you will be in a better position to get in touch with what motivates all of your thoughts, actions, and reactions so that you can become more effective, happier, and maybe healthier.*

In order to do this, I believe that you need two things:

> ➢ *Just enough knowledge about how brains work, in general, and how your brain works in particular.*
> ➢ *An understanding of how to apply that knowledge to your life and its inevitable challenges and changes.*

I have attempted to write these the books with just the right amount of theoretical knowledge about your brain so that you can apply what you are learning in a practical way to your daily life, both work and social.

In many cases, the examples and much of the terminology I use in this book are oriented towards the life of a leader or manager in a business, but, in many ways, we are all leaders so I believe that much of what is contained in the book is applicable to all of our daily lives. It is applicable to anyone that has a brain. ☺

Why This Book in Particular?

But why write this book? Or should I say, yet another book? I know there is a small section just a couple of pages back on why I wrote it. But that was about me. That was more about how I came to write it. I wrote this book with the following thoughts in mind (or should we say, brain ☺):

> ➢ I have a fundamental belief that as we all start to understand our own brains and those of other people, we can start to understand behavior that would otherwise leave us puzzled.

> ➢ As I contemplated writing the book, President Obama announced that he was going to push Congress to spend $100 billion on brain research. The brain is becoming mainstream…people even have started talking about it at cocktail parties. Maybe this book can help although, personally, I generally like to steer clear of cocktail parties. ☺

> ➢ It is my belief that with the new things that we are learning about the brain, we just might have a new tool to address the leadership issue. In using the understandings of the brain, maybe we can make better leaders. And better teams. And maybe in the process we can make each of us a little more effective and a little happier. Maybe we can influence some of the dysfunction and chaos that seems to be churning around us at the moment.

Some Brief Comments About Leadership

Leaders think and influence others for a living, often in environments of stress, pressure, and ambiguity – even more so these days in the new VUCA* world. It does not matter whether we are talking about business leaders, political leaders, school leaders, church leaders, scout leaders, or any other type of leader. Every leader in each of these contexts faces similar challenges: how do I get more done for less, how do I make sense of what's going on, how do I make decisions, how do I help others make decisions, and so on. This is just a start: the list of what a leader is required to do and know goes on and on. As I mentioned in my earlier comments, there are literally thousands of books that list, in excruciating detail, all of the competencies that a leader needs to have.

With the brain operating as the control center of everything you do – what you think and feel, how you choose your focus, and how you understand, react to, behave with, and relate to others – your brain is your single most valuable resource. As such, understanding your brain is no longer something that is interesting or nice to have but is an imperative. This is true for all of us but particularly so for people in leadership roles.

Some More Context

The next few paragraphs give me the opportunity to offer a few more detailed comments about context, to provide a few more remarks about my intent, and to give a few general caveats. If you have no interest in this type of topic and have decided that you have had enough background, then now would be a good time to skip to the next section.

---

*VUCA = Volatility, Uncertainty, Chaos, Ambiguity

Let us start with why I believe that a brain-based approach is extremely important. As I mentioned earlier, about ten years ago I was privileged to be able to study for a Master's program called "Coaching for Change" [5] It addressed how people change as individuals, how teams change, and how organizations change. The program offered a wide variety of viewpoints at each of these levels. Some resonated with me and some left me quite cold. One of the viewpoints presented, however, changed everything. As I mentioned earlier, it was "The Brain as the Fundamental Leadership Genome!"

Even though I had been in the business of coaching, counseling, and consulting to change for the previous twenty-five years, this brain-based approach explained a lot. It explained why some of the approaches that I, and many other consultants like me, had been using were effective or not. Mostly by accident, I had indeed taken into account some ways in which the brain works.

A brain-based approach also explained why some – rather too many if I am truly honest – of my approaches had failed. In these instances, I had failed to align my approach with the way in which the brain functions. In retrospect, I am very surprised at how lucky I was that any of the approaches worked at all given how little most of us knew about what was going on at the biological level of the brain.

Since those early days of learning about the brain, I have spent a great deal of time learning as much as I can about the brain from all sorts of perspectives. I now use a brain-based approach in all of my professional engagements and, to a large degree, in my social life. It seems to help. Even if I explain just a small amount about how the brain works to people, I often receive responses based on the overall theme, "Oh that explains... [*fill in the blank*]," and it has amazed me how long those people remember and apply those small pieces of knowledge. The understanding of the brain and the application of that knowledge seems to be highly "sticky." On the other hand, I really do try not to bore people at dinners and cocktail parties (those that I do go to)!

It seems, therefore, that the bottom line is this: using the fundamentals of the brain as a starting point to our understanding of leadership seems to work. It seems to explain a lot that, hitherto, was shrouded in mystery.

Neuroscience and Other Things

Talking of neuroscience, the very word causes some people to roll their eyes and head for the hills. Let me take this opportunity to state that I have no intent in this book to attempt to provide lots of detailed explanatory diagrams about the brain with a multitude of Latin names. At least no more than I have to. It was the one thing that put me off when I started reading in this field. Most books start with a detailed diagram of the brain. That is almost like giving a detailed diagram of the central computer of a car when all you are trying to do is learn how to drive the thing.

I am convinced that most of us do not need to know that level of detail about the brain. Rather, we need to know the impact of what is going on in the brain and what we need to do with that knowledge. So, you will only find a few Latin or scientific names in this book, the ones that are really, really necessary. If you want to know more, then I have provided references where you can read greater detail about the brain to your heart's (or your brain's) content.

There is a debate, especially when there is a group of scientists (neuro or otherwise), that if something cannot be scientifically or rigorously "proven" then it should not be considered as part of the discussion. I do not take such a strict view: if something has been included as part of the general framework of scientific opinion, then that is great. I like that and will use it.

Additionally, if something appears to work, seems to have some wide applicability and appears to be useful, I will include that too. To the pure scientist, its validity may still have to be proven to their satisfaction. I believe that if something seems to be useful and makes reasonable sense, it informs the debate even if it has not been rigorously proved valid. Of course, the difference between the two needs to be identified in any written material.

Let me illustrate the difference. Several years ago, Dr. Evian Gordon developed a model of the brain that he called the 1-2-4 model. Dr. Gordon has been in the neuroscience field for over thirty years. His model, albeit on the surface very simple, is the result of the integration of hundreds, if not thousands, of other brain models and ideas. Each of these other models was subject to the rigor of the scientific process. It is reasonable to think, therefore, that the 1-2-4 model has a sound scientific foundation.

In this book, I use a construct that looks at threats and rewards using five categories. Let's call it the 5 P's model. While there is a large amount of scientific evidence behind all of the facets in these five categories, the categories and elements that comprise them have not been subjected to the same degree of rigor as, for example, the 1-2-4 model. The 5 P's model does seem, however, to provide a good foundation for our thinking. The model has proven over the past several years to be extremely useful to many people in a wide variety of settings.

A final comment upon the scientific debate and terminology. There are some scientists (and some non-scientists) who will want to point out that some of what I address in this book is not in fact "neuroscience" but is "psychology." To be truthful, I don't know exactly where one ends and the other begins. There are also new terms springing up on a regular basis, for example, "neuropsychology," "neuropsychotherapy," and even "neurodharma." For my purposes in this book, I do not believe that the distinction is important. What is important is that we understand the overall concepts and know how to leverage that knowledge in our day-to-day lives. Whether the information came as a result of a neuroscientist's work last month or a psychologist's work two decades ago is irrelevant if the end result is useful.

What is important is the concept of "integrative." This term was introduced to me by Dr. Evian Gordon through the concept of "integrative neuroscience." [6] As I understand it, this concept implies that multiple views of a subject and adjacent subjects are integrated into a holistic view. For example, the cover of Evian Gordon's book identifies the following subjects as being included in the book: philosophy, evolution, anatomy, dynamics, neurons, physiology, imaging, psychiatry, psychology, neurology, psychotherapy, and computer models. That is what this book is intended to do - integrate the knowledge from neuroscience, psychology, leadership development, and any other subjects that help us understand what is going on!

Lastly, in the same Master's program that I referred to earlier, I was introduced to the term "pracademic" which I have used on many occasions since.* The intent of the term is to refer to someone who offers a balance between the rigor behind an academic approach and the pragmatic, practical approach of someone who has to take an action

---

*I met Irwin Turbitt who was then at the Business School at the University of Warwick. He was a guest speaker at my Master's Program and spoke about adaptive leadership and how he had applied it in order to solve "the troubles" in Belfast. He coined and introduced me to the term "pracademic" for which I give him many thanks.

as a result of the learning. This is the approach that I intend to offer in this book. I have read many of the scientific papers and books so that you don't have to. ☺

To summarize, I hope that this book offers a balance between academic rigor and useful and practical application in a manner which integrates many fields of knowledge.

Some Disclaimers

The Mind:

When discussing the brain, we can rapidly reach the philosophical morass of the differences between the mind and the brain. I am not going to go down that path. It's too open-ended and too large of a problem for me to tackle here. There are lots of experts, much better qualified than me, that have published on this topic. A Google search will give you many, many results.

Scientific Discovery:

Throughout the book you, will read statements like "It appears that…" or "It is thought that…" in connection with my comments about the brain. The current wave of research about the brain and the application of that research is still in its early stages. While researchers and practitioners like myself are starting to understand many parts of the brain, we are probably only scratching the surface. New discoveries are being made every day. Some of these discoveries support what we think we know about the brain. On the other hand, some discoveries are disproving what we thought we knew. Hence, when I write a phrase such as "We believe that…" or "It appears that…" or "Research indicates that…," I am allowing for the fact that we may find new knowledge that changes what we think today. It is very difficult to get a scientist to state categorically that something is true, especially in the field of neuroscience. Hence, why I use phrases that allow for something new to be discovered which might cause my opinions to change. It is an exciting time to be following this field of research and, occasionally, ambiguous and frustrating.

Limitations of Brain Research:

There is no doubt that brain research is in full-swing. I was recently told that there are over 100,000 neuroscientists engaged in full-time research. Whether true or not, I don't know. If it is true and each of them published just one research paper per year, then you would have to read nearly 300 papers per day to keep up! And that's not counting the backlog of papers that have been published over the past two or three decades nor other references. You get the picture.

Wait. It's actually a lot tougher than that. I wrote that paragraph some time back. Mlodinov (don't even try to pronounce it) reports: [7]

"In 2017, for example, there were more than three million new scientific papers."

Three million! Now, some of those are not in fields that are relevant to this topic, but many are. And finding them either got easier or harder depending on which way you look at it:

"That rate of production isn't just greater than the practitioners in any field can assimilate; it is greater than the journals can contain. As a result, in the decade between

2004 and 2014, publishers had to create more than five thousand new scientific journals just to accommodate the overflow."

That's the really good news. There's lots of research being done. Some of it confirms other research that has been published already. Some of it starts to challenge prior research. We shouldn't be surprised. That's the way it is with scientific research. It confirms, it builds, or it refutes. So, when we start to look at brain research, we have to remember that it is still in its early stages, and some of what we believe to be true may be proven not to be. And some of what has not yet been researched will turn out to give vital clues as we move forward.

As a closely related example of this, I was recently in a private conversation with a plastic surgeon focused on breast reconstruction in women. He was saying that just five years ago, there was one gene that was identified as possibly causing breast cancer. Now over sixty have been identified.

When I was studying computer sciences in the late sixties, our professor, John Buxton, suggested that, at that time, the state of computer science was the equivalent of steam engines in the 1820s. The computer, like steam engines, mostly worked, but occasionally it blew up and no one knew why. The good news was that it didn't kill many people.

Similarly, we have to be careful in where we take the interpretation of brain research today. We are probably still where the steam engine was in the 1820s. ☺

That is, when the research is good quality research, the results and claims are limited in scope, the results, conclusions, and claims are reasonably interpreted, and they are objectively reported in the scientific and public media. Unfortunately, there are many cases where one or more of these is not true, so we need to be doubly wary.

There have been a number of books that have been published over the past decade that have started to shine a light on the poorer quality research. They warn of published research that reaches conclusions that are based on a handful of cases. These studies are then picked up by the mass media and all of a sudden become truths or myths.

But wait. It gets worse. It has been shown that almost all articles having a scientific bent to them and showing a picture of the brain or including some reference to "neuro-something" are seen as being true by the lay public. It still remains a case of caveat emptor.

In addition, like all good science, not all researchers agree. The best, and somewhat tongue-in-cheek illustration of this, is simply by looking at the titles of two books *You Are Not Your Brain* [8] and *We Are Our Brains.* [9]

So, by way of an overall caveat at the end of this opening section, while I have done my best to sort the wheat from the chaff in the way of research, please use your own judgments. I have included many references. If you trust me, then don't bother reading them. I spent many years of my life doing so, so that you wouldn't have to. If you don't trust me or are just curious, then please follow up the references.

[1] Pfeffer, J. (2105). Leadership BS: Fixing Workplaces and Careers One Truth at a Time. Harper Business.

[2] FORUM: The Minds of Others: The art of persuasion in the age of Trump. (2018, February). Harpers Magazine, 27–36.

[3] Greenspan, N. T. (2005). The End of the Certain World: The Life and Science of Max Born. Basic Books.

[4] Johansen, B. (2012). Leaders Make the Future: (2nd ed.). Berrett-Koehler Publishers.

[5] https://www.sbs.ox.ac.uk/programmes/consulting-and-coaching-change

[6] Gordon, E. (2000). Integrative Neuroscience: Bringing Together Biological, Psychological and Clinical Models of the Human Brain. CRC Press.

[7] Mlodinow, L. (2018). Elastic: Flexible Thinking in a Time of Change. Pantheon.

[8] Schwarz, J. (2012). You Are Not Your Brain. Avery.

[9] Swaab, D. F. (2014). We Are Our Brains: A Neurobiography of the Brain, from the Womb to Alzheimer's. (J. Hedley-Prole, Trans.) (1st ed.). Spiegel & Grau.

Section A Part 2: Getting the Very Most Out of This Book

Each of us approaches our tasks in slightly different ways, and it is impossible to say what is best for everyone. There are way too many factors involved. However, there are some common factors that seem to apply so here's a few suggestions that you might want to consider as you go about reading this book:

1. Write It Down!

Keep a pen or a pencil with you as you read. Write in the book.* If an idea gets triggered or you think of something that you might want to do, scribble a note in the margin. One author I read recently summed it up well:

> *"…even the faintest pencil is better than the strongest memory."*

It's what the brain needs. Write it down then and there. Highlight what you like. Write in the margins or at the top. It's your book. Do with it what you want.

In addition, or instead of that approach, you could buy or find a blank notebook and use that book for taking notes about you and your brain. It appears that the very act of taking notes assists in memory and recall. It seems also that the act of writing has more of an impact in the memory process than the act of typing something into a computer or electronic pad. It appears that it consolidates learning. So, I recommend keeping a notebook to add to your learning. This notebook can also act i) as a notepad when you wake in the middle of the night, ii) as a journal for your thoughts as you go on your learning journey, and iii) as a place to record those insights or ideas that you will probably have as you read through the book. And remember, only you are going to read your notes, so write down whatever you want and push your own edge.

2. Attention!

If you prefer electronic notetaking, and I understand many people do these days, then here is something else you might want to consider. While you are reading, turn off your phones (smartphones or otherwise), your tablets, your email, your RSS feeds, your voicemails, your instant messaging systems – in fact anything that provides random, uncontrolled interruptions. (I know that some of your random, uncontrolled interruptions, for example, your children, spouse, pets, etc. don't come with an on-off switch, but turn off anything that does.)

Linda Stone **named a phenomenon known as continuous partial attention (CPA). CPA indicates that when these various devices and applications are on, part of our brain pays attention to them non-consciously. Some more recent research from the University of Texas gives support to this idea. The end result of this diverted attention is that if one of these devices or tools is switched on, your brain will "devote" some of its cycles to wondering whether there are any messages, emails, etc., and as a result

---

*I was recently delivering a workshop on the brain where I made the statement about writing in a book. One of the participants freaked out and stated that she could never write in a book. A discussion ensued where we looked at the background of where this resistance came from. Childhood and parents. Like many other things!

** Linda Stone coined the phrase Continuous Partial Attention (CPA) in 1998 and has written and lectured about CPA in many places. Her website is www.lindastone.net.

you lose cognitive ability. The best approach is to switch them off and put them in another room. This effect also applies if you are in meetings, one-on-ones, etc. So, if you want to be kind to your brain and your learning, turn your digital devices off, and leave them somewhere where you cannot see them.

3. Exercise

And here I am not just referring to your regular workout or daily exercise that you take for your mental health, bodily health, and well-being. I am referring to the occasional stretch. Or jump. Or jog. If you get tired, then learning and memory gets impaired. If you find yourself getting tired while reading, then get up, stretch, go for a small walk, or play with the dog. There is much evidence that exercise is one of the best activities for the brain and some evidence that one of the best times for us to learn is immediately after exercise.

4. Rest

The brain cannot concentrate for very long before it needs to take a break. The estimates that we have at the moment is that the brain needs to rest and change modes of thinking about every 7 to 12 minutes. If you don't take a break from time to time, your brain will do so on your behalf. If you find that there are times when you feel that it would be useful to stop, step back, and reflect, then let your instinct be your guide. That instinct is pretty well honed for all of us.

5. Focus

We know that the brain cannot focus on many things at the same time. We know, for example, that with a few small exceptions, multi-tasking makes the brain explode. Not literally, of course. What masquerades as multi-tasking is, in fact, the brain rapidly changing focus and contexts from one task back to the previous. It is extremely energy consuming from the perspective of the brain. So, one topic at a time.

6. Small Steps.

If you choose to do something different as a result of reading this book, then do two things. Choose an overall goal, and then employ small steps to get there. Chewing off something too large, no matter how exciting or compelling it might be, is often the first step to nothing happening. Research shows that even in the light of large projects or changes, we should tackle something small first. This gives the brain a reward that it is accomplishing something and sets us up for tackling the next small thing.

7. Sequence.

One aspect of the brain that you will learn more about in the pages that follow is that the brain's need to feel safe. And one way that the brain feels safe is predictability. Prediction is a word that will come up again and again.

Reading the sections of the book in the sequence in which they are written is predictable and makes the brain feel safe. For some people, predictability is an absolute requirement. The sequence of the book is designed to help you make sense of each of the following chapters and, as such, there are no surprises (other than new knowledge), and it is highly predictable. For many people, that predictability is extremely important.

But, in the earlier piece about different strategies for reading the book, I offered a few options on how you can go about reading it. For some people, choice is more important than predictability. It really is your choice as this is intended to be a brain-friendly book. But I strongly recommend reading it in the sequence in which it is written.☺

Section A Part 3: Acknowledgments

This section is where I say thank you to the many people who have helped and influenced me over the years. It is also the place where I apologize to anyone who I forgot to say thank you to as I went along. In my first privately published book, I made a few acknowledgements that still apply today. In addition, I have added quite a number.

In the years since I did my Master's degree, I have read many hundreds of books about the brain, about leadership, about teams, about personalities, about behavior…the list goes on. In some way, every one of those books has influenced my thinking so I wish to say thank you to all of those authors, especially Daniel Kahneman who wrote *Thinking Fast and Slow*, the book that I wish I had been capable enough to write.

As I reflect upon my leadership and neuroscience journey to date, I realize I have been incredibly lucky to have met many mentors, teachers, coaches, and role models. These have been in a variety of fields including leadership, business, neuroscience, personal growth, and leadership development. I wish to say thank you, most of all, to the people below who have been foundational in providing with me with information, theories, guidance, and assistance in developing some of my own insights over the past several decades:

- Fred Allen
- Katherine Benziger
- Denis Bourgois
- Ian Browde
- Tom Cavallo
- Alan Cypher
- Jim Ewing
- Tim Gallwey
- John Grassi
- Nancy Hauge
- Prasad Kaipa
- Susan Larson Kidd
- Mike Markkula
- Dan McCammon
- Sal Melilli
- Janine Nahapiet
- JR Parrish
- Barry Rhein
- David Sibbett
- Jim Stuart
- Teller
- Gregg Ward
- Jim Whittaker

- Fred Baca
- Joe Black
- Bill Bridges
- John Buckley
- Alan Christensen
- Savannah DeVarney
- Doug Frye
- Jerry Gibson
- Jason Greer
- Steve Jobs
- Neil Kiefer
- Tom Lawrence
- Graham Marriott
- Walt McFarland
- Debby Meredith
- Tyler Nelson
- Don Paul
- David Rock
- Soren
- David Surrenda
- John Thompson
- Cheryl Wicks
- Ken Zerbe

- Dave Barram
- Susan Black
- Greg Brodsky
- Bill Campbell
- Debi Coleman
- Gary Edwards
- Michelle Gale
- Evian Gordon
- Hermann Gyr
- Carmel Judd
- Jim Kouzes
- Trevor Linger
- Harry Max
- Steve McMahon
- John Montgomery
- Kevin Ochsner
- Dan Radecki
- Richard Scott
- Carla Street
- Marshall Tanner
- Bill Underwood
- Stefan Winsnes

Some have illustrated role model leadership. Some have provided theories. Others have helped me understand the theories. Others have heeded my advice and applied it.

I would, however, like to focus on one person in particular. Dr. Susan Larson Kidd and I met at a "Learning & the Brain" conference in 2014. We immediately struck up a friendship (we had a common bond…we were both lost and trying to find our way to the lecture hall), and that friendship continues to this day. She provided much of the early encouragement to tackle this book, has seen me through several versions, has hung in there, and also took care of me during hip surgery. Thank you, Susan.

As I have studied and learned over the past decades, it has become clear to me how much our family backgrounds provide the foundation for who we become. I have come to realize how privileged I have been, and still am, to have had a loving, encouraging, and supportive family. I always knew, regardless of what happened, that they were always there for me. So, to Pat & Harry Dixon and Annette, Rita, & Gill, I give my love and sincere thanks.

I honor and say an additional thank you to the following people who have all, in different ways, added to my experience, knowledge, and understanding: Stephanie Giles, Pat & Doug Robinson, Richard Scott, Carla Street, Heidi Hanna, Teri Dahlbeck, Robin Pitman, Lisa Friedman, Lazlo Gyorffy, Barry Rhein, Linda Henson, Winston Churchill, Harry Max, Linda Sharkey, Savannah DeVarney, Michele Soukin, Winston and Clemmie, and Rex, Pia, Nico, Jake, and Spike. You may not know the role you played, but let me tell you, it was important to me – thank you.

In addition, I would like to say special thanks to all of the people that reviewed the book at various stages, doing various levels of proof-reading and giving me crucial feedback. There are a few people I would like to call out in this respect. First, I would like to thank my sister, Rita, who not only read through the book in detail but provided an extremely useful proof-reading effort in the process.

I would like to thank Scott Fitzgerald, MBA, my co-author. He not only provided invaluable feedback during the latter stages of the book-writing activity but added his own blend of counsel, wisdom, and humor to the book's content. En route, he also kept me intellectually honest as to what should be included and what should be omitted.

I have worked with Cheryl Whiting Kish for almost fifteen years at this point and would like to thank her for taking the risk of incorporating some new thinking and new models into her consulting and training practices.

I have also been extremely lucky to have met Victoria Dozier in the final few weeks of writing the book. Tori came into my life bringing with her persistence, consistency, diligence, and the discipline required to run the final ten yards to the finish line. She is the person that read it through countless times, challenging, questioning, polishing, and re-writing. Thank you so much.

Finally, and by no means least, I would like to give special thanks to my wife, Cathy, who has not only provided love, tolerance, forgiveness, support, proofreading, many cups of tea, and acted as a wonderful sounding-board but has put up with me spending endless hours of research and writing at my desk.

Section A Part 4: Dedication

This book is dedicated to the following people who were close friends or family and who have had a major influence on my life but who, alas, are no longer with us:

Joe Black
John Buckley
Bill Campbell
Uncle Charlie
Harry Dixon
Pat Dixon
Stephanie Giles
Mrs. Harvey
Krista Henley
Mike Homer
Pete Kavanagh
Deb Marriott
Lee Milligan
Tom Lawrence
Little Nan
Doug Robinson
Ron Smith
John Thompson
Craig Wells

Your presence on this planet made this book possible.

Your wisdom infuses it.

Your absence is keenly felt, and I miss every one of you.

Section B.
Understanding Your Brain

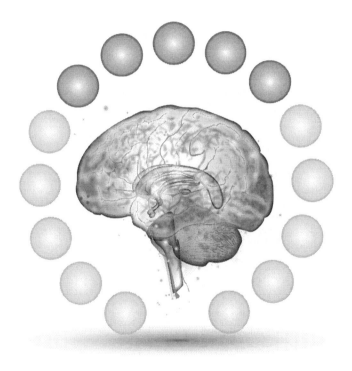

This is what is in Section B.

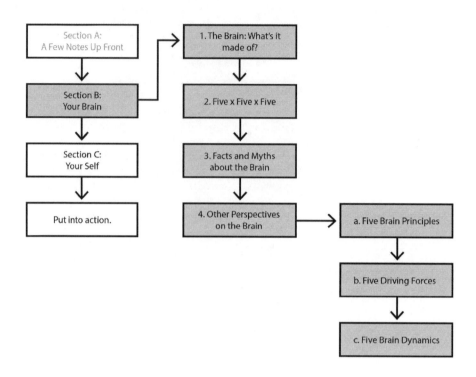

Section B Part 1: What is the Brain Made Of?

The brain is the most complex of all of our organs, and we are still only just beginning to understand some of its complexities. The next few pages contain some fundamentals that I will be referring to during the rest of the book so it's good to understand them from the start. Let's take a look at some numbers and the structure of the brain.

1. Weight and Size

The average adult brain weighs about 3 lbs. (or 1.4 kilograms) and occupies about 100 cubic inches (1.7 liters) and represents approximately 1 – 3% of our body weight. For a 100-pound (45 kg.) person, this would be 3%. For a 150-pound (68 kg.) person, this would be 2%. And for a 225-pound person, it would be 1.3%. I am told that it's the texture of soft tofu, although I have personally never seen or touched one. In general, most researchers believe that we have a higher ratio of brain size to body weight than most other animals, although the exact ratio and what is being compared varies from researcher to researcher.

However, our brains are shrinking. Not each of us on a daily basis. But, over the past five thousand years, it seems that the human brain has been getting smaller. We know from archeological data from Europe, China, South Africa, and Australia that brains have shrunk about 9 cubic inches from an average of about 82 cubic inches, i.e., approximately 10%. Researchers really don't know why this is. As you might suspect, there are many theories. One of these is that our brains are evolving to become more efficient. Another theory is that our skulls are getting smaller because our diets include more things that are easily digestible, and so we don't need the big strong jaws like our prehistoric ancestors.

Conclusion: Before you get too entranced with our comparatively large brains, remember – they're not as large as they used to be.

2. Energy Consumption

The degree to which the human brain consumes energy is amazing. Let's think about other species first. The brains of rodents and dogs, for example, use about 5% of their total energy. Monkeys' brains use about 10% of their total energy. Humans use 20% of their energy to manage their brain on a moment to moment basis. [10] [11] Compare this to the 1.3 – 3% of body weight! If you look at the brains of children who have a developing brain, a full 50% of their energy deals with running their brain. In infants, the number is even higher at 60%.

Even though the brain uses a lot of energy, it is actually very efficient. As you will see as we move through the discussion of the brain, everything about the brain and its functioning is designed to be efficient. The brain uses about 12 – 15 watts [12] of power compared to 70 watts for the whole body when the body is at rest. To put it into perspective, 12 watts is one-fifth of the power that is required for a standard 60-watt light bulb.

Compared to most other organs, the brain is really greedy in terms of energy consumption with a disproportionately large amount of this energy consumption being taken up by the prefrontal cortex. We will discuss the prefrontal cortex, or PFC, in more detail later.

Another way of looking at this energy consumption is that it is about 15 – 20% of the total cardiac output, i.e., the blood flow from the heart that is directed to the brain every minute.

Conclusion: The brain is an energy hog and will need lots of feeding.

3. Fuel

The brain uses glucose as its primary energy source and needs oxygen in order to be able to utilize the glucose. The glucose used by the brain comes from dietary carbohydrates in the bloodstream and gets to the brain by crossing what is known as the blood-brain barrier. The brain cannot store glucose and needs a constant supply. At any given point in time, it has about ten minutes available to it.

Conclusion: So, not only is the brain an energy hog but a demanding one at that!

4. Two Halves and Three Layers

The human brain is not just a 3-pound cohesive lump. If we look at it physically, the brain is divided into two halves – the left half and the right half – which are connected by a large bundle of neurons called the corporate callosum. The physical split between the two halves is known as lateralization and, until a couple of decades ago, we used to think that this was REALLY important. Many "experts" made reference to the "left-brain" and the "right brain," assigned characteristics to each side, and taught many organizations to do "whole-brain thinking." While this separation of the two halves IS real and is obviously important, with more recent knowledge about how the brain is highly networked, we are attaching less importance to this division.

Within each of these halves, there are three distinct layers with different physiology and different purposes. I will expand upon these three layers in the next section.

Conclusion: The three layers are just as important to our understanding of the brain as the two halves.

5. Neurons

The brain is made up of nerve cells called neurons.* There are lots of pictures of neurons available on the Internet, but the example here simply illustrates the major part of a neuron and how information flows along one. (I have deliberately not included the fancy Latin names.)

The brain is made up of a large number of these neurons. Some older texts, and even some newer ones, put this number as high as 100 billion. More recent estimates are 85 billion, and one researcher has even refined

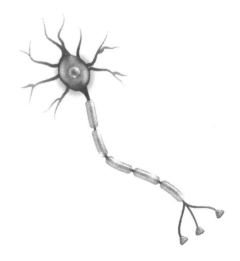

---

* I know, I know. I stated up front that I would not try to make you into a brain expert and would not introduce lots of Latin words (and I have blown that already); however, the neuron is such a basic part of the brain that talking about the brain without talking about neurons would be like talking about the body or the heart without mentioning blood.

it to 86 billion. [13] No one actually knows. Even the latest research describing the 86 billion adds that it is plus or minus 8 billion! We have never been able to actually count them, and all of the numbers are just estimates arrived at by a variety of algorithms and logic. If you go with 85 or 86 billion you probably won't be far wrong. They look like the image to the left:

There are different types of, or specialized, neurons, and my guess is that as we move on in the field of neuroscience, there will be many more that will be discovered. Mirror neurons, spindle neurons, and grid neurons are three examples of such specialized neurons that have already been identified.

Wait. Three days after I wrote that sentence, there was yet another type of neuron discovered – the Rose Hip neuron, named because it looks like one. The excitement among neuroscientists is almost palpable as it appears that this type of neuron is unique to humans. Watch this space.

Conclusion: There are a lot of neurons, and the exact number probably doesn't really matter. There's a lot. And there are different types.

6. Networks

Neurons are highly interconnected. Estimates vary as to how many other neurons each neuron is connected to. Some researchers say there are 1000 to 10000 connections to each neuron while others suggest that it might be as high as 10,000 to 50,000 connections per neuron. These connections form networks or circuits which are referred to as neural networks or neuronal networks. The best estimate that I have found is that there are 10^{15} such networks in each of our brains. I think that this number is a quadrillion, but I may well be wrong. Way too large of a number for most of us to understand, and, once again, the exact number probably doesn't really matter except to say that it's very, very large.

Before I go any further, however, I need to make a clarification. When I say "connection," in general, the neurons don't actually connect. They come very close, but there's an all-important gap between the end of one neuron and the beginning of the one it is connecting to. This gap is referred to as a **synapse**. There's a lot of activity that goes on, very quickly, in these synapses. It's one of the places where **neurotransmitters** (essentially, chemical messengers) hang out.

In turn, each of these neural networks are linked together to form a large number of "maps" which seem to be specialized to address certain topics or activities.

In an infant's brain, as many as 2 million new connections are formed every second. By age two, a child has over 100 trillion connections, double the number an adult has. [14] These networks are in a constant state of change. They are being formed and are being changed all of the time; in certain occasions, they are also being pruned.

With all of these highly interlinked, parallel networks, there doesn't seem to be one orchestra conductor or Master of Ceremonies that controls the rest of the brain in a hierarchical fashion. Everything runs in parallel and intercommunicates with many other neurons and networks. The phrase that best describes it is "massively parallel."

Conclusion: The Internet is probably the best metaphor for how the brain is networked.

7. Glue

The neurons are all surrounded by glial cells, [15] and they are outnumbered ten to one by them. Once again, there is disagreement about this neuron/glial ratio. Some researchers state it could be as high as 50:1. [16] It was originally thought these glial cells were just to hold everything together ("glia" comes from the Greek word for "glue"), but, increasingly of late, researchers believe that these glial cells may play a much more important role in the transfer of chemical messages which are essential to all brain processes. [17]

Glial cells may play a significant part in the mopping up of excess neurotransmitters which have been diffused in the synapse and need to be removed – just like a janitorial service! They may provide immune protection. They may also promote synaptic growth and function and neuronal plasticity. Some neuroscientists refer to the glia as "the silent majority," but, at this time in the neuroscience of the brain, it is the neurons that get all of the attention.

One possible downside of these glia is that they are so numerous that they can reproduce unchecked and might be the cause of some cancers. Many of the most commonly found tumors in the brain are associated with these glia cells.

Conclusion: Watch this space. We're likely to learn a lot more about glial cells and their importance as time progresses.

7. Wrinkles

The brain is wrinkly. If you take a look at a brain, it is convoluted and wrinkled. The wrinkles or folds are called gyri or a gyrus. The hillocks or bumps in between the gyri are each called a sulcus (and for those of you that are fascinated by this sort of thing, the plural is sulci.) The secret to our species' intelligence and the wonderful abilities of our brains may lie in these wrinkles.

These wrinkles make up the surface of the brain, as shown in this picture. Because the brain is folded in a wrinkled manner, the whole surface area takes up less space than if it is not folded. The skull is a finite size so we want to get the maximum use and efficiency within that size. A wrinkled brain gives us that efficiency. If we compare the human brain to a mouse brain or the brains of other primates, we don't find all of these grooves and fissures. Those brains are smooth, i.e., wrinkle free.

These wrinkles allow us to have more neurons, with more connections, in a smaller, more efficient space and, we presume, ultimately, to have more brain power.

Conclusion: Despite the opinions of plastic surgeons and the use of Botox, not all wrinkles are bad. ☺

8. Visual

Some estimates suggest that between 60 – 70% of the networks of the brain are visual networks, i.e., are devoted to processing visual signals. Other research suggests that it might be lower. The processing of visual signals is handled by the visual cortex (a thin sheet of tissues about the size of a dollar) which is located at the back of the head. Both hemispheres of the brain contain a visual cortex. Just to complicate our understanding, the visual cortex in the left hemisphere receives signals from the right visual field, and the visual cortex in the right hemisphere receives signals from the left visual field.

Conclusion: With that explanation, this is the time when you, the reader, might say, "Ah, I see."

9. Neuroplasticity

The brain has an amazing ability to change itself. We refer to this as neuroplasticity. These changes occur due to changes we make behaviorally, physically, and mentally. Indeed, with the reading that you have done of this book so far, your brain has already changed ever so slightly. These changes are changes in the interconnections between the neurons and networks that we mentioned earlier.

Conclusion: The fact that the brain changes is one of several new ways of looking at the brain – we used to think of the brain as a static. Not anymore!

10. A Chemical Cocktail

There are many chemicals found in the brain. The exact number varies with the researcher that you read. Some estimate as low as 30 – others over 100. It is also estimated that every second there are over 100,000 chemical reactions that go on in the brain. Examples of chemicals that are involved in such reactions are cortisol, oxytocin, dopamine, and serotonin.

Conclusion: As my colleague Dr. Evian Gordon used to say, "We all live on a chemical knife-edge."

11. Information Handling

The brain handles 11,000,000 bits of information per second. [18] We will come back to this number when we talk about how the brain handles all of this information.

Conclusion: The brain is busier, all of the time, than most of us credit it for.

For something a little more lighthearted, I couldn't resist finishing this section by referencing a brief science fiction piece written by Terry Bisson and published in the now defunct *Omni Magazine* in 1990. It concerns an alien reporting back to home-base after spending time on Earth. The article was entitled "Meat All the Way Down" and here is a part of it:

"Nope. They're born meat, and they die meat. We studied them for several of their life spans, which didn't take long. Do you have any idea what's the life span of meat?"

"Spare me. Okay, maybe they're only part meat. You know, like the weddilei. A meat head with an electron plasma brain inside."

"Nope. We thought of that, since they do have meat heads, like the weddilei. But I told you, we probed them. They're meat all the way through."

"No brain?"

"Oh, there's a brain all right. It's just that the brain is <u>made out of meat</u>! That's what I've been trying to tell you."

"So ... what does the thinking?"

"You're not understanding, are you? You're refusing to deal with what I'm telling you. The brain does the thinking. The meat."

"Thinking meat! You're asking me to believe in thinking meat!"

"Yes, thinking meat! Conscious meat! Loving meat. Dreaming meat. The meat is the whole deal! Are you beginning to get the picture, or do I have to start all over?"

"Omigosh. You're serious then. They're made out of meat."

Notes and References for "Understanding the Brain: What's It Made Of?:

[10] D F Swaab. We Are Our Brains: A neurobiography of the brain from the womb to Alzheimer's. 2014. Spiegel & Grau, New York. p 7.

[11] Herculano-Houzel, S. (2012). The remarkable, yet not extraordinary, human brain as a scaled-up primate brain and its associated cost. Proceedings of the National Academy of Sciences, 109 (Supplement 1), 10661–10668. http://doi.org/10.1073/pnas.1201895109

[12] D F Swaab. We Are Our Brains: A neurobiography of the brain from the womb to Alzheimer's. 2014. Spiegel & Grau, New York. p 7.

[13] Azevedo, F. A. C., Carvalho, L. R. B., Grinberg, L. T., Farfel, J. M., Ferretti, R. E. L., Leite, R. E. P., et al. (2009). Equal numbers of neuronal and nonneuronal cells make the human brain an isometrically scaled-up primate brain. The Journal of Comparative Neurology, 513(5), 532–541. http://doi.org/10.1002/cne.21974

[14] Eagleman, D. (2015). The Brain: The Story of You. Pantheon.

[15] D F Swaab. We Are Our Brains: A neurobiography of the brain from the womb to Alzheimer's. 2014. Spiegel & Grau, New York. p 7.

[16] Herculano-Houzel, S. (2012) Op cit

[17] Fields, R. D. (2011). The Other Brain: The Scientific and Medical Breakthroughs That Will Heal Our Brains and Revolutionize Our Health (1). Simon & Schuster.

[18] Brooks, D. (2012). The Social Animal: The Hidden Sources of Love, Character, and Achievement. Random House Trade Paperbacks.

Section B Part 2: Five x Five x Five[*][**]

Section B Part 2a. Five Brain Principles

We can identify five major principles of the brain that influence everything else.

Everything!!!

These are:

	Principle	Brief Description
1	**ONE Purpose: Survival**	We have ancient brains that haven't caught up with society's progress. They are constantly scanning for threat in order to ensure our safety and, hence, our survival.
2	**TWO Modes of Operation**	Our brains have two modes – a conscious mode and a nonconscious mode. We are mainly driven by the nonconscious part of our brain. It drives most of our decisions and reactions.
3	**THREE Layers**	Our brains have three layers. Parts of two of them are in a constant struggle.
4	**FOUR Processes**	There are four distinct processes that occur: cue recognition, thinking, feeling, and self-regulation. During these processes, the brain experiences social threat and physical threat in a similar fashion.
5	**FIVE Driving Forces**	We are driven by the need for Protection, Participation with others, and Prediction. Once we feel safe, we pursue our Purpose and Pleasure.

Now let's take a look at each one in more detail…

---

* Before we go any further, I need to make a major disclaimer. What I am about to describe is not actually how the brain works! I describe a number of models or metaphors. What actually happens is way more complex than this, but this is good enough for what we need to address now. If you want more detail, you can find lots of articles, books, and papers if you search Google Scholar.
** Evian Gordon introduced me to his Brain 1-2-4 model several years ago. We were using it with a client, and one of the attendees kept asking, "What happened to the 3?" So, these five principles fill in the "3" and add one for the "5."

Brain Principle #1: We have Ancient Brains with <u>ONE</u> Primary Objective.

ONE Purpose - Survival

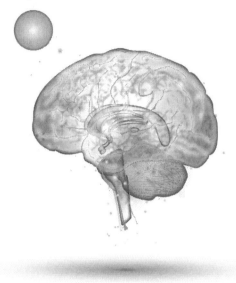

The brain is geared towards one thing. Survival! Your survival and, subsequently, the survival of the species. In order to achieve this, the brain seeks safety. In his book *Brain Rules*, John Medina [19] describes how the brain has evolved since we were early human beings out on the African Savannah. He states that the brain is:

> " .. *a problem-solving mechanism for survival in an outdoor environment while constantly on the move under constantly changing conditions.*"

Bessel Van Der Kolk [20] adds another layer of detail to the brain's "mandate":

> *"The most important job of the brain is to ensure our survival, even under the most miserable conditions."*

The organizing principle of the brain, therefore, is survival via safety. Safety first, and far above every other consideration. In order to survive when we were on the Savannah, we had to be and feel safe. It was important to deal with danger or threats (like being eaten) before anything else. Once the threats had been dealt with, and we felt safe, then we could seek reward. Like food, warmth, shelter, sex, etc.

Fast forward a few millennia, and the world has changed. There are few people that have to face a saber-toothed tiger in real life today (although I have met many people who describe their bosses that way). But our brains don't know that! Our brains treat the threats we experience at work today exactly the same way as our ancestors' brains experienced that tiger.

Society has moved on, but our brains haven't. Even if you go back 600 or 700 years (a blink of the eye in terms of evolution), most people around the world were still in real danger for much of their life. Medieval villages were probably no picnic to live in. Nowadays, the worries that we face are more likely to be the traffic on the way home, the bills that have to be paid, or the presentation that we need to prepare to deliver to a potential client next week. But our brains haven't evolved to anywhere near the same extent. Brain 2.0 hasn't come along yet.

Our brains are extremely good at picking up these threats. The brain scans its environment every 1/5th of a second, looking for threats and rewards. [21] Let me repeat that. Every 1/5th of a second! Our brains are constantly searching for signs of danger. These signs, or "cues," are primarily visual and auditory. A sudden move to one side can make us jump involuntarily. A loud noise can have a similar effect. Many years ago, had you not reacted quickly that way, you would likely have been eaten. Hence, your genes wouldn't have evolved into the gene pool of today.

Once we feel safe, we are also looking for signs of reward. The response to this constant search, however, is not evenly distributed. There are 5 times as many networks in the brain that are attuned for responding to threat than there are networks that respond to reward. We have significantly greater awareness of negative stimuli that we do to positive ones and, as a result, more negative emotions than we do positive ones. Don't forget about Van Der Kolk's and Medina's statements about the brain's mandate, a problem-solving mechanism for survival. Hence, the brain is heavily oriented towards picking up threat in order to ensure our survival.

The brain can correctly identify images seen for as little as 13 milliseconds, which is about 1/75th second. [22] By way of comparison, here are timings of some other brain responses:

13 milliseconds (1/75th second)	The brain can identify that an image is present – not what it is.
50 milliseconds (1/20th second)	Basic shape is recognized (e.g., is this round or elongated?)
120 milliseconds (1/8th second)	The image can now be identified as an object – and "named."
160 milliseconds (1/6th second)	Object classified or categorized (e.g., plant or animal)
200 milliseconds (1/5th second)	Scanning repeated

Brain Principle #2: We Have <u>TWO</u> Modes, Conscious and Nonconscious.

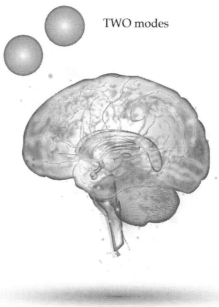

TWO modes

The brain has two modes in which it operates: a conscious mode and a nonconscious mode.* These two modes have been referenced by many researchers too numerous to mention. The two modes have also been referenced by different names by other authors; for example, Daniel Kahneman called them "System 1" and "System 2" [23] and, much earlier, Tim Gallwey referred to them as "Self 1" and "Self 2." [24]

As mentioned earlier, the brain handles about 11,000,000 bits of information per second. However, only 40** bits are handled by the conscious part of the brain; the nonconscious mode handles the rest. The other 10,999,960!

Conscious processing is relatively obvious. You are consciously reading and understanding this book. At least, let's hope that is the case. ☺

Let me illustrate nonconscious processing by way of blushing, yawning, and chicken skin*** as examples. Blushing is something that most of us have little control over and, often, don't even know what causes us to blush. Lots of research has gone into what makes us yawn; it has been shown that most of the time, it is not only about a physiological process. There are many hypotheses as to why we yawn. I give just one reference from the many that are available. For some people, a touch or a sight or a sound will cause them to get chicken skin.

Biases, triggers, habits, and tendencies are all other examples of largely nonconscious responses. I will be dealing with these at various stages throughout the book.

---

* I use the term "nonconscious" to mean everything that is "below" our conscious thinking. It was introduced to me as the best term to use. Unconscious is a physical state introduced by violence or chemicals and subconscious has a built-in implication of being able to gain access to those activities.
** Some researchers say it is as low as 15. Others credit us with handling 100. Wow! That's still only 0.01% of the total.
*** Chicken skin is called goosebumps in many parts of the world.

In his book, *The Brain Revolution*, Evian Gordon has the following to say about the nonconscious brain:

> *"The speed and pervasiveness of your nonconscious reactions affect everything about you. This means that when you have a conscious thought, it happens only after you have already non-consciously processed and weighted the most beneficial outcome and response to any situation."*

The conscious mode is slow (by comparison to the nonconscious mode), deliberate, tends to be verbally oriented, and is primarily driven by words. It involves thinking, logic, details, and context. By contrast, the nonconscious mode is fast, automatic, picture and symbol driven, tends to be nonverbally oriented, and is triggered by cues. It is the default mechanism for our reactions to most situations.

If we now combine the drive towards survival and safety together with the enormous percentage of nonconscious processing, then we can start to see that we are primarily driven towards safety in a highly nonconscious manner.

The brain is a pattern junkie. It loves to detect patterns, and once it finds a pattern, it hardwires it in. The hardwiring then drives automatic (nonconscious) responses once the brain sees a repetition of the pattern. This is the basis of many of our biases, habits, and paradigms.

The neural networks that I referred to earlier exist throughout the brain and integrate the conscious and nonconscious modes.

The specific words that we use cause different reactions in the brain. In addition, the context of the words that we use can cause different reactions in the brain. For example, the question "How fast was the blue car going when it hit the red car?" will cause a different estimate from witnesses than "How fast was the blue car going when it smashed into the red car?" [25] "Did you see the broken headlight?" will get a larger number of positive answers to "Did you see a broken headlight?".

It gets worse. The words that we use can get misinterpreted by our brains and have the opposite effect than what was intended. The famous "Don't think of a pink elephant" will often cause us to do just that. Further, we might make a statement that we intend to be positive, but it gets received as something negative. For example, if we say, "Don't worry," the important word that the brain actually registers is "worry," i.e., the opposite of what we intended. Words like "feedback," "change," "stress," "reject," "failure," "frustrate," "anger," "sad," "depressed," "worthless," etc. are heard by the brain as a threat regardless of the context in which they are used. So, statements like "Let's not get frustrated" would probably have a better impact on the recipient if they were changed to "Best to stay positive."

In contrast, positive words like "sooth," "connect," "calm," "reward," "succeed," "gratitude," "joy," "happiness," "meaning," etc. will always tend to come across as reward oriented.

If we now take a look at combining some of these brain principles, we can start to see the relationship between the scanning brain and this nonconscious aspect of the brain. We are driven by nonconscious responses to the many cues (verbal and nonverbal) that the brain picks up. An example of that is with physicians. Physicians need to be seen as both warm and competent. In a recent study (2017), Kraft-Todd [26] demonstrated that just two empathetic nonverbal behaviors (eye contact and leaning forward rather than away) caused a significant increase in participants' view of the physician's empathy, warmth, and competence.

One more item not strictly related to conscious and nonconscious processing but still relevant. It was known from the 1930s that the brain was constantly active, but it wasn't until much later that a curious phenomenon was noticed. It was noticed that when the brain was supposedly at rest, i.e., thinking but with no specific mental task to focus on, some parts of the brain were more active than normal. The network of these active areas is known as the default mode network.

This network seems to be activated when we are "miles away," for example when we are daydreaming, reflecting, or ruminating.

I bring this topic up here as it seems to be somewhere between the conscious and the nonconscious modes. There is much current research going on in this field so expect many more discoveries about this network.

Conclusion: The nonconscious brain drives many, if not most, of our thoughts, decisions, and actions, and we need to take it very seriously!

Brain Principle #3: The Brain Has <u>THREE</u> Layers.

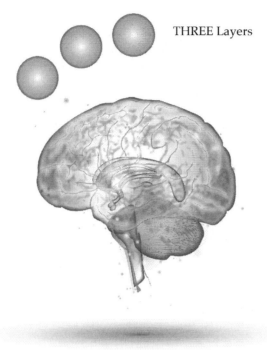

THREE Layers

In essence, the brain is essentially three brains in one. This is known as the triune brain.*

Let's start with the oldest layer.** It is known as the **reptilian brain** (or sometimes the lizard brain) and is located where the spinal column enters the skull. It can be regarded as the core of the brain.

The next (and slightly younger) layer is the mammalian brain, which is also called the **limbic system**.

The final and physically largest layer is the rational brain (or **neocortex**), which is the newest of all the layers.

Each of these layers are anatomically separate, can be distinguished from each other, and contain different chemicals. Each layer is responsible for different groups of behaviors and makes different contributions to the overall operation of the brain. The reptilian brain is all about feeling safe and is on autopilot. The limbic system is concerned with emotion and sociability and makes rapid decisions. The neocortex is about prediction and knowledge and reason and rationalization.

The diagram on the nest page shows what the three layers look like. If you search on the Internet, you will find a whole variety of similar diagrams, but I think this one does a good job. The table that follows the diagram lists the primary functions of each of the three layers:

---

* The term Triune brain is attributed to Paul McClean who was Director of the Laboratory of Brain Evolution and Behavior at the National Institute of Mental Health.
** By "oldest," I mean the oldest from an evolutionary viewpoint. In addition, the sequence described is the sequence in which the brain develops as we are born and grow.

The Triune Brain

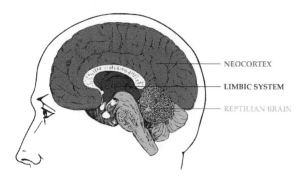

Rational Brain	**NEOCORTEX**	Language, abstract thought, imagination, consciousness	Reason and rationalization
Mammalian Brain	**LIMBIC SYSTEM**	Emotions, memories and habits	Decisions
REPTILIAN BRAIN	**Brain Stem and Cerebellum**	Fight or Flight	Autopilot

Van Der Kolk [27] gives us a great explanation of the three layers with some additional functions and detail (and says it much better that I can):

> *"The reptilian brain is in charge of the moment to moment registration of our body's physiology. It is responsible for all the things that newborn babies can do: eat, sleep, wake, cry, and breathe; feel temperature, hunger, wetness, and pain; and rid the body of toxins by urinating and defecating. The brain stem and the hypothalamus together control the energy levels of the body. They coordinate the functioning of the heart and lungs and also the endocrine and immune systems, ensuring that the basic life-sustaining systems are maintained within the relatively stable internal balance known as homeostasis"*

> *"The mammalian brain (the limbic system) is concerned with the identification of comfort, safety, threat, hunger, fatigue, desire, longing, excitement, pleasure, and pain. Development of this part of the brain truly takes off after the baby is born. It is the seat of the emotions, the monitor of danger, the judge of what is pleasurable or scary, the arbiter of what is or is not important for survival purposes. It is also a central command post for coping with the challenges of living within our complex social networks."*

> *"This system is shaped in response to experience, in partnership with the infant's own genetic makeup and inborn temperament."*

> *"The rational brain (the neocortex) is primarily concerned with the world outside us: understanding how things and people work and figuring out how to accomplish our goals, manage our time, and sequence our actions."*

Taken together, the reptilian brain and the limbic system make up, in Van Der Kolk's words, the "emotional brain." They comprise the very basis of the central nervous system whose key task is to keep you safe and look out for your welfare.

Brain Principle #4: There Are <u>FOUR</u> Processes Going On.

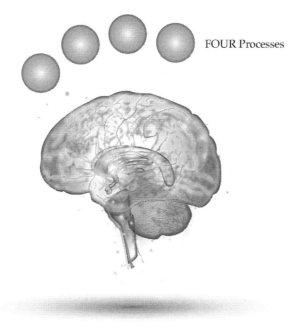

FOUR Processes

In their paper, [28] Williams et al describe four processes that occur in the brain. These are, in their words, emotion, thinking, feeling, and self-regulation. Their definitions of the four processes are as follows:

> *"**Emotion** – Adaptive action tendencies that are mobilized by signals of potential danger or reward. They involve a 'feedforward' mode of brain and body activity that is triggered automatically and without the need for conscious awareness of the triggering signal.*
>
> *For example, when walking in a laneway at night, a dark shape appears abruptly just ahead of you, signaling potential danger. Before you are aware of it, direct sensory input from this visual signal has triggered a feedforward sweep of brain activation, heart rate acceleration, and repertoire of motor reflexes that define the action tendency of fear and the readiness to flee.*
>
> ***Thinking** and **Feeling** – Rely on conscious awareness and a 'feedback' mode of brain-body activity. **Thinking** is when you are consciously aware of information and can represent it to yourself in words or images. **Feeling** is when you are aware of the emotion you are experiencing and can describe it to yourself. Thinking and feeling allow us to selectively attend to information, extract its context, make controlled, voluntary responses, and link these to what we know and remember.*
>
> *To continue the example, with brain-body feedback over the next few hundred milliseconds, you identify the dark shape as a person and your feeling as 'scared.' The context – the person is moving towards you – confirms your perception of danger. You reinforce the tendency to flee and run until you are out of the laneway and in a busy, well-lit street.*

Self-Regulation – The modulation of emotion, thinking, and feeling to minimize danger and maximize reward over time. Self-regulation is inextricably linked to our well-being and adaptation.

In the above example, the outcome of the experience of walking in the laneway will contribute to our self-regulation such that we minimize our feelings of being scared by avoiding such situations in the future. We may plan so that we do not walk in similar environments at night."

In summary, then, the brain receives a cue which gives rise to an emotion. This triggers off thoughts (cognitive analysis) and feelings (bodily sensations) which we then use as the basis of deciding what to do.

Personally, I have found that simple diagrams are easier to understand as shown in the one below.

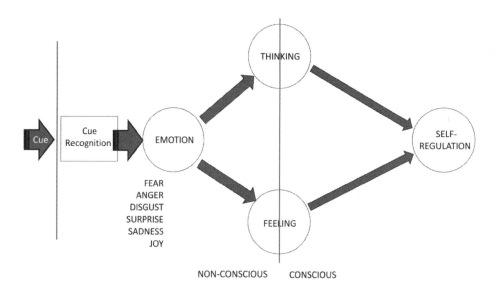

Let's talk a little more about these four processes, and in order to do so, I am going to lean heavily on Gordon's work [29] where he summarizes the processes way better than I could:

*"**Thinking** is your verbal, conscious brain process (you think in words) including memory, focus, and planning. It determines what is most significant to you.*

Thinking relies on memory to give you the context necessary to assess the consequences of your past actions, store them, and plan for your best future options.

***Focus** gives you the ability to concentrate on a selected task while ignoring distractions (internal and external) so that you can complete the task.*
***Planning** (executive functioning) uses memory and focus to implement the best strategy to achieve your goals.*

***Cues** are the triggers of **emotion**. An example of a threat cue would be a very loud noise, a sudden movement, or a threatening shape.*

Such nonconscious triggers are basic to human behavior, and your nonconscious processing is particularly attuned to these cues.

Your primary emotional reactions to cues allow each emotion to empower you to rapidly avoid/deal with potential danger or to deal with reward:

> *Fear: for flight*
> *Anger: for fight*
> *Disgust: for withdrawal from food contaminants or social mismatches*
> *Surprise: for dealing with novel information and increasing reward*
> *Sadness: for withdrawal and the elicitation of soothing comfort*
> *Happiness: for social engagement and approach behaviors*

***Feeling** stems from your conscious awareness of feedback from your body in the form of changes in your heart rate, sweating, and breathing that are triggered by your reaction to emotional cues.*

Feeling is a subjective, conscious experience of a reaction to an emotion cue.

***Self-regulation** is your capacity to be aware of, manage, and align, your thinking, emotion, and feeling to achieve your best short- and long-term goals.*

Self-regulation reflects how well you master feelings of stress and can help you in making decisions and planning – it is the extent to which you effectively integrate your emotion-thinking-feeling."

As this is all happening, if the brain feels either physically threatened or socially (emotionally) threatened, it treats both types of threat the same way. [30] [31] [32] Eisenberger, and others, have done a huge volume of research on this. What it means is that if you feel socially threatened (for example, if someone trashes your great idea at work) or emotionally hurt (for example, if someone dumps you or fires you via text), the brain responds in the same way as if you had been physically threatened or physically hurt. The brain networks that are recruited (i.e., become active) under physical pain or the threat of physical pain have a large degree of overlap with those that are recruited under emotional or social pain.

OK. Let's get down to brass tacks. Tigers, snakes, and spiders to one side, what are some of the threats and rewards that we actually find in today's workplaces and social environments? I am sure that you will be able to come up with many of your own examples, but here are a few to start your thinking:

***Threats at work:** Folded arms, angry looks, being ignored, being ridiculed, being shouted at, being criticized, having someone else getting or taking credit for work that you did, being treated unfairly, being overruled, being micro-managed, having processes or systems changed on you without being told or involved, not being in the in-crowd or in the know, not being invited to meetings that you thought you should be at, losing a potential deal...the list goes on.*

***Threats in our social life:** If you re-read the list above and translate the context to that of your social life, you will see that many of them are exactly the same and still apply. We can probably add a few more that would then reflect back into the workplace; for example, an argument with a spouse or significant other, being disciplined by a parent (especially if you are already an adult), a scowl or raised eyebrow, an unpleasant comment, being late for a date, having a birthday (or some other important event)* *forgotten, not being invited to a party, feeling like you are worse off than your neighbors...again, the list goes on.*

Rewards at work: Someone paying attention to you and/or your ideas, someone simply listening to you, giving you an (authentic) smile, someone saying "thank you," being given a raise, being given a bonus, someone congratulating you on a job well done...and so on.

Rewards in our social life: Once again, if you re-read the list above and translate the context to that of your social life, you will see that many of them are exactly the same and still apply. We can probably add a few more that would also then reflect back into the workplace; for example, seeing a friend that you haven't seen for a long while, holding someone's hand, being given a hug, being spoken kindly to, helping someone else out, someone commenting on how nice you look...or your car...or your house.

Now let's dig even deeper and look at what happens when these cues arrive. This is where we are going to discover the brain's main internal and ongoing struggle. The struggle is between the prefrontal cortex (PFC) which is located in the neocortex, just above our eyes, and the amygdala, which is located in the limbic system.*

Let's go into some detail about each of these two parts to start with.**

For the explanation of the PFC I am going to use the write-up in Wikipedia:

"The PFC has been implicated in planning complex cognitive behavior, personality expression, decision-making, and moderating social behavior. The basic activity of the PFC is considered to be the orchestration of thoughts and actions in accordance with internal goals. It is likely to be the center of concentration, orientation, abstracting ability, judgment, and problem-solving ability.

The most typical psychological term for functions carried out by the prefrontal cortex area is executive function. Executive function relates to abilities to differentiate among conflicting thoughts, determine good and bad, better and best, same and different, future consequences of current activities, working toward a defined goal, prediction of outcomes, expectation based on actions, and social 'control' (the ability to suppress urges that, if not suppressed, could lead to socially unacceptable outcomes). It assists in rule learning and the ability for abstract thought."

Now let's look at the other physical system that I referred to, the amygdala (more precisely we should say amygdalae as there are two of them, one on each side of the brain, but let's keep it as simple as possible)

The role of the amygdala is as an emotional watchdog or gatekeeper. It appears that it is involved in many things, probably the most important of which is the processing of emotions such as fear, anger, and pleasure. It has an important role in our responding appropriately to cues of danger.

Van Der Kolk [33] has a vivid description of the relationship between these two areas so, once again, I am going to use some of his description with a variant of the four-

---

* OK. Once again, I have to apologize. I know that I promised the minimum amount of brain science and Latin words. Trust me on this. This is important. We can't go much further without naming and talking about these two parts of the brain.
** I will have many neuroscientists up in arms at the simplicity of this model, as the brain is clearly a lot more complex that this, but it will give you a good basic model to work from.

process diagram that I introduced earlier. Once again, I want to emphasize – this diagram is NOT precisely what happens – it is a simplified model to explain the general concept and relationship between the various regions in the brain triggered by a sensory cue.

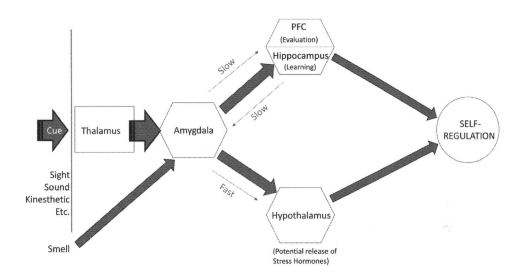

Let's look at this process carefully:

1. Sensory information about the environment and the body (from the scanning brain) is received by the eyes, ears, nose, touch, kinesthetic sense, etc. and converges on the thalamus, where it is processed.
2. The signal about that information is then passed on to the amygdala. (This is not 100% true. Smell has a fast track direct to the amygdala.)
3. The amygdala then interprets its emotional significance. This occurs at lightning speed.
4. If a threat is detected, the amygdala sends messages to the hypothalamus to secrete stress hormones to defend against the threat.
5. Meanwhile, a message is sent along a second neural pathway which runs via the hippocampus to the prefrontal cortex.
6. The PFC (our rational brain) then does a conscious and more refined interpretation of what is going on. This takes several microseconds longer.
7. If the PFC determines that there is no real threat (that rustling sound was only the wind in the trees not a snake), then it will send a message back to the amygdala to "stand down." The PFC wins the struggle.
8. If the interpretation of threat by the amygdala is too intense, and/or the braking system from the PFC is too weak, people lose control over the automatic, amygdala-driven response. The amygdala wins the struggle.

As I mentioned earlier, the amygdala and the PFC have this constant tug of war going on between them. The amygdala is ready to react to any stimulus that appears to be a threat. The prefrontal cortex acts as a "brake" on the amygdala [34] and keeps it in check. It is a relationship that is in constant tension.

This works OK until "the filtering system from the PFC is too weak." This happens when the PFC goes "off-line." The PFC goes off-line for a number of reasons:

- ➢ when it is tired
- ➢ when it has become temporarily worn out moderating our social behavior
- ➢ as a result of being placed under too much stress
- ➢ due to lack of sleep

Under these conditions, the PFC is no longer able to act as an effective brake on the amygdala. This means that the amygdala has "free rein" to respond to emotional and social threats without any moderating influence by the PFC.

Let's take a look at one of these conditions, i.e., the PFC is stressed.

In simplistic terms, when our brains are placed under a threat state, cortisol gets released. The "job" of cortisol is many-fold, but there are two impacts that I want to focus on here. The first job of cortisol is to close down the PFC; in effect, it reduces the ability of the PFC to do its job. The second job of cortisol is to boost the functioning of the limbic system (and hence the amygdala). The overall effect of this is to reduce your executive function's thinking ability and to trigger off your biases, habits, and automatic responses.

Activity	Physiological states	Affected brain portion
Whenever we feel threatened, we instinctively turn to the first level. We call out for help, support, and comfort from those around us.	Social Engagement	Cortex
If no one comes to our aid or if we feel that we are in immediate danger, we revert to a more primitive way to survive. We attempt to fight off the attacker or get to a safe place.	Fight or Flight	Limbic System
If this fails, we try to preserve ourselves by shutting down and expending as little energy as possible.	Freeze or Collapse	Reptilian Brain

If we go back just for a moment to the Savannah and being chased by that tiger, then this all makes sense. You don't want the PFC taking time to think about whether you should run from the tiger. Doing so would be too late...you want the limbic system to react as quickly as possible and get you and your brain to safety. But we are no longer on the Savannah. In most cases in our social and work environments, we want a fully online, fully functional, and fully effective PFC. We don't want to be driven by our amygdalae. It would be safer for all of us to have them under control!

So. Let's take a moment and look at what happens next. Once again, Van Der Kolk describes it better than I can, so I will use some of his words:

> "The autonomic nervous system regulates three fundamental physiological states. The level of safety determines which one of these is activated at any particular time"

While the fight or flight response has become well-known over the past several decades, the other two levels are equally important. The first of these levels has become known as "tend and befriend" and tends to be more practiced by females than males.

This makes sense from an evolutionary point of view. Many millions of years ago, it may not have made survival sense for females to have fought (they may have been physically smaller, although recently this has come into debate), and it may not have made survival sense to run (they may well have had offspring to protect). Hence, a survival strategy may have been to address the threat through social engagement. You can see remnants of that in today's meetings. If someone feels threatened, then the first thing you will often see is them look around at their colleagues for help.

This constant battle underlies many of the issues that we face, and I will explore it to a much greater degree in the next book in the series.

Notes and References for "Understanding the Brain: Five Basic Brain Principles":

[19] Medina, J. (2014). Brain Rules: 12 Principles for Surviving and Thriving at Work, Home, and School (2nd ed.). Pear Press.

[20] Van der Kolk, B. (2015). The Body Keeps the Score: Brain, Mind, and Body in the Healing of Trauma. Penguin Books. p 55

[21] Carter, R. (2014). The Human Brain Book: An Illustrated Guide to its Structure, Function, and Disorders. DK. Page 80

[22] http://www.kurzweilai.net/where-and-when-the-brain-recognizes-categorizes-an-object?utm_source=KurzweilAI+Weekly+Newsletter&utm_campaign=33e0e74157-UA-946742-1&utm_medium=email&utm_term=0_147a5a48c1-33e0e74157-282026345

[23] Kahneman, D. (2011). Thinking, Fast and Slow (1st ed.). Farrar, Straus and Giroux.

[24] Gallwey, T. (1997). The Inner Game of Tennis: The Classic Guide to the Mental Side of Peak Performance. Random House Trade Paperbacks.

[25] Eagleman, D. (2015). The Brain: The Story of You. Pantheon.

[26] Kraft-Todd, G. T., Reinero, D. A., Kelley, J. M., Heberlein, A. S., Baer, L., & Riess, H. (2017). Empathic nonverbal behavior increases ratings of both warmth and competence in a medical context. Plos One, 12(5), e0177758–16. http://doi.org/10.1371/journal.pone.0177758

[27] Bessel van Der Kolk, The Body Keeps the Score, p 54.

[28] Williams, L. M., Gatt, J. M., Hatch, A., Palmer, D. M., Nagy, M., Rennie, C., et al. (2008). The INTEGRATE Model of Emotion, Thinking and Self-Regulation: An Application to the "Paradox Of Aging." Journal of Integrative Neuroscience, 7(3), 367–404.

[29] Gordon, E. (2012). Brain Revolution: Self, Relationships and Society. Brain Revolution Publications.

[30] Eisenberger, N. I., & Lieberman, M. D. (2004). Why rejection hurts: a common neural alarm system for physical and social pain. Trends in Cognitive Sciences, 8(7), 294–300. http://doi.org/10.1016/j.tics.2004.05.010

[31] Eisenberger, N. I. (2012). The pain of social disconnection: examining the shared neural underpinnings of physical and social pain. Nature Reviews Neuroscience, 13(6), 421–434. http://doi.org/10.1038/nrn3231

[32] Eisenberger, N. I. (2012). The Neural Bases of Social Pain. Psychosomatic Medicine, 74(2), 126–135. http://doi.org/10.1097/PSY.0b013e3182464dd1

[33] Van der Kolk, B. (2015). The Body Keeps the Score: Brain, Mind, and Body in the Healing of Trauma. Penguin Books. p 61

[34] Lieberman, M. D. (2009). The brain's breaking system (and how to 'use your words' to tap into it). NeuroLeadership, (2), 1–8.

Brain Principle #5: There Are <u>FIVE</u> Driving Forces.

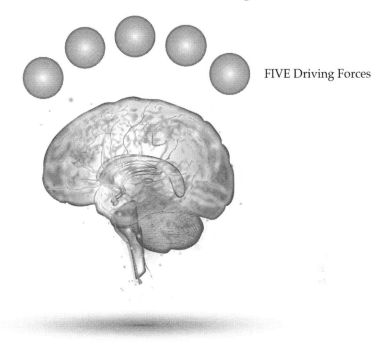

FIVE Driving Forces

We can identify the threats and rewards that the brain faces in five domains:

- ➤ Protection: i.e., to feel safe, secure, and, hence, survive
- ➤ Participation: i.e., to join in and be welcomed as part of a tribe
- ➤ Prediction: i.e., to be able to foresee what is going on
- ➤ Purpose: i.e., to be able to have a sense of meaning
- ➤ Pleasure: i.e., to enjoy ourselves

This is <u>SUCH</u> an important brain principle that it is in a section of its own, Section B, Part 2c, page 66.

Section B Part 2b. Five Brain Dynamics

Now that we understand the five brain principles, we can look at some other dynamics that affect the brain and consequently our thoughts, decisions, and actions.

	Dynamic	Brief Description
1	**We are biased.**	We are biased and habit driven, most of it nonconscious, much of it very important to how we react.
2	**We behave irrationally.**	Not only are we driven by the nonconscious part of our brain, but many of our actions are irrational.
3	**We are severely impacted by stress.**	Stress plays a very important role in the effective working of the brain; we need an optimal level.
4	**In general, we don't like change.**	For many of us, our brains do not like change; others take change in their stride.
5	**We are subject to some innate brain rhythms.**	We are driven by a number of rhythms or cycles that impact our energy.

Now let's take a look at each one in more detail.

Brain Dynamic #1: Bias and Habit

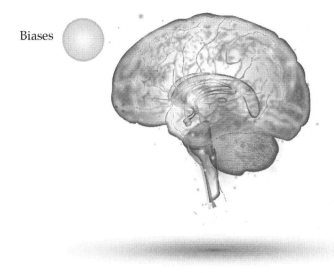

Biases

As one of the basic brain principles, I will briefly address the topic of bias here but will go into a lot more detail in the second volume, *Your Brain with Another Person.*

We are all biased. Period. (Full Stop.) We have to be for the sake of our brain. Biases, habits, patterns, or whatever you call them, the brain needs to have efficient ways to deal with the vast volume of data that is arriving second by second. Biases are one way of handling this information. Purely from the perspective of the brain, biases are useful shortcuts. Biases can deal with some of those 11,000,000 bits of information that the brain is handling in the background. Quick, easy, and highly energy efficient. It has worked well for us over many millennia. Biases are the brains way of not having to consciously think about everything all of the time.

There are many different types of bias. First, there are the obvious ones like race, skin color, gender, etc. but there are other types as well. Some of them are less obvious ones like maybe a bias against people who chew gum or towards people who dress a certain way. I am going to label these as "social biases."

Then there are the biases that are buried slightly deeper at a nonconscious level. One common example of this is called conformation bias. The conformation bias posits that we search out and give greater credence to information that we already know or that supports particular beliefs that we hold. At the point of writing this book, there are over 170 different cognitive biases identified on *Wikipedia.* [35]

Finally, I introduce a third type of bias - "neurodiversity bias." * These are biases that we use with people who behave or think differently than we do. For example, most of us have a bias with regard to extroversion and/or introversion. If we are introverted, for example, we may naturally shy away from someone who is extroverted.

There is a longer list of each of the three different types of biases in Appendix A.

---

* I am aware that this term has been used to refer to people who are on the spectrum. I use it because it best describes the biases that I am talking about.

I now want to peel one more layer off the bias onion. While these biases are set up for the purpose of saving energy for the brain, they are difficult to get our arms around. What I mean by that is this:

> ➢ We often don't believe we are biased (although we are).
> ➢ Our biases are mostly at a nonconscious level, and so we don't know they are there.
> ➢ Even when we know they are there, they are almost impossible to control.
> ➢ Even when we try to control them, we don't do a very good job at it.
> ➢ Trying to train ourselves is very difficult.

In their book, Banaji and Greenwald [36] describe the situation very well so I will use their original words:

> *"Once lodged in our minds, hidden biases can influence our behavior towards members of particular social groups, but we remain <u>oblivious to their influence</u>."*

The underlines are mine. But get this. "We remain oblivious to their influence."

But wait, it gets worse. They go on:

> *"In talking with others...people find it unbelievable that their behavior can be guided by mental content of which they are unaware."*

The sad thing is that even when we know that we are biased, we are not good at doing anything about it.

And Lieberman [37] adds that training, in general, doesn't seem to work. Some researchers might challenge his premise. Although the solution might be a little indirect, Frederickson [38] reports an interesting approach:

> *"A long series of experiments had already confirmed that people are notoriously bad at recognizing individuals across racial lines...i.e., own-race bias in face recognition. Not much seems to budge this entrenched bias – not even years spent in ethnically diverse schools and job sites."*

and

> *"We notice a person's race within about 100 milliseconds. By comparison, we notice their sex within about 150 milliseconds.*
>
> *Positive emotions didn't simply diminish the entrenched racial bias, it eliminated it altogether: under the influence of positivity, people become just as good at recognizing individuals of another race as they are at recognizing individuals of their own race."*

So, just maybe, we are doing the wrong forms of training.

In researching and writing about bias and viewpoints about bias, it is important to point out that there is some debate about why biases exist. Haselton et al [39] demonstrate that taking an evolutionary view of bias reframes the whole issue of bias.

They present an argument that suggests that rather than some cognitive biases being "flaws," they are adaptively useful.

Here is the best summary of their argument that I can find:

> *"We ultimately conclude that the mind is best described as adaptively rational. By adaptively rational, we mean that the mind shows evidence of psychological design for coping with recurrent adaptive problems our ancestors encountered over evolutionary history – the mind is equipped with mechanisms that are constrained and sometimes imprecise but nevertheless clear products of natural selection showing evidence of good design."*

Biases and habits are vitally important to the brain, to save conscious thought, and hence, energy. They are also drivers of much of our behavior, so understanding them is key. I'll be talking a lot more about them throughout the rest of the series as they impact everything ... our behaviors when we are on our own, when we are interacting in any way with other people, whether singly or in groups.

Brain Dynamic #2: Irrationality

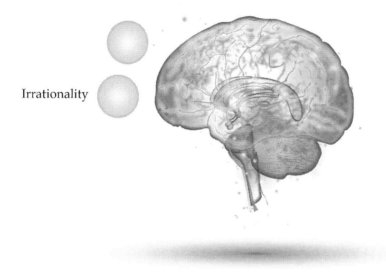

Irrationality

Despite our wonderful brains and the incredible power that they have, we all behave irrationally. There are a number of reasons for this, and many books and papers have been written on each. For example, we may behave irrationally if:

➤ we see something that is unfair, either to us or to other people.
➤ specific words or metaphors are used.
➤ something is framed a certain way.
➤ something has been "anchored" in our brain.
➤ we are subject to certain influences.

Let's take a look at some of these in a little more detail, leveraging the work done by Dan Ariely who has many books on the advantages and disadvantages of irrationality, this reference being one of them: [40]

Unfairness and Rationality

This subject, or more accurately, this combination of subjects, has been the topic of much study and experiment over the past several decades, most notably by Kahneman and Tversky. [41] Their work has been extremely well-documented and made very accessible by Michael Lewis. [42]

One process underlying many of their studies is a behavioral economics game referred to as the ultimatum game. The essence of the game is very simple. It consists of two players. Player A is given a sum of money, let's say $100. Player A, however, must share the money with Player B. Player A can make a determination of any amount that they share with Player B. Player B, however, can make the ultimate decision of whether they like the way that Player A has shared the money. If Player B likes the way that Player A has shared the money and accepts the offer, then they both get to keep the money. If Player B does not like the way that Player A has shared the money and rejects the offer, then neither player gets to keep the money.

The "rational" theory is that it does not matter what amount Player A offers Player B, then Player B should accept it. After all, any amount is better than nothing, and Player B had nothing beforehand. Ah, yes. But wait. Player B's brain, if it is not a "reasonable" or "fair" offer, frequently rejects the offer as being "unfair." In a truly rational world, all offers would get accepted. But it's not. Our emotions come into it and can sometimes rule the roost. There is some evidence that the "drop off" point for acceptance of unfair offers is about 20% of the original amount.

The experiment has been repeated many, many times, but Daniel Kahneman and Amos Tversky get the credit for developing it and the associated theory. As a small aside, they were awarded the 2002 Nobel Memorial Prize in Economic Sciences which displeased many economists as Kahneman and Tversky are/were psychologists not economists. ☺

The experiment has many variants. In one such variant, the researchers [43] examined whether gender made a difference to the average offers and acceptances that were made and found, indeed, that gender influenced the offers and acceptances. In yet another variant, [44] they found that the attractiveness of the person did positively affect the amount of the offer. These demonstrate an interesting interaction between these different fundamentals of the brain, in this case, the interaction of bias and irrationality.

I have run this experiment informally on many occasions and have found that the fairness issue seems to vary from country to country, culture to culture, and, maybe, context to context. During a visit to the Czech Republic a couple of years ago, I ran a brief version of the ultimatum game. While I understand that I had not established a sound scientific study, I was surprised at the differences in the participants' reactions to what I experienced when I had carried out similar experiments in the US. They were, to a person, much more willing to accept lower shares of the financial pie. Even down to a single $1. In a subsequent discussion, the participants pointed out that they, or their parents, had lived under a communist regime for a long time. They were happy to receive any amount of money no matter how fair or otherwise it seemed. I suspect that we need to do a lot more research for different regions, countries, cultures, and contexts to flesh out these research findings.

Words Matter

The words that we use when asking questions can have a significant impact on the answers that we get. Consider the following two questions aimed at the same event:

"How fast was the car going when it hit the other car?"

"How fast was the car going when it smashed into the other car?"

The speed estimates that we get from the second question are much higher than in the first.

There are many other examples of the impact of words. One such example is the use of metaphors. For example, a recent study [45] determined that how we describe discoveries shapes people's perceptions of both the inventions and the inventors. The metaphors we use for the discovery influence perceptions of the quality of the idea and the ability of the creator.

The "light bulb" and the "nurtured like a seed" metaphor were used as comparisons. The idea was seen as more exceptional when the light bulb metaphor was used. In addition, there was a gender difference: the results were different for female inventors. Women were judged as better idea creators than men when ideas were nurtured over time, i.e., using the seed metaphor. Gender stereotypes play a role in how people perceive the inventors. The seed metaphor increased perceptions of female inventors whereas the light bulb metaphor increased perceptions of male inventors

Framing Effect

How we frame something impacts the responses we get even though the event, the data, and the context are the same. A group of doctors were given a simple scenario. There was an illness about to affect a whole town and without help everyone would die. There was a remedy, but it was not wholly effective. The doctors could choose whether to administer a drug or not. Half the doctors were told that if they administered the drug, they would save 80% of the town. The other half of the doctors were told that if they administered the drug, 20% would die. In the first instance, most of the doctors elected to administer the drug. In the second case, most of the doctors decided not to administer the drug.

The Anchoring Effect

First, a definition… "The anchoring effect (or priming effect) is the tendency to rely too heavily, or 'anchor,' on one trait or piece of information when making decisions (usually the first piece of information that we acquire on that subject)."

Kahneman [46] describes this effect as

"… so common and so important in the everyday world …"

that we all need to know about it. He goes on to describe "its absurdity" when referring to the fact that people are influenced by "an obviously uninformative number." There are many examples of the anchoring effect, and they tend to have a couple of pretty significant impacts on our daily lives, some where the single piece of information has no relation to the topic under consideration and some where the information may have some bearing. Let's take a look at both cases.

In the first case, the experiment cited by Kahneman describes how he and Tversky rigged a roulette wheel to stop only at 10 or 65. Participants were then asked to write down the number when they spun the wheel. They were then asked a question that had absolutely nothing to do with the spinning wheel or roulette. They found that the simple act of writing down either 10 or 65 impacted the degree of freedom that they exhibited when making their next estimate. This experiment has been repeated hundreds of times, and one famous study had people write down the last two digits of their social security number. The experiment demonstrated that this had an impact on the amount that the participants bid when they took part in an auction.

The second case is demonstrated in a number of ways, for example, in a wine menu. If you are in the mood for a reasonably nice bottle of wine, you may peruse the menu and see several bottles going for approximately $50. You glance at the bottom of the page, and you see a bottle at $84. You think to yourself that price seems too expensive even for a good California Cabernet Sauvignon. On the next page, you see several bottles in the $100 to $150 range and one at $420. As you pass through the menu a second time, that $84 bottle seems like reasonably good value.

You might think that these effects are small and subtle, but that turns out not to be the case. The effects can have impacts of 30 – 50% differences.

Once the priming effect is in operation, then we have to exert extra effort to move away or adjust from the anchor. People adjust less when their mental resources are depleted (the brain's struggle rears its head again).

Influence

Cialdini [47] has done much of the research on how much we are non-consciously influenced, and all of his books are well written and packed with examples. The one that comes to mind whenever I think of the issue of influence is the first that Cialdini addresses: reciprocation.

Reciprocation

Reciprocation recognizes the fact that people feel indebted to those who do something for them or give them a gift. This indebtedness is felt even if the gift they are given is not something that they asked for or even want. And it happens at a nonconscious level.

When I use this next example in workshops, people are blown away. In advance of telling them about the influence, I ask them what influences the amount of tip they give at a restaurant. The answers, if they don't have an automatic number in mind, which some people do, are typically the quality of the food, the service from the wait staff, and the ambience of the overall dining experience. I then show them the following data:

Behavioral Scientist David Strohmetz examined the impact of leaving a gift (a piece of candy for each diner) on the same plate as the bill by the wait staff at the end of a meal in a restaurant.

Condition	Increase in tip
A single piece of candy left on the plate	3.3%
Two pieces of candy left on the plate	14.1%
A single piece of candy, followed by a return to the table with an extra piece	23%

So, the bottom line of all of this – we are nowhere near as rational in our thinking and decision-making as we think we are.

Brain Dynamic # 3: Stress

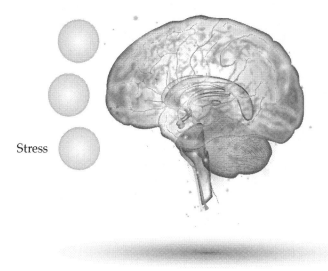

Stress

The heading for this part of the book really should be "The Need for Just the Right Amount of Stress." You may have heard that cortisol is equated with stress, and cortisol and stress are both bad. Well, yes and no. It's not as simple as that. Cortisol is, indeed, equated with stress, but we all need some degree of stress. Indeed, we probably wouldn't wake up if it weren't for cortisol. [48] But we need the "right amount" of stress in order to "perform" at our best. The relationship between stress (or arousal as it is technically known) and performance has been documented many times since it was first described over 100 years ago. [49]

For simple tasks, our performance increases to a certain point after which extra stimulus has little effect. That's the top line shown in the next diagram. For more complex tasks, there is a peak before which we don't perform as well and after which we don't perform as well. That's the lower of the two lines.

This is best illustrated by the following diagram:

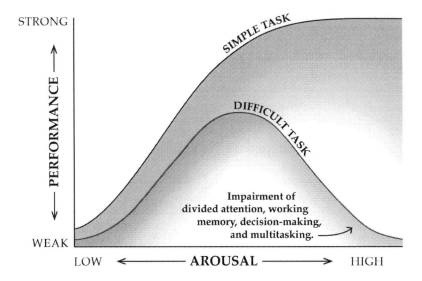

Some neuroscientists refer to this as the Goldilocks syndrome because the amount of stress, and hence our position on the curve, has to be "just right." Stress is necessary for us to get organized, get going, be efficient, and get creative. Too much, however, will push us too far, and we start to lack focus, lack concentration, become less productive, get distracted more easily, and, in many other ways, become less productive. In addition, we are likely to become more emotional. This arousal curve helps us to understand why stress impacts different people in different ways. We all have a "natural" place somewhere on the curve, which is different for all of us. And it is different for extroverts and introverts.

The way that we all handle stress, what stresses us, and how we respond to stress is different for everybody. I call that mixture of things your Personal Threat Profile.

The exact shape of the curve, and where we will sit on the curve at any given time and for any given task, depends on a number of things in addition to the task complexity, illustrated above. The mixture of things I refer to is the Personal Threat Context, and it covers things such as:

> - The skill level of the person doing the task
> - The newness of the task to the person
> - The newness of the context to the person
> - The degree to which the person feels like they have control over their situation
> - The person's personality
> - The person's trait anxiety
> - The degree of support that the person perceives that they have
> - The person's current stress levels from other activities or from the context
> - The amount of information that the person has about what is going on

Let's now take a look at the impact of chronic stress.

We need some amount of stress as I mentioned above. The stress response, however, evolved to meet an immediate threat. The threat of seeing a saber-toothed tiger caused us to run. The threat was dealt with and life would go on (assuming that you survived).

59

The various chemicals that had been injected into your body and brain would dissipate and your breath, heart rate, and other physiological changes would return to normal relatively quickly.

Nowadays, however, the stresses that we are faced with don't just "go away." We are often faced with social or emotional threats that are around for a long while. For example, Hogan and Hogan [50] found that the biggest stressor at work for approximately 75% of people in corporate America is their boss! Much of the time, that is a stress that you cannot get away from.

There are many studies that show chronic stress has serious negative impacts on our brains. Studies have shown that the length of neurons and the number of branch points of these neurons changes as a result of chronic stress. In the PFC and hippocampus (a center of memory and learning), the length of the neurons and the number of branch points reduce with chronic stress. The impact of this is that we find it harder to learn and memorize under chronic stress. On the other hand, in the amygdala, the length of the neurons, and the number of branch points increases under chronic stress. The theory behind this is that if the amygdala is under constant stress, it resolves to strengthen in order to deal with the stress, initiating a vicious cycle.

In *The Blue Zones*, [51] Dan Buettner identifies that effectively dealing with stress is one of the nine factors for a long and happy life. His summary:

> *"Even people in the Blue Zones experience stress, which leads to chronic inflammation, associated with major age-related disease. The world's longest-lived people have routines to shed that stress: Okinawans take a few moments each day to remember their ancestors. Adventists pray, Ikarians take a nap, and Sardinians do happy hour."*

Bottom line: some stress is necessary and healthy. Too much isn't. Too much will cause your performance to decrease in the short term. Over time, too much stress results in undesirable physiological changes to the brain.

Brain Dynamic #4: Change

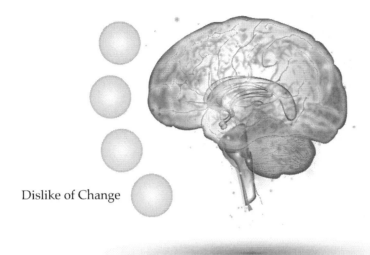

Dislike of Change

Change is often (usually?) met with some resistance because the brain basically dislikes change. In essence, change is the inverse of all the aspects that make the brain feel safe. The brain craves consistency, commitment, certainty, clarity, information, knowing what's going on, etc. so that prediction, and hence safety, is possible. The very concept of change, even for the good, threatens that consistency, commitment, and clarity.

It is generally thought that the brain uses image schemas (more correctly schemata, but who cares?) as mental imagery or concepts that hang together in some way to represent everything about our world. From when we are very young, we build up these schemas to represent and remember everything that we learn. Everything from a banana (being a yellow, curved fruit, eaten by monkeys, the skin of which is slippery if you tread on it) through to a castle (being a large, cold, foreboding, cold building often perched on top of mountains in Europe). Thus, these schemas represent knowledge structures. The brain tends to keep them at a high level and fills in the detail when required.

These schemas are good news and bad news. The good news is that they provide easy constructs for us to make judgments. In a similar fashion to biases, they provide the brain with quick mental shortcuts. They guide and draw attention to whether a piece of data is "new" and hence not yet in our schema. The bad news is that they can "also guide our attention to selectively ignore information that is not consistent with the schema."

All the while, we add additional data and information that matches or fits into the schema that we have, then the brain is happy to do so. Indeed, because of some our biases that we have, e.g., confirmation bias, we actively seek out data and information that match the schema. If additional data arrive, however, that doesn't match our schema, then it causes the brain difficulty. So, if all of a sudden you come across a purple banana, then it will disorient your brain's image of what a banana should be. When the new data matches our schema, we feel rewarded. The brain likes to be right. When the new data does not match, we feel threatened.

DiSalvio [52] gives a great brain-based explanation for this. He cites Axelrod's [53] schema theory of how our brain's store information.

"As these schemas develop, the parameters for what information can be included, tighten."

I quote again from DiSalvo, as he describes it so well:

"When a well-established schema is called into question by new information, the brain reacts as if threatened. The amygdala fires up (threat response) and the ventral striatum revs down (reward response). This is not a comfortable place for the brain. The supercharged clay in your head doesn't like being on guard – it likes being stable. Ambiguity, which might result from considering the new information, is a threat. We can either allow that threat to stand by considering the inconsistent information or block it by dismissing it or ignoring it. Or we might subcategorize the information and store it away as an 'outlier' case, something that can't be ignored but does not challenge or change the existing schema."

There are some theories that this schema-based process mismatch is the underlying problem when people are faced with change. Faced with change, many of the brain's schema would have to be changed, something that some brains are unwilling to do easily. If it was as simple as that, then that would be easy. But as you have probably gathered by now, nothing is simple and easy as far as the brain is concerned. If that were all there was to it, then we would all react the same way to change. If the data matches, then we will feel safe. If the data doesn't match, then we will feel threatened.

That doesn't explain, however, why some people seem just to go with the flow with change, and others find even the slightest of changes very threatening. Once again, this all depends on your Personal Threat Profile, which we will address in the next section.

One of the roles of sleep is to help us to sort through the data of the day. It is probable that this sorting process assists with the integrating of new data into existing schema. [54]

Whenever we talk about change, then the biggest question that follows is, well can people change? If so, how do we change? For example, can we change our habits? Research indicates that yes, if we are ready to change, and that is a big "IF," then we can change some things. Others are more difficult, but in any case, any approach to change needs to take the brain into account and develop a strategy that addresses both the PFC and conscious change together with the limbic system and nonconscious resistance.

Brain Dynamic #5: Brain Rhythms

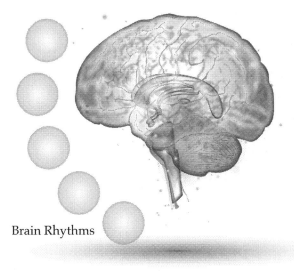

Brain Rhythms

It appears that the brain is affected by four main cycles or rhythms. These are ultradian rhythms, the circadian rhythm, the owl-lark cycle, and the infradian cycle. The first of these cycles is the shortest and the last is the longest. Let's look at them in a little more detail, starting with the shortest cycles first.

Ultradian Rhythms

Rhythms or cycles that repeat periodically for lengths of time of less than an hour to several hours. They seem to drive a rhythm that leads to optimal vs. less optimal functioning. They drive some hormonal activity and the REM sleep cycle (of approximately 90 minutes), and there is some evidence that this 90-minute cycle continues during wakefulness as well as sleep.

Circadian Rhythms

A (roughly) 24-hour cycle in the physiological processes of living beings including plants, animals, and fungi. They are internally driven, although they can be modulated by external cues such as sunlight and temperature. They impact the sleeping and feeding patterns of all animals, including human beings. There are clear patterns of brain wave activity, hormone production, cell regeneration, and other biological activities linked to this daily cycle.

Owl-lark Cycle

People find their performance peaks at specific times of day. A contribution to this variation appears to be driven by the difference between early risers or "larks" and late-night people or "owls." Researchers refer to it as "'morningness" or "eveningness." It appears that female larks are awake on average an hour or so before male larks. There is some recent evidence that this tendency could be driven as a tribal evolutionary advantage in that there was always someone on guard for the community.

Pink, in his book *Time*, [55] suggests that there is a large percentage of the population who are neither one nor the other.

Infradian Cycle

These are cycles that occur with a period of greater than one day; a typical example of this is the female menstrual cycle. They are independent from ultradian and circadian rhythms.

The net effect of the combination of all these cycles means that the brain has "its ups and downs" on a regular basis. Not all times of the day are equal when it comes to brain activity. Not all times of the month are equal when it comes to brain activity. Understand and make use of your optimum times to do different activities.

Finally, all of these rhythms can be affected by other contextual dynamics. For example, diet, nutrition, sleep, exercise, other stress, and our own positivity/negativity bias can all have impact on our energy cycles. I will deal with these in a little more detail in the next few sections.

Brain Dynamics: Summary

I have looked at each of these brain principles and brain dynamics as separate aspects. In practice, while these are good descriptions of what is happening, the actual process is a lot more complicated than I have described it. In addition, these principles are all going on in parallel and are interacting with each other.

Notes and References for "Understanding the Brain: Five Brain Dynamics":

[35] https://en.wikipedia.org/wiki/List_of_cognitive_biases

[36] Banaji, M. R., & Greenwald, A. G. (2013). Blindspot: Hidden Biases of Good People. Delacorte Press.

[37] Lieberman, M. D., Rock, D., & Cox, C. L. (2014). Breaking Bias. Neuroleadership Journal, 5, 1–20.

[38] Frederickson, B. L. (n.d.). Positivity: Top-Notch Research Reveals the Upward Spiral That Will Change Your Life. Harmony.

[39] Haselton, M., Bryant, G. A., Wilke, A., Frederick, D., & Galperin, A. (2009). Adaptive rationality: An evolutionary perspective on cognitive bias. Social Cognition, 27(5), 733–763.

[40] Ariely, D. (2010). Predictably Irrational, Revised and Expanded Edition: The Hidden Forces That Shape Our Decisions. Harper Perennial.

[41] Tversky, A. (2003). Preference, Belief, and Similarity: Selected Writings. MIT Press - Bradford Books.

[42] Lewis, M. (2016). The Undoing Project: A Friendship That Changed Our Minds. W. W. Norton & Company.

[43] Solnick, S. J., & Schweitzer, M. E. (1999). The Influence of Physical Attractiveness and Gender on Ultimatum Game Decisions. Organizational Behavior and Human Decision Processes, 79(3), 199–215.

[44] Solnick, S. J., & Schweitzer, M. E. (1999). The Influence of Physical Attractiveness and Gender on Ultimatum Game Decisions. Organizational Behavior and Human Decision Processes, 79(3), 199–215.

[45] Elmore, K. C., & Luna-Lucero, M. (2016). Light Bulbs or Seeds? How Metaphors for Ideas Influence Judgments About Genius. Social Psychological and Personality Science, 8(2), 200–208. http://doi.org/10.1177/1948550616667611)

[46] Kahneman, D. (2011). Thinking, Fast and Slow. Farrar, Straus and Giroux.

[47] Cialdini, R. B. (2008). Influence: Science and Practice. Allyn and Bacon.

[48] Smyth, N., Thorn, L., Hucklebridge, F., Evans, P., & Clow, A. (2015). Detailed time course of the cortisol awakening response in healthy participants. Psychoneuroendocrinology, 62, 200–203.

[49] Yerkes, R. M., & Dodson, J. D. (1908). The relation of strength of stimulus to rapidity of habit formation. Journal of Comparative Neurology and Psychology, 18, 459–482.

[50] Hogan, R. (2006). Personality and the Fate of Organizations (1ᵉ ed.). Routledge.

[51] Buettner, D. (2012). The Blue Zones: 9 Lessons for Living Longer From the People Who've Lived the Longest. National Geographic.

[52] DiSalvio, D. (2011). What Makes Your Brain Happy and Why You Should Do the Opposite. Prometheus Books

[53] Axelrod, R. (1973). Schema Theory: An Information Processing Model of Perception and Cognition. The American Political Science Review, 67(4), 1248–1266.

[54] Lewis, P. A., & Durrant, S. J. (2011). Overlapping memory replay during sleep builds cognitive schemata. Trends in Cognitive Sciences, 15(8), 343–351. http://doi.org/10.1016/j.tics.2011.06.004

[55] Pink, D. (2018). When: The Scientific Secrets of Perfect Timing. Riverhead Books.

Section B Part 2c. Five Driving Forces: The Five P's of Threat and Reward

Before we take a look at the specific domains of threat and reward, I want to put the brain into the framework of our daily lives. The context that I want to start with is this: "What do we want as human beings?" This is a subject that people have been writing about for years. This brief commentary will be a little different in that I am going to take a look at it, mostly, from the brain's perspective.

If you examine the literature, you can find many papers and books on what we want as human beings. The list of items that results from this research gets to be quite long and can become very disorganized. If you look at it from the viewpoint of the brain, however, it can become a little easier to see what's going on.

One of the concepts that I addressed in Brain Dynamic # 3 is the three "layers" of the brain (Page 39 and 40) As a reminder, the 'bottom' layer is known as the reptilian brain, the next layer is known as the limbic system, and the 'top' layer is the neocortex. If we look at the "focus" of each of these three parts, it can help us to understand what it is we want…or, more specifically, what each of these layers of the brain wants:

Area	Role	Focus	Threatened By and Rewarded By
Neocortex	**Prediction**	Conscious Thought Reasoning	Threat: Uncertainty Reward: Learning, Flow, and a Higher **Purpose**
Limbic System	Social **Participation**	Emotions Learning Emotional Memory	Threat: Social and Emotional Danger Reward: Feeling Trust, Social Activities, Higher Status, and **Pleasure**
Reptilian Brain / Brain Stem	Personal **Protection**	Danger	Threat: Physical Danger Reward: Feeling Safe and Secure

If we pull this apart, we can see that there are five major drivers that impact these three layers:

> ➤ Protection: i.e., to feel safe, secure, and, hence, survive
> ➤ Participation: i.e., to join in and be welcomed as part of a tribe
> ➤ Prediction: i.e., to be able to foresee what is going on
> ➤ Purpose: i.e., to be able to have a sense of meaning
> ➤ Pleasure: i.e., to enjoy ourselves

Let's explore these in a little more detail. I will take each of the five areas, or domains, and expand into some specific facets. These facets have come from a variety of sources, and I believe it to be fairly comprehensive. The list, however, is not intended to be totally complete or rigorous from a scientific viewpoint. Rather it is to provide a basis for you to start to think about the types of things that you want and/or are driven by. In what areas do you find yourself emotionally or socially threatened or triggered? This is one of the first steps to self-awareness.

The list came from an analysis of various books, assessments, and treatise on human needs and the human condition. I gathered various words or groups of words that seemed to come up again and again. Some of these words seemed as though we might react differently to them according to our context, i.e., whether we were at work or at home or in our social or private lives.

I then grouped all of these facets into the five domains.

The list of the facets is on the next two pages, followed by some overall comments about how you might think about them. Then I go into further explanation of each of the facets, some of the science behind them and finish with a question about how that facet might apply to you.

As you read the list (if you read the list) you might find yourself for certain facets saying something to the effect... "Well that's not important to me." For other facets, you will nod your head in agreement. That's perfectly natural. We all assign different weightings to each of these facets. As you read this list, it might be useful to assign a numeric value to each of the facets on a scale of 1 to 10, according to how important that facet is to you.

And how would knowing a value be of interest to you? Let's say you score very high on any given facet, i.e., it is very important to you. If you are faced with a situation that causes that facet to be in question, then your brain might experience the situation as a threat which can trigger off your brain's reaction to threats. In addition, if something is important to you, and you see someone else not doing it, then that too might trigger a reaction in you.

Let's take an example. Let's say delivering against your commitments is important to you. You will strive to deliver what you say you will deliver. You will want to live up to your word. If something or someone prevents you from delivering, then that might cause you to get triggered. In addition, if other people don't deliver against their commitments, that also might cause you to get triggered.

Protection

We each, to a lesser or greater degree, want to:

1. Feel physically safe, i.e., have warmth and shelter
2. Feel emotionally safe in our personal, work, and social relationships
3. Feel financially secure and avoid financial losses
4. Experience a balance between short-term reward and long-term gain
5. Know where we stand – geographically and in our social and work environments
6. Be treated fairly, see other people treated fairly in our social and work environments, and see animals treated fairly
7. Be treated as equal partners in our primary relationship and see other people treated as equal partners in their primary relationship
8. Feel resilient, i.e., we want to be able to bounce back from life's troughs
9. Be and feel healthy – physically, mentally, emotionally, and spiritually

Participation

We each, to a lesser or greater degree, want to:

10. Be trusted and be with people we trust
11. Be associated with people with whom we have something in common, with whom we feel we belong and are accepted, and who we like
12. Differentiate ourselves from the group and be able to proffer opinions that are different from others in the group
13. Play and work on teams
14. Have a sense of self-respect and self-esteem, to feel equal to or better than others, and to see life as a competition where we want to win or beat other people
15. Receive recognition from people who are important to us, be valued and respected by them, know that they care about us, and know that we have some level of approval from them
16. Have some sense of power and influence in our work and our social lives
17. Have some sense of status and prestige in our work and our social lives
18. Treat other people in a benevolent fashion
19. Avoid looking incompetent or stupid
20. Avoid feeling like an imposter/fraud

Prediction

We each, to a lesser or greater degree, want to:

21. Feel certainty about the future and be clear in our work and our social lives
22. Know what is expected of us in our work and our social lives
23. Know how we will be measured and evaluated in work situations
24. Know if and how we will be rewarded at work
25. Have a degree of control of our own destiny, i.e., autonomy, in our work and our social lives
26. Be able to move into action and make things happen in our work and our social lives
27. Know what's going on
28. Be right and achieve some degree of perfectionism
29. Have no changes – keep things the same in our work and our social lives

30. Understand what is going on and make sense of things in our work and our social lives
31. Have things be consistent
32. Have some ambiguity in work and our social lives – but not too much
33. Have some things be spontaneous, but surprises at work and socially can scare us
34. Feel that we can take care of ourselves
35. Have some sense of tradition
36. Have some sense of conformity
37. Have some sense of harmony and stability at work and socially
38. Be sure – we don't like feeling doubt
39. Have people be authentic with us
40. Minimize risk at work and in our social lives
41. Be curious and learn
42. Know that we are heard and our opinions count
43. Be able to "go with the flow" at work and in our social lives
44. Have commitment from others at work and in our social lives

Purpose

We each, to a lesser or greater degree, want to:

45. Achieve mastery in our fields and have an opportunity to practice it on a regular basis
46. Develop ourselves/self-actualize
47. Have a Mission/Purpose/Meaning
48. Live in accordance with our core values and work with people/organizations that align with those values
49. Express ourselves artistically
50. Explore and live our spirituality
51. Feel passionate about something
52. Have a challenge
53. Seek the truth

Pleasure

We each, to a lesser or greater degree, want to:

54. Experience joy and happiness
55. Experience sensual gratification
56. Experience instant gratification
57. Experience stimulation and excitement
58. Play
59. Be loved

The sequence with which the brain "deals" with these five P's is also important. It turns out that the brain cannot address "rewards" until it feels safe, i.e., until all of the threats have been dealt with. Then it can turn its attention to what might be rewarding. Hence, Protection, Participation, and Prediction figure higher in what we regularly pay attention to than Purpose and Pleasure. We are triggered by those things in Protection, Participation, and Prediction that threaten or potentially threaten us. We are triggered by events or actions that might prevent us from getting what we want in the Purpose and Pleasure spheres.

While I have arranged each of these social facets into these Five P's, some don't fit nicely into just one area. They overlap two or more. For example, we want to be and feel healthy. This could be viewed as the need for prediction, to be sure that we will be able to take care of ourselves in the future; it could, however, be the need for protection because otherwise we will not survive.

In addition, for simplicity's sake, all of these social facets are listed separately whereas in reality most, if not all of them, interact. For example, if I increase your certainty about the future (Prediction – giving you a better sense of what will happen), I might, in parallel, decrease your sense of control (Participation – you weren't involved with my decision about the future and also Prediction – you weren't in control of what I decided).

The degree to which we want each of these different facets varies widely from person to person and sometimes within each of us. We are likely to perceive social or emotional threats and rewards in each of the facets which we rank highest. The degree to which we are affected by these threats and rewards will depend upon the value or weighting we attach to each of these social facets. For example, there are some people for whom change is no big deal. They take it in their stride. They would attach little value to the need for things to stay the same. On the other hand, as I am sure you will have experienced, there are people for whom the slightest change sends them into a tailspin. They would rate this facet very high, i.e., as extremely important to them.

If we just take a look at a couple of examples, it will illustrate this point:

For our first example, let's look at Protection. Some people have a great need to feel safe and wouldn't dream of putting themselves in physical harm's way. Being asked to participate in a ropes course at work, for example, could feel like a major threat to them. Yet other people will bungee jump off the side of a bridge without a second thought.

Yet, that same person who bungee jumps every second Sunday (Protection) might not be willing to share their emotions with other people (Participation). They will face physical risk but shy away from emotional risk.

For our second example, let's say there are two people named Mary and Fred who are work colleagues. Mary likes things to be very predictable. She is most happy when she knows exactly what is going to happen. She wants to do the same task on a regular basis with only very gradual change, if any at all. On the other hand, Fred has a real need to do different things all the time or he gets bored. Or worse, he may even sabotage the very systems or processes that make Mary feel safe and secure. And he may not even recognize that he is doing so.

And even Mary every so often will do something off the wall. Even she may not really know why. It was just on a whim. It was as if another part of her took control for a brief period. Other people might see it as so out of character.

Finally, we need to add in one other very important facet into our considerations. That is the concept of the Self. We will be examining the Self in a lot more detail in the second half of the book, but for now let's just say this: we all bring our own story to any situation. This story is a product of our environment growing up and our experiences which include joy, happiness, sadness, trauma, etc. These experiences shape the way we experience the world and the filter by which we experience our daily lives. While all of the other social facets are general, there are some that will be highly specific, and maybe even unique, to an individual, i.e., the Self. These individual ones may be so powerful that they can eclipse the general ones.

I recently spent a week with two of my sisters. One evening we were discussing some of the "truisms" under which we had grown up. For them, a memorable one was not being allowed to sing at the dinner table. At which point, naturally, the three of us started to sing. ☺ Another that we all remembered was that whenever we drove somewhere, our father would drive us back a different way. To this day we all still do it! Trivial examples, obviously, but good illustrations of the power and longevity of these social facets.

So, the overall purpose of this section is to look at each of these facets in more detail so that you can understand what will likely trigger a stress response in you and what will likely have no significant impact. Once again, I will be simplifying. Spoiler alert: the real life of the brain is way more complicated than how I will describe it.

I will be suggesting that you think about yourself in relation to each of these separate facets. Let's take an example:

One of the facets of Participation is the following statement:

"We want to be associated with people with whom we have something in common."

For some people, this aspect of being social and sociable is extremely important, and they will take steps in their life to ensure that happens. This might manifest itself in activities such as joining clubs, attending church, and, even more so these days, joining like-minded people on social media. The idea of joining a group links our need for Participation together with our need for Protection – physically, we feel safer with a group.

For other people, being around other people is not necessary at all, let alone being around people that are just like them. They prefer to be on their own and don't seek out others that are just like them.

And some people are in the middle. They have a few activities that bring them in contact with other people that are like them, but it is not a dominant part of their lives.

We can quantify this by using a simple scale of 1 to 10. If you had an absolute need to be with people with whom you have a lot in common, then you might score yourself as say 9 or 10 out of 10. On the other hand, if the thought of spending time with people who have a similar mindset to you sends shivers down your spine, then you might score 1 out of 10. And the people in the middle? They probably score themselves 4, 5, or 6 out of 10.

On many occasions, when people are asked to make a personal assessment like the one I mention here, they get confused. The true answer that they want to give is "It depends." And indeed, that is most often the case. It depends on a whole variety of factors, some of which we can identify in advance, but many are too varied to be predictable. We know that one of the factors that we need to consider is time. What timeframe are we looking at? Long-term, medium-term, or short-term?

Some of our personal characteristics seem to have been with us for a long time. Experts say that these, known as someone's temperament, are identifiable at a very young age and do not tend to change. Others tend to be around for a long period of time but are changeable. Others tend to be driven by what is happening in our world during the recent past or back a couple of months or a couple of years.

Experts say that we have two sorts of conditions in our mind – the long-term ones they call traits, and the shorter-term ones they call states.

I suggest that as you think about your own view on these different facets, you consider the following different time frames.

> ➤ Trait – your behavior and preferences over the long-term
> ➤ State – your behavior more recently, let's say anywhere between the past several years and the past month or so
> ➤ Recently – your behavior in the past couple of days or week

Clearly, these are not specific timings. They are meant to be general, but I have found this division to be helpful in giving people a framework for how to put their thoughts in context. For example, I was working with a person several years ago. She described that, as a trait, her need for things to stay the same was very low. Then she was laid off from work and went without a job for approximately nine months. She recognized that her need for things to remain secure had changed. She now valued consistency and certainty in her work life. Even though she had found a new job and had been in it for over a year, she valued that things would stay the same. But she had started to realize that she needed some other things to change in her life. That's where we focused our discussions.

One of the other factors that we can predict is that we don't always act the same way for any given set of circumstances, although we would like to believe that we are rational and behave consistently. We will examine this in a lot more detail in the section under "Self."

One small caveat. As I describe the things that we want in more detail and make some comments on how we react, I am doing so within the context of a "normal" brain. Without getting into a long discussion of what I mean by "normal," I will not be making comments about aspects of abnormal personalities, characteristics, illnesses, or injuries. So, I will not be addressing the specifics of, for example, sociopaths, psychopaths, narcissists, etc. These specifics have major impacts on those that possess them and on the people around them, but to address them effectively would require a much longer book.

Let's get back to the specific facets.

The purpose of looking at these in more detail is to help you determine your own combination of responses to all of these facets – i.e., your Personal Threat Profile. Any given action by other people, or any given thought of our own, can trigger threats and/or rewards in any of these facets. Which of these facets, however, causes you major stress and which do you just blow by with hardly a second thought? We are all different. For each of the 5 P's, I will explain a little of what the neuroscience says about that facet.

As you read each of these facets, and think about your response, ask someone else who knows you very well to offer their opinion of your answers. You just might be surprised.

It is, of course, necessary to describe these aspects one at a time; in fact, their impact rarely occurs independently. They all interact with each, in some cases to cancel out an effect, or, in some cases, to multiply it.

In addition, in this section I will be discussing how your Personal Threat Profile might be impacted by the situation that you find yourself in right now, i.e., Your Threat Context.

Let's dig into the different facets within the 5 P's.

Driving Force #1: Protection

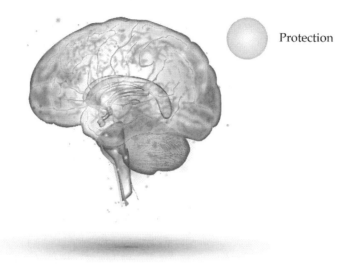

Protection

1. We want to feel physically safe.

The need to feel safe is the primary driver of the brain. We can refer back to the comments made by Medina and Van Der Kolk in Brain Principle #1. While most of us don't have to face the same dangers that we used to face on the African Savannah 5 million years ago, the brain responds to fear in the same way that it responded back then. Our brains were, and still are, preoccupied with "safety first."

Let's examine our preoccupation with regards to our need for safety even further.

Sometimes this preoccupation comes as a result of misinterpretation of one of the many stimuli that we receive. For example, a loud flash, a fast movement, or an unknown noise will still trigger off some of our fear-based reactions even though they are the result of a flash-gun, a bird flying close by, or a rustle in the leaves. All of these things can send our amygdalae into a split-second tailspin, only to be rescued an instant later by our prefrontal cortex, reassuring us that everything is OK.

Sometimes the misinterpretation has much more to do with the changes that have come along with society, as we discussed in Brain Principle #1. The fear that we may not get to work on time or may not be able to deliver the report to our boss on time or that we may not be able to close the deal with that important potential client. All of these, once again, require the reassurance of our prefrontal cortex, this time reasoning out, over a longer period of time, that we are not going to die if we don't get to work on time or get the report done or don't bring that new client in.

As Gordon states in his book [56]:

> "Behaviors that evolved to deal with a short life on the African Savannah are now being played out in 21st century cities that require new behaviors of a more effective and adaptive brain."

Finally, however, there are occasions, real or imagined, when we are not misinterpreting the threat. The threat is as real as it was back then. Or, at least the brain perceives it as such. Bullying, either at work or at school. Hostile work environments. Harassment, sexual or otherwise. Domestic violence. Gang violence. I am sure there are many other situations where the end result is the same: the brain perceives a real threat.

When I was first describing this facet to a colleague, she described a situation when she was recovering from an operation. By an unfortunate set of circumstances, the pain-killers that she needed were not available. She described the moment of panic that she had at the thought of having to experience real physical pain and how vulnerable she felt. This is the fear of physical safety.

At the time of writing this book, there is an increasing sense that many of us are in a state of constant physical threat, for example by terrorists, gun violence, or short-sighted politicians.

Take a moment to think about your own needs with regard to physical safety. How important is this to you in day-to-day life, and how much attention do you give it?

2. We want to feel emotionally safe in our personal, our work, and our social relationships.

I found it difficult to find a reliable definition of emotional safety. Even that fount of all knowledge, *Wikipedia*, stated that the entry on emotional safety had "multiple issues," i.e., there might be things wrong with it.

For the purposes of this book, let's assume that it is best described as feelings of connectedness and acceptance, accessibility, respect, involvement, clear boundaries and expectations, openness, transparency and vulnerability. When any of these are violated, either real or perceived, then we don't feel emotionally safe, and we will respond. Unless specifically trained to do otherwise, this response is typically either an attack on the other person or a withdrawal from the relationship. Both of these reactions can cause the other person to feel less emotionally safe and hence, begin a downward spiral.

The Gallup Organization has done a large amount of research into organizational culture, engagement, and attitudes. One of the questions that they ask in their employee engagement survey is "Do you have a best friend at work?" Their research, and the reason why they ask that question, indicates that employees that have a best friend at work perform better. In a recent Gallup bulletin, AnnaMarie Mann [57] cites that women who strongly agree they have a best friend at work are more than twice as likely to be mentally engaged (63%) compared with the women who say otherwise (29%). In addition, "two-thirds of women say the social aspect of a job is a 'major reason' why they work."

Let's take a quick look at what I am calling "social safety." Some authors and researchers call it "psychological safety," a term that has been around for some time. Amy Edmondson defines psychological safety as "a climate in which people are comfortable being (and expressing) themselves." A study carried out by the People Analytics team at Google found that it was the single most important factor in predicting high-performing teams. [58]

Social safety, or lack of it, can come from many dynamics or events: rejection, humiliation, having an idea dismissed, being ignored, being overruled, and many more are all aspects of social safety. Some of the work in the early part of this century, most notably by Eisenberger and Lieberman, significantly added to our body of knowledge with regard to the neuroscience of social safety. Their original studies were focused on the reaction of the brain to rejection. [59] Since then, they, and many others, have published many studies on the topic.

The response to the lack of social safety has also been studied, for example, in a recent study by Chester and DeWall. [60] They report that, predictably, rejection damages mood, leaving individuals motivated to recover and that retaliatory aggression is often a pleasant experience. That is, when we feel hurt, we feel better by taking revenge in an aggressive manner.

For the purposes of this book, the primary difference I am using between emotional safety and social safety is as follows, although clearly there is overlap: emotional safety is focused on one-to-one relationships, and social safety is when there are more than two people involved.

And you? How much mental time and effort do you spend in thinking about your emotional and social safety?

3. We want to feel financially secure and avoid financial loss.

Many of us claim that we want financial security. By way of illustrating how important the issue might be, a recent Google search on long term financial security that I did resulted in 117 million responses. Needless to say, I didn't read them all!!!

In a recent article, Nicole Dieker [61] quotes the second tip from Dan Buettner's book [62]:

"Financial security is also, obviously, huge. It really does deliver more happiness over time than most anything that money can be spent on – after your needs are taken care of, and you maybe treat yourself occasionally. If you have money left over, you're much better paying down your mortgage or buying insurance or signing up for an automatic savings plan than you are buying a new gadget or new pair of shoes."

In a large UK study, [63] researchers showed that how we each think about our social status is a predictor of ill-health. They further show that our opinion of our social status is made up of a number of things, including occupational position, education, household income, satisfaction with standard of living, and *feeling of financial security* regarding the future. (Italics are mine.)

So, it seems that financial security, or at least our subjective sense of it, seems to impact health and happiness. Wow! Not bad for starters.

As I stated earlier, we all hold different weightings for these facets, and this is certainly true with regard to financial security. For some people, it is of paramount, almost overwhelming importance. To others, much, much less so. I was once coaching a female engineer in Silicon Valley who had become wealthy as a result of a startup buyout. She was wondering what to do next with her life, and part of her considerations was financial security. She calculated that with her current assets and her current and anticipated rate of spending, she had financial security for over 50 years. She still decided to go back to work.

But there are many things that we all regularly do that don't help us achieve that goal of financial security and confound some of the positive actions that we do take. The next couple of facets address some of the ways we shoot ourselves in the foot.

Loss aversion is now a well-researched topic and was first reported in 1984. [64] The bottom line is that losses have a greater impact on us than gains do. The sadness of losing $5 has much greater impact than the happiness of gaining $5. We will not take certain risks if we fear that we might lose rather than assign an equal possibility of gaining. There is much debate about what is going on in the nonconscious part of our brain with regard to loss aversion, but it is probably driven by the amygdala. Loss triggers the amygdala sufficiently so that the PFC is unable to exercise a sense of control.

The disposition effect (one of our many biases) states that we are more likely to sell an asset that has risen in value than we are to sell one that has lost in value. See any connection here? Once again, we are acutely aware of loss – and will hang on to a depreciating asset long after we should have unloaded it because we don't want to recognize the loss.

At this stage of your life, how important is financial security to you?

4. We want a balance between short-term rewards and long-term gains.

Let's talk about hyperbolic discounting (or delayed discounting) for a moment. (Now there's a conversation starter for your next cocktail party!!!) It has a fancy name, but it is basically about our need for short term gratification. In an ideal world, we would balance short-term incentives with long-term advantages, but we tend not to. We tend to take short-term payoffs rather than opt for greater but longer-term advantages. It is even wrapped up in a common saying: "A bird in the hand is worth two in the bush."

A Google Scholar search for either of those terms will generate a large number of responses; there has been much research done on this topic. It's impact, however, goes across many short-term vs long-term reward domains. Money is a clear and obvious example, and there is some research indicating that obesity might be linked: "Obesity seems related to a preference for immediate gratification." [65] It seems possible that even the domain of extramarital affairs maybe the desire for short-term vs long-term reward. I will research this for the next version of the book.

So, do we have control over this balance? Maybe. Some research seems to indicate that if we are specifically focused on the future by providing "vivid mental simulation of general future experiences," [66] our attention can be diverted from those short-term, diet-killing temptations and influence our decisions to eat more healthily.

Further, it also appears that natural environments tend to influence a more future-oriented thinking than buildings or abstract images. [67] On the other hand, it seems that our tendency to discount the future might have some genetic components to it. [68]

In addition, it seems that the more anxious, depressed, and stressed we are, the more we are inclined to go for that short-term reward. Why? An argument could be made that from an evolutionary perspective, it would make survival sense to go for the short-term reward if/when you are under stress. Maybe that short-term reward will increase your chances of survival. The eons old equivalent of the extra cookie might have given you an extra amount of short-term energy to run away from the saber-toothed tiger. ☺

Now, you. How important is it to you to balance the short-term vs. the long-term?

And how well do you do with that balance?

5. We want to know where we stand – geographically and in our social and work relationships.

Some people want to know exactly where they are. By this, I mean that some people want to know where they are physically at all times. When they enter a building, they keep track of ingress and egress pathways. When they are traveling, their route is calculated meticulously even with GPS available. For some people, being lost is just a way of life, and they don't worry about it, being self-assured that they will soon recognize somewhere they know. For others, even being slightly off the beaten track is nerve-racking.

This need can be taken one step further. For many people, sitting with their back to the door in either an office or in a restaurant can be nerve-wracking. Many will refuse to sit in such a situation and request that they be moved.

As an interesting anecdote, those of us who grew up with printed maps learned map-reading (more or less) as a necessary skill for survival. The younger population that has grown up with GPS, especially once GPS arrived in the smartphone, has never been lost. Maybe the brains of digital-natives are changing in this respect.

The need to know exactly where we stand might also come less from the protection aspect and more from the participation and prediction aspects. The need to know where I am with regard to an individual or group is about both participation and, possibly, prediction. Some people tend to worry on a daily basis whether their relationship with others is still OK. They are constantly asking questions as to whether everything is fine. Their "ancient brains" are constantly wanting to know, in effect, whether they are still a valuable part of the tribe or if they going to be thrown out and left to fend on their own. The slightest cue or clue that things are not well, as interpreted by them, can send them into a tailspin.

Some people want to know what's going on between them and a potential partner the minute they meet. Others are much more laissez-faire about it.

The need to know where I am with regard to work issues can take a couple of forms. It can be relationship-oriented or task-oriented. Where I am in relationship with a work colleague or where am I in with regard to progress on a project, for example.

In the case of the former, it bears many similarities to the previous facet, but some overtones in terms of position in the organization. Boss, peer, subordinate. and team member relationships all make this more complex.

As I described in Brain Principle #1 (we want to feel safe), we are scanning for these clues all of the time. Most of the time we are pretty good at interpreting the cues and using them as clues. But occasionally we get it wrong.

As an amusing example, many years ago I was at an IT conference with another colleague of mine. One of the guest speakers was doing a session on body language. After her presentation, she came up to my colleague and I and asked how long we had been married. We were both aghast as we couldn't dream of being married to each other. In further discussion, however, the presenter explained that she had noticed how close we stood with each other. Much closer than "normal" work colleagues would. What she hadn't taken into account was that I am from England, and my colleague was very experienced with working in Europe. Our need for personal space, presumably, was much lower than "normal."

So, knowing where you stand can take many different angles.

How important is it to you to know exactly where you stand? In work situations? In social situations?

6. We want to be treated fairly, see others be treated fairly in social and work environments, and see animals treated fairly.

These, clearly, are all about fairness. It seems that fairness is a very important facet for many people and frequently is identified as the single most important facet. Since it is such an important facet, I will devote significant space to it.

In summary, as humans we need to see that exchanges that occur around us are fair, both to us and to others. Fair exchanges are intrinsically rewarding to the brain, independent of other factors. When we deem that what we see or experience is unfair, the brain reacts the same way that it does for disgust, one of the six fundamental emotions. On the other hand, when we see or experience activities around us that are fair, our brains react in the same way as if we have been rewarded.

We don't have to go very far to find some more unique ways of researching the issue. Sarah Brosnan's "Letter to Nature," [69] in connection with capuchin monkeys and inequity of treatment, describes the results of her work with scientific clarity and brevity. She describes what happens when two monkeys are treated unequally, and it is a stunning show of what happens when these primates observe inequity.

It seems that our dislike of fairness is shared by other animal species. In another article, Brosnan and de Waal [70] report:

> "… there is mounting evidence that at least some comparison of rewards and aversion to unequal rewards are found across a wider variety of species than just ourselves or even non-human primates. Although no other species thus far shows the inclusive sense of fairness seen in humans, aspects are present in a wide variety of species and situations."

Fairness makes sense from an evolutionary sense. In past eras, if you didn't receive your fair share of the resources of your tribe, then your survival might have been in question.

People with a high need to see fairness in how they are treated and how other people are treated will probably react to unfair situations with anger and disgust.

Some research has shown some gender differences in how people respond to unfair behavior. Singer et al [71] concluded that:

> "…in men…empathic responses are shaped by valuation of other people's social behavior, such that they empathize with fair opponents while favoring the physical punishment of unfair opponents…"

But before we go any further, let's take a moment and examine what is meant by fairness. Some of my readers will feel that is was unfair of me to get so far into the discussion of fairness before defining what is meant by fairness. ☺

It will probably come as no surprise to you to learn that, once again, there is much debate. In a very readable article, Andreoni et al [72] not only describe two different views of fairness but also how we can change our minds, over relatively short periods of time, about what we believe is fair. They identify the following two approaches: fairness of opportunity vs. fairness of outcomes. Then, when they come to address fairness of outcomes, they talk about whether the outcomes arose out of luck or out of choice. Other authors talk about "material fairness" and "non-material fairness."

My own experience in this domain is that there is no one definition. It is both highly individual and highly context-driven. From an individual point of view, what is seen as unfair to one person can be judged as fair by another with both of them having equally sound logical and emotional reasoning to support their position. From a context point of view, I had the opportunity to run an ad hoc version of the ultimatum game in a European country that had been part of the USSR. The game failed to replicate the results that it always seems to when I run the game in the US or UK. Their view of fairness seemed to be very different. When I asked for some explanations, they suggested that many years of frustration, lack of opportunity, and lack of resources made them look at any opportunity as fair. Their view had been normalized downward.

From a context point of view, one's own childhood background seems to have an impact on our view of fairness. Gilles Le Garrec [73] found that:

> "… when children observe during childhood, how adults have collectively failed to implement fair redistributive policies this lowers their concern during adulthood for fairness or the moral cost of not supporting fair taxation."

So, where does all of this happen in the brain? This is still under investigation, although we are starting to get some clues. We do know that, once again, our two "usual suspects" are involved, i.e., portions of the PFC and the amygdalae.

Bottom line? We all want fairness to some degree or other, how we measure it is very individualistic and can cover many dimensions, and the degree to which we value fairness can be driven by our background.

If we consider "social environment" in its largest context, this could be one of the most important issues facing the world today. The fair treatment of one country by another, wars and tension between countries, the fair treatment of refugees, the fair treatment of people of different racial and ethnic backgrounds within a given country, state, or town. The list goes on and is too big for me to address within the confines of this book. So, I will selectively pick a couple of topics recognizing that taking this approach is woefully inadequate to the overall topic.

In the abstract to their paper, Killen et al [74] expand upon these themes:

> "Yet, social exclusion from groups and the denial of resources reflect societal issues pertaining to social inequality and its counterpoint, fair treatment of others. Social inequality occurs when opportunities and resources are distributed unevenly in society, often through group norms about allocation that reflect socially defined categories of persons. This occurs at multiple levels of societal organization, from experiences of

exclusion in childhood, such as being left out of a play activity to being denied access to resources as a member of a group. These situations extend to larger level experiences in the adult world concerning social exclusion from voting, for example, or participation in educational institutions. Thus, most decisions regarding social exclusion and the denial of resources involve considerations of group identity and group membership, implicitly or explicitly, which contribute to prejudice and bias, even though this has rarely been investigated in developmental science."

In a 2001 article, [75] Van Den Boss and Lind provided us with a summary of some of the outcomes of fair treatment (or justice). The end results?

"The studies show that, at least under some conditions, the treatment of others is as potent a consideration in justice judgments as is one's own treatment."

En route, they discuss:

"Being treated fairly typically leads to things such as higher commitment to the organization or institution within which the treatment is experienced, more prosocial citizenship behavior, and greater acceptance of authorities. People who experience unfair treatment, on the other hand, are more likely to leave their jobs, show lower levels of commitment, and may even start behaving in antinormative or illegal ways."

I couldn't have put it any better than these three quotations.

The need for fair treatment is probably as alive and well and impactful in the workplace as anywhere. We are sensitive at work as to who gets the best projects, who is selected to travel to events, who gets away with doing nothing and who does most of the work, who gets a bonus and who doesn't, who gets a promotion and who doesn't, and do women receive equal pay for equal roles?

I know that it might seem strange to include the topic of fair treatment of animals as one of the facets that drives us, but when I was researching the fairness topic and developing the list of threat and reward facets around fairness, the issue of how far our thinking about fairness and justice extends, kept coming to the surface. This ranged from discussions about the treatment and adoption of domestic animals at one end of the scale through to the possibility of extinction of many animal species as the result of human activities.

Since a large number of people have now been exposed to the Personal Threat Profile, it has been interesting to note participants' responses to the issue of fairness in the treatment of animals. At this early stage, it appears to be bimodal. Responses indicate that it is either really important to one group of people who rank it 9 or 10 out of 10 or relatively unimportant to the group who rank it around 2 or 3 out of 10.

How important is fairness to you?

7. We want to be treated as equals in our primary relationships and see other people treated as equals in their primary relationships.

In his book on love, [76] John Gottman writes about fairness in relationships as follows:

"It is very difficult to establish deep and lasting trust in a relationship that has an unwelcome power symmetry, one in which distribution of power feels unfair to at least

one person. Unless the power distribution feels fair to both partners, and feels equitably balanced, trust will erode. (p 51)"

Some people focus on their own relationships while others seem equally concerned with how their friends are treated, hence, the two questions.

Equality in relationships. Yours and others. How important is this facet to you?

8. We want to feel resilient, i.e., we want to be able to bounce back from life's troughs.

Resilience, stress, and control are inextricably intertwined. In some ways, they are three sides of the same coin, but I may be mixing metaphors here. ☺ If an individual has a high degree of resilience, then they are more likely to be able to respond adaptively to stressors. Similarly, if an individual has a sense that they have control over those stressors, they can respond adaptively.

In the next book in the series, I devote a complete section to stress mastery and resilience.

Your resiliency? How well do you bounce back?

9. We want to be and feel healthy – physically, mentally, emotionally, and spiritually.

Being healthy almost seems too trite to include in this list, but I do so deliberately for several reasons.

> ➢ First, when we are healthy, the concept of being unhealthy tends not to attract our attention. Yet, that is precisely the time when it is best to pay attention.
> ➢ Second, this lack of attention has a bigger impact the older we get.
> ➢ Third, the older we get, it does seem to be something we focus on. The need to be healthy.

The purpose of spending some time expanding on what might seem to be an obvious topic is to help you, the reader, to ensure that as you think about your overall health, you spend some time looking into more detail than you might otherwise do.

And, while each of the questions addresses a specific aspect of health, in practice they are highly interlinked.

But first let's define "health," or at least attempt to. WHO (the World Health Organization) gives us a definition:

"… health is a state of complete physical, mental, and social well-being and not merely the absence of disease or infirmity."

Hmm, useful, I guess, but it really doesn't get us very far. In fact, this definition has been under attack for some time now as "lacking operational value."

So, let's try again, and go back to that knowledge source, *Wikipedia*. This gives us a definition, and makes reference to another:

"Health is the ability of a biological system to acquire, convert, allocate, distribute, and utilize energy sustainably."

and

"Health is the ability to adapt and manage the physical, mental, and social challenges we face through life." [(77)]

Hmm, interesting but still not getting us to where we need to be. Maybe it's a bit like the definition of pornography – I cannot define it, but I know it when I see it. ☺ I cannot define health, but I know when I am feeling unhealthy.

It was even more interesting for me to see that the "formal" definitions don't seem to include a spiritual element, yet there is more and more research showing that people who have a strong spiritual element to their lives live healthier and longer lives. *Wikipedia* introduces us to a couple of studies supporting the positive impact of social activities, for example volunteering, but not on spirituality.

It wasn't until I searched *study.com* [(78)] that I found a wider definition:

"Physical health is critical for overall well-being and is the most visible of the various dimensions of health, which also include social, intellectual, emotional, spiritual, and environmental health. Some of the most obvious and serious signs that we are unhealthy appear physically. Addressing this dimension is crucial for anyone attempting to sustain overall health and wellness."

If we pull apart the different aspects of health, however, we can get some better guidance as to what we need to attend to.

Let's start with physical health. *Study.com* comes to our assistance here too:

"Traditional definitions of physical health prior to the onset of modern medicine would have considered someone physically healthy if he or she was not stricken with a serious illness. With modern medical innovations came longer life spans, which changed the way we define physical health. Today's definition can consider everything ranging from the absence of disease to fitness level.

While physical health consists of many components, here is a brief list of the key areas that should be addressed:

> ➢ *Physical activity – includes strength, flexibility, and endurance*
> ➢ *Nutrition and diet – includes nutrient intake, fluid intake, and healthy digestion*
> ➢ *Alcohol and drugs – includes the abstinence from or reduced consumption of these substances*
> ➢ *Medical self-care – includes addressing minor ailments or injuries and seeking emergency care as necessary*
> ➢ *Rest and sleep – includes periodic rest and relaxation, along with high quality sleep."*

For the definition of mental health, WHO gives us:

" … a state of well-being in which the individual realizes his or her own abilities, can cope with the normal stresses of life, can work productively and fruitfully, and is able to make a contribution to his or her community"

I found the most useful description of emotional health on *familydoctor.org*:

> *"Emotional health is an important part of overall health. People who are emotionally healthy are in control of their thoughts, feelings, and behaviors. They are able to cope with life's challenges. They can keep problems in perspective and bounce back from setbacks. They feel good about themselves and have good relationships."*

> *Being emotionally healthy does not mean you are happy all the time. It means you are aware of your emotions. You can deal with them, whether they are positive or negative. Emotionally healthy people still feel stress, anger, and sadness. But they know how to manage their negative feelings. They can tell when a problem is more than they can handle on their own. They also know when to seek help from their doctor."*

The "thoughts, feelings, and behaviors" relates directly back to Dr. Evian Gordon's INTEGRATE model. [79]

And let's go back to *study.com* for spiritual health:

> *"One specific definition does not completely summarize spiritual health. While organized religion and prayer – two concepts familiar to most in Western societies – can certainly be part of spiritual health, they are not all that should be considered. Spiritual health can also consist of more broad concepts, such as hope, purpose, and peace.*

> *Some common criteria that fall within the category of spiritual health include belief in a supreme being, unity with a greater force, a guiding sense of meaning and value, an organized religion, balance, introspection, and meaning. While all of these aspects are not necessary to be spiritually healthy, addressing the main concepts can provide a foundational understanding to this way of approaching one's health.*

> *Overall health can be positively impacted by high levels of spiritual health. For example, people experiencing a life-changing event may deal with their situation in a more positive manner if their levels of spiritual health are high. In other words, people can become more resilient by properly addressing their spiritual health."*

How much of your mental time and effort do you devote to thinking about and worrying about your health in all of its aspects?

Driving Force #2: Participation

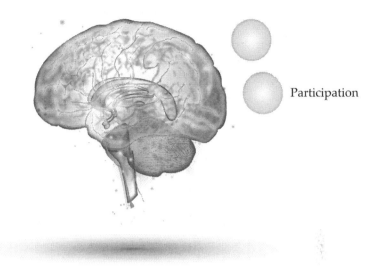

Participation

10. We want to be trusted, be trustworthy, and be with people we trust.

We make judgments about who we trust in a very short period of time. Various researchers put this at between 1/5th and 1/10th second. And that decision tends to stick with us for months, if not years.

Our brains evolved to treat strangers as enemies or foes. This makes sense from an evolutionary point of view. If your theoretical ancestors trusted too many strangers, then they probably aren't your ancestors. They were probably taken out of the gene pool or did not survive long enough to reproduce. So, even today, if we don't have something in common with another person upon our initial meeting with them, the brain circuitry that "handles" the initial relationship is that which deals with foes. We are cautious, defensive, and wired as ready to fight or flee.

This is, of course, fully understandable. If we found a stranger approaching our tribe, due to our survival drive, we naturally assumed that they weren't there for a good reason. Contrary to our assumptions, however, it is possible that they were simply lost, in which case they might have been relatively friendly, and it might have been your natural assumption of danger that was causing them "stranger stress." In those days, however, it was more likely that they were not there for a good reason and were there scouting out how they might steal your food, shelter, etc.

Once we have established something in common with that person, then several things happen. Internally to the brain, the first thing to happen is that the circuitry used to handle the relationship changes. Our friend the PFC is involved in both cases, in assessing similarity and closeness of the other person. [80]

The second thing that happens is that we start to trust that person.

The third thing is that we also tend to see them as more credible and competent.

I go into a lot more detail about behavioral ways that you can increase (or decrease) trust in the section "Your Brain with Another Person" in the next book in the series. But here I am focusing on what happens inside the brain. Paul Zak has devoted a large amount of the past couple of decades to research on trust in human beings, and much of this summary is based upon his work. [81] So. Trust. What's it all about? One word. At least one word for now. Oxytocin.

In Paul's words:

> *"Oxytocin appears to do just one thing – reduce the fear of trusting a stranger."*

It seems that oxytocin is a double-edged sword but in the nicest possible way. It works both ways. An increase in our oxytocin levels increases our trust of others, and increasing trust in others increases our oxytocin levels.

An increase in oxytocin also increases our empathy for another person. It seems natural that trust and empathy would go together.

It also seems that having a higher sense of purpose (see the "Purpose" section on page 102) also increases oxytocin production. So, trust and higher purpose seem to work hand in hand.

It seems that the relationship between oxytocin and trust is universal.

There are several things that get in the way of oxytocin production, high stress being one of them.

The trust question: How important is it to you to have trust in, and be trusted by, others?

11. We want to be with people with whom we have something in common, with whom we belong and feel accepted, and who we like.

In many ways, these are all corollaries to the previous facet on trust. We develop trust once we find we have something in common. And we want something in common with a group of people.

This is often called our need to be in an "in-group." We are social animals, and we like being with people who like the same things as us. Facebook has made it a fundamental part of their platform and business model. Cialdini has these aspects as two of his fundamental principles of influence, i.e., social proof and liking. (See Appendix B, "Influences," for longer descriptions.)

Milanov et al [82] describe this "in-group dynamic" so perfectly, that I will simply cite it here:

> *"Group identification is a central aspect of many theories within psychology, sociology, anthropology, and related areas, and it is a core factor for explaining phenomena such as prejudice, collective self-esteem, in-group favoritism, and intergroup bias. Membership in social groups does not only impact individuals' judgements about fellow in-group members but also influences their perception of other groups in the society and affects their interpersonal relationships in everyday life."*

This is just one example of the large amount of research that has been carried out over the past fifty or so years on this subject, with many books and papers having been written. A Google Scholar search will get you thousands. Among the research there is also some debate regarding:

> ➤ what the criteria are for an "in-group"
> ➤ the impact that the in-group dynamic has on one's self identity
> ➤ the impact that the in-group has on the way that in-group members treat members of an out-group

Milanov et al [83] identified the following five criteria for an in-group:

> ➤ Salience, importance, significance, and centrality of the group membership for the self
> ➤ Perceived similarity to the group, self-categorization, and depersonalization
> ➤ Close identification with other group members, commitment to the group, common bond, and in-group ties
> ➤ Reciprocal and behavioral interdependence between the group members
> ➤ Evaluative, affective, in-group attraction, superiority, and satisfaction element

Some years ago, I was involved with consulting to an outsourcing effort. It was an IT function that was being outsourced. The announcement had been made that the department would be outsourced, and staffing numbers would be reduced by about 5%. All the people that were going to be laid off had been told and the appropriate arrangements made. The staff that remained would have the same salary, the same job, the same boss, sit at the same desk and would be evaluated in exactly the same manner. Yet, one gentleman who was assigned to me to coach had not yet told his wife that he was being outsourced. And this was six weeks after the original announcements had been made.

After a couple of hours of discussion and much anger, frustration, and tears, the cause of the angst came to light. He felt like he had been "thrown out of the club." He had worked for the company for nearly twenty years, and now he felt that he had simply been tossed aside.

The desire to belong to an in-group can sometimes create very strange behavior. In a recent discussion, some colleagues and I were talking about a phenomenon that had taken place a while back. Pokémon GO. It was released in the summer of 2016 and became an overnight hit. Communities started to form. People would stop each other in the street – even complete strangers. At the time of writing this section of the book, February 24, 2018, according to the *Forbes.com* website, [84] the second ever Pokémon GO Community Day is being held. In our discussion, one my colleagues described how her sister, an extreme introvert, would drive along the street, stop her car, and approach people who appeared to be playing Pokémon GO.

Some people have a high need to be associated with an "in-group." Others have little or no need. What about you? How important is it to you to be part of an in-group?

12. We want to differentiate ourselves from the group and be able to proffer different or even oppositional viewpoints from the group.

On the other hand, Berger [85] spends a whole chapter on the fact that, although some of us want to identify with an in-group and non-consciously copy their thoughts and actions, we also want to be seen as different to the other members of the group.

For some people, the need to belong to an in-group is very high. Other people do not require such a high level of attachment to an in-group and are driven much more towards differentiation from the group or, indeed, disassociating with or from any group.

LWS (Leadership WorkStyles ©) [86] is a 360-degree behavioral assessment that has been around for a long while. One of the twelve characteristics that they assess is called the "Oppositional" style. Like many character attributes, this style is a double-edged asset/liability. On the positive side, the ability to think differently to the group helps breakthrough solutions and creativity and avoids "groupthink."

On the other hand, just coming up with ideas that are in opposition to those of the group can cause threat and dissent among other members of the group. They can see it as obstructionist, elitist, and ego-driven. Especially if it is a typical, automatic, probably nonconscious habit. I have found this behavior to be destructive to the overall functioning of teams.

How important is it for you to differentiate yourself from other people, whether you are part of an in-group or not?

13. We want to work on a team – or some of us do.

Some people thrive when working in teams. That is where they do their best work. They engage with other people on the team and become very productive. Indeed, some people have so much of a need to work on a team that, if they are not on a team, their productivity, performance, and effectiveness is significantly reduced.

Other people far prefer individual roles and have a tough time on teams.

In the corporate world, there has been a tendency to emphasize the role of team players and to reward those people that play well on a team. Let me be clear. There are many significant products and breakthroughs that are the result of team efforts. But not everyone plays well on a team. They prefer and work better when left to be on their own. At least not on the team all of the time.

You? Team or individual player?

14. We want a sense of self-respect and self-esteem, to feel equal to or better than others, and see life as a competition where we want to win or beat other people.

There are many, many studies on the topics of self-respect and self-esteem. I am sure that we could find them going back many thousands of years if we chose to go looking. These two topics seem to have a major impact on many aspects of our day-to-day lives. Issues of self-esteem have been correlated with psychological and psychiatric disorders such as depression and anxiety and physical disorders such as over or undereating.

As I write, there is a huge amount of research going on with regard to self-esteem and the brain. Consider some of the following findings:

> Low self-esteem has been found to increase our responsiveness to social pain.[87]
> Self-esteem biases our view of positive and negative feedback from others. [88] [89]
> Self-esteem impacts the effect of mindfulness meditation on anxiety and depression. [90]
> Self-esteem appears to rise from the interconnection of neural systems integrating information about the self. [91]
> Self-esteem appears to impact the volume of certain brain areas associated with the ability to deal with issues such as emotion/stress regulation, pride, and theory of mind (i.e., our ability to frame up what others are thinking). [92]

In addition, across multiple cultures, self-esteem increases from late adolescence through middle adulthood, and, in general, males consistently report higher self-esteem than females.

So, it seems that self-respect and self-esteem are key to much of how we interact in our daily lives.

If you are interested in a quick evaluation of your own self-esteem, then please refer to the Rosenberg Self-Esteem Scale which I have included in Appendix C.

How we see ourselves in relationship to others was well written up by Matthew Hutson. [93] Since he did it so well, I am going to cite his small article in its entirety*:

"No wonder we constantly measure ourselves against our peers. In a survey of faculty, students, and staff at the Harvard School of Public Health, nearly half of the respondents said they'd prefer to live in a world where the average salary was $25,000, and they earned $50,000 than one where they earned $100,000, but the average was $200,000. Similarly, a majority favored relative over absolute advantage when it came to their own intelligence and attractiveness, their child's intelligence and attractiveness, or praise from a superior. Apparently, the survey respondents would rather the planet be filled with stupid, ugly children than have their own child left behind.

H. L. Mencken was on to something when he defined wealth as 'any income that is at least $100 more a year than the income of one's wife's sister's husband.' According to one analysis of labor statistics, sisterly competition may have contributed to rising female employment after World War II. Among grown sisters not in the workforce, a woman was more likely to get a job if her brother-in-law out-earned her husband.

People also suffer from a phenomenon known as 'last place aversion.' Although players in an economics game tended to give money to those with fewer assets, this tendency waned when a player was ranked second to last. The researchers who ran the game also found that in real life, people making just above the minimum wage were among the least supportive of a minimum wage hike.

---

* I haven't cited his sources – you can Google them if you wish.

And yet, competitive though we clearly are, we underestimate the influence of social comparison. In one study, call center employees said that achieving mastery at their job was more important than achieving superiority (ranking better than peers). But in reality, relative rankings affected their self-evaluations, and mastery did not.

Our desire for relative advantages is not irrational: such advantages may make us happier. In 1974, Richard Easterlin, an economist, found that although a country's richer citizens are happier than its poorer ones, as countries become richer, their citizens do not become happier – a contradiction known as the Easterlin paradox. Happiness, Easterlin reasoned, must depend on one's wealth relative to one's compatriots: when everyone gets richer, no one gets happier.

A study of 12,000 British citizens would seem to support Easterlin's conclusion, revealing that increased income boosted life satisfaction only when income rose relative to peers of a similar age, educational level, or region.

And so, it goes. We decry the goal of 'Keeping Up with the Joneses,' even as we struggle ferociously to keep one step ahead of them. Perhaps this is with good reason. If we don't, our rivals will win all the glory, and we'll become bear food."

With regard to our need to win or beat other people, some people view life as a "zero-sum" game. Somebody has to win, and somebody has to lose. The LWS assessment that I mentioned earlier has one dimension that measures that characteristic. Great leaders want to focus on and beat the real competition, not everyone that they come across. As I write this book, I am compelled to look at the political environment and leadership through this particular facet.

And your approach? Do you see life as winning and beating others or just doing your best?

15. We want to receive recognition from people who are important to us, be valued and respected by them, know that they care about us, and know that we have some level of approval from them.

Let's start with recognition and respect. The assertion that I am going to make here, that "we want to receive recognition from people who are important to us," is really the tip of the recognition iceberg.

First, at the foundational level of the iceberg, as I will expand upon below, is the recognition that my "group" is real and that it is of equal importance to other "groups."

The next level up is that "we" as a group are respected and valued.

After that is the level that focuses on the individual rather than the group: I am generally respected for my attributes and behaviors.

The fourth level is that I am recognized, respected, and potentially rewarded for my specific tasks and achievements.

Then, at the top of the iceberg is the question from above. Recognition and respect from people who are important to us.

Charles Taylor [94] directly addresses the issue of group recognition and associated individual identity. Very early in his book he points out:

"The demand for recognition…is given urgency by the links between recognition and identity, where this latter term designates something like a person's understanding of who they are, of their fundamental defining characteristics as a human being."

Then he continues:

"The thesis is that our identity is partly shaped by recognition or its absence, often by the misrecognition of others, and so a person or group of people can suffer real damage, real distortion, if the people or society around them mirror back to them a confining or demeaning or contemptible picture of themselves."

And:

"Non-recognition or misrecognition can inflict harm, can be a form of oppression, imprisoning someone in a false, distorted, and reduced mode of being."

So, at a very philosophical level, we have a very high need to be recognized for who we are. If not, then some pretty powerful words get dragged in… "oppression," "imprisonment," "distortion," and a "reduced mode of being."

On the next page, he twists the knife even further:

"Within these perspectives, misrecognition shows not just a lack of due respect. It can inflict a grievous wound, saddling its victims with a crippling self-hatred. Due recognition is not just a courtesy we owe people. It is a vital human need."

A vital human need!

Some people have a high need for recognition from others. In some cases, especially where someone is more narcissistically-oriented, the individual needs that recognition from as wide an audience as possible. In other cases, the recognition need only come from a much closer circle. In very special instances, it need only come from a group of one's peers or from one of our in-groups.

Yet, some people have little need for any external recognition.

It is no accident that I placed these facets immediately after the facets about self-respect and self-esteem. In the first instance, self-esteem is generated from our internal values. In the second instance, looking for recognition, respect, care, and approval from others is clearly externally driven. None of these, however, is black and white, or all or nothing. We all have them to varying degrees.

Let's take a look at a couple of ventures that might, at first glance, seem to have little or nothing to do with the topic at hand. Open-source software and *Wikipedia*.

First, what is "open-source" software?

"The open source development model fundamentally changes the approaches and economics of traditional software development. Typically, open-source software is developed by an internet-based community of programmers. Participation is voluntary, and participants do not receive direct compensation for their work. In addition, the full source code is made available to the public. Developers also devolve most property rights to the public, including the right to use, to redistribute, and to modify the software free

of charge. This is a direct challenge to the established assumptions about software markets that threatens the position of commercial software vendors."

What would motivate programmers to want to voluntarily give their time for no direct compensation? My contention is that, in addition to many other factors such as altruism, independence, and other internal motivations, the lack of need for recognition from others contributes to these programmers' willingness to give highly of their time.

I assume that most readers know what *Wikipedia* is. Within the Internet world, it is one of the most widely recognized collections of encyclopedic information. It might be the largest. It has, however, likely been the major cause of the demise of other encyclopedic efforts like *Encarta* and *Encyclopedia Britannica*. But, like open-sourced software, the contributors receive little or no recognition.

We want recognition, but along with that, we want respect from people that matter to us. As I said when I first started talking about the facets of the 5 P's, we all have different weightings that we apply to each of these facets. This is a case in point.

Using the "iceberg" metaphor I introduced above, at the base of the iceberg is your group's position in society. If your group has traditionally been recognized as a fundamental part of society (or organization) then the need for recognition as a group probably doesn't even register with you. It may also not register with you that the lack of recognition will be important to people in groups that haven't typically been recognized.

As I write this book, I can see this aspect being played out at the international, country, and state political arenas on a daily basis.

At the top of the iceberg for some people, recognition from those that are important to them, whether it be peers, boss, clients, or their profession, is very important. Many awards ceremonies are as a result of this need. On the other hand, there are many people who don't need or want that type of recognition and will actively attempt to avoid it.

Let's move on to the caring facet. Being cared about is probably an important aspect of the ancient survival drive of the brain. Once again, in that weird logic, the fact that you are here indicates that your far distant ancestors did care about their offspring. If they hadn't then their genes wouldn't have been passed on.

So being cared for is a very deep need for us in general and specifically for those that are close to us. For some people, the need to maintain the "relationships" with those that they care about is one of their prime drivers. It can impact what they say and what they do on a daily, if not hour by hour and minute by minute, basis. Someone who is constantly evaluating whether they are upsetting those that they care about and/or those that care for them will often behave in ways that, at least in the long term, are not in the "relationship's" best interest. This might, for example, manifest itself in the "go along to get along" dynamic.

It almost goes without saying that the need to be cared for starts at a very young age. The National Association for the Education of Young Children has a number of articles on the impact of caring on a child's brain development. [95]

Finally, let's look at the issue of approval. Once again, we each vary greatly in our need for approval. Some people rarely, if ever, seem to act in accordance with approval from those around them. Others seem to be paralyzed into inaction unless they are sure that what they will be saying or doing will be approved of. In a landmark study, Burkland et al [96] demonstrated that at a neuronal level, disapproval, to some people, may have a greater impact than anger. The parents who are constantly telling their kids that they are "so disappointed in them" may be having more of an impact than if they were angry at them.

What is your need for recognition and approval from others that are important to you?

16. We want some sense of power and influence in our work and our social lives.

The need to have some degree of power has been studied widely. Once again, in the LWS assessment, the need for power is one of the twelve dimensions. Power can come from a variety of sources. Positional power. Behavioral power. Knowledge power. Financial power. Political power. Personal power. There are probably many more different types. I think we have all felt and experienced different types of power. Some people seem to have a high need for power while others have much less so.

There has been research on alpha male gorillas with regard to power. When they were taken out of their group for whatever legitimate reason and placed in a different group, they frequently fell sick and, in some cases, died. Their need for that positional power was high.

One way at looking at the opposite of power is "helplessness," and there has been much research on the impact of helplessness. In one example, research on older people in Mexico showed that helplessness was the single largest factor in predicting high blood pressure.

There is an argument to be made that the facet of "power" deserves to be located in the "Prediction" domain of the 5 P's. The argument would be that if a person has power, then one can make life that much more predictable as the person with the power can determine what will happen. The Golden Rule: "He who has the gold sets the rules."

I have taken the tack, however, to include power in the "Participation" domain for one main reason: the impact that the use of power, and the mis- or overuse of it, can have on the individual and on others. Power provides the individual a platform to direct and participate in their environment on their own terms, as opposed to the terms of other people or groups.

There is an old saying, "Power corrupts."* This statement has been proven at a societal level and at a research level many times over. I will leave the societal issues for another book and another author but will address some of the research side.

Let's start with the now infamous Stanford Prisoner Experiment.** There is much debate with regard to the validity of the process, methodology used in the experiment,

---

* The historian and moralist, who was otherwise known simply as Lord Acton, expressed this opinion in a letter to Bishop Mandell Creighton in 1887: "Power tends to corrupt, and absolute power corrupts absolutely. Great men are almost always bad men."
** From Wikipedia: "The Stanford Prison Experiment was a 1971 social psychology experiment that attempted to investigate the psychological effects of perceived power, focusing on the struggle between

and the ethics involved. This debate has cast some doubt on the reliability of the results. The nominal conclusions, however, indicate that when given power, people will use it, then abuse it.

This in turn can lead to stepping on to a slippery slope. There has been much recent research on the effect on the brain of the "person in power." The constant availability of power in some people appears to reduce certain aspects of the brain. This was named the "hubris syndrome" [97] and is described as:

> "...a disorder of the possession of power, particularly power which has been associated with overwhelming success, held for a period of years and with minimal constraint on the leader.
>
> Its 14 clinical features include: manifest contempt for others, loss of contact with reality, restless or reckless actions, and displays of incompetence."

Once again, I couldn't help but ruminate over how this seems to apply to politics at all levels over many generations.

So, as you think about your need for power, think about the downsides of actually acquiring that power – if you care.

How important are power and influence to you?

17. We want some sense of status and prestige in our work and our social lives.

When I first ventured into the field of consulting rather than a real job, I was consulting to the senior team of a large, nonprofit volunteer organization. The organization doesn't exist anymore, but at the time it had approximately fifty thousand members and regularly held conferences with twenty thousand or more attendees.

I was astounded at the hubris (now we have been exposed to that syndrome ☺) of the members of the senior team. I came to realize that while their day jobs were relatively mundane and low level, the status and prestige that they gained for being at the senior levels of the volunteer organization was huge. I was warned that, even as an external consultant explicitly brought in to increase the effectiveness of the team, I shouldn't say anything that would cause any of the team to want to leave their role. After all, they were volunteers and should be treated as such.

That was in my early, naïve years. Now I am in my late naïve years, I realize that this need is very important for many people and can manifest itself in many ways. I am well over six feet tall; I learned very early on the impact of being that tall on many people, especially short men. I think it's called the Napoleon complex. [98] I

---

prisoners and prison officers. It was conducted at Stanford University between August 14–20, 1971, by a research group led by psychology professor Philip Zimbardo using college students. In the study, volunteers were randomly assigned to be either 'guards' or 'prisoners' in a mock prison, with Zimbardo himself serving as the superintendent. Several 'prisoners' left mid-experiment, and the whole experiment was abandoned after six days. Early reports on experimental results claimed that students quickly embraced their assigned roles, with some guards enforcing authoritarian measures and ultimately subjecting some prisoners to psychological torture, while many prisoners passively accepted psychological abuse and, by the officers' request, actively harassed other prisoners who tried to stop it. The experiment has been described in many introductory social psychology textbooks, although some are beginning to exclude it because its methodology is questioned."

compensated, when I could, by sitting down. This need is clearly related to the facet of constantly comparing ourselves with other people.

In more recent years, research has shown that the brains of macaque monkeys reflect some of their social hierarchy with changes taking place in the amygdalae, hypothalamus, and brainstem. [99] These status comparisons and changes are taking place in the area of the brain largely responsible for the emotional processing and perception of threat. Our ancient brains experience the threats emotionally, and therefore we respond accordingly as we relate to how we will survive.

Now that we have seen the impact of fairness, a 2015 study showed that our view of what is fair is affected by our sense of status as I have said before. [100]

But wait! It gets worse. Our view of our own status seems to become hardwired and, even when we are told to ignore it, we can't. [101]

I reflect back on that consulting assignment and wish I had understood more about the impact of status and prestige and the comparisons that we all make around these topics.

With those data in mind, you might be able to better evaluate your own need for social status and prestige. Or maybe not.

18. We want to treat other people in a benevolent fashion.

It turns out that benevolence just feels good! In an article in *Psychology Today*,[102] Dan Schulman summed it up:

> *"When it comes to altruism, the brain seems to pat itself on the back. The choice to cooperate stimulates pleasure centers in the brain and can even overcome the urge to strive for increased financial gains. This reward circuitry may provide a biological basis for altruism, selfless behavior that is unique to humans."*

Take a look at these! Some other amazing research on generosity and benevolence, downloaded from an article in *Lifehack* [103]:

> *"The reward and pleasure centers in the brain light up in the same way that they would upon receiving a gift. Oxytocin floods the body lowering stress and contributing to an overall sense of wellbeing.*
>
> *Another study found giving money increased the happiness of participants as opposed to spending it on themselves (Norton, 2008).*
>
> *In another comprehensive study of 40 different families from diverse classes, races, and neighborhoods, people choosing to be more emotionally available and generous to others were shown to be in 48% greater overall health.*
>
> *The findings showed much lower depressions rates among individuals who donated more than 10% of their incomes (Smith, 2009)."*

And it's not just about money. Donating time and non-monetary resources such as giving to blood banks or donating hair are all equally rewarding activities.

"Studies are finding average individuals who volunteered around 5.8 hours each month would describe their existence as very happy. On the other end of the spectrum, those confessing to feelings of inadequacy and stating they are very unhappy clocked volunteer methods at around 0.6 hours per month (Davidson, Smith)."

And the discovery of the importance of benevolence is by no means new. Take a look at Adam Smith's comments in *The Theory of Moral Sentiments* (1759): [104]

"How selfish so ever man may be supposed, there are evidently some principles in his nature which interest him in the fortune of others and render their happiness necessary to him, though he derives nothing from it except the pleasure of seeing it."

So, there you have it. We are benevolent because it feels good. So, we might do it just because of that.

But, we might also do it because it supports some of the other things we want like pleasing other people and, hence, getting approval from them, for example. Or maybe because we have learned to trust them. And they, us!

As you think about how important benevolence is to you, you might also think about why.

19. We want to avoid looking incompetent/stupid.

The brain loves to be right. (I'll address that in detail in the section on being right in the "Prediction" domain.) If we're wrong, there can be a number of consequences. Some of which are feeling stupid, humiliation, embarrassment, or shame. Or, indeed, other emotions associated with being socially hurt. This is especially so if we are in front of people who are important to us like work colleagues, professional peers, family, etc. From a psychological perspective, it probably reminds us of the pain we experience when something went wrong when we were growing up, and we were bullied, teased, or ridiculed for it.

Not only do we (in fact, our brains) like to be right, but if it feels like we are wrong, we will often resort to that stress response process – and one way is to fight our way out. If we "win," the brain reinforces the process and the addiction to being right begins. I won so I must have been right.

Many people will go in the other direction to avoid feeling stupid. They will avoid proffering an opinion. The internal argument is "... if I say nothing then I can't be wrong."

There are, of course, many people who believe in the title of one of two books chronicling Richard Feynman, *What Do You Care What Other People Think*? But, because most of us do, we worry about looking incompetent or stupid.

Where are you? Or maybe you don't want to tell me, for fear of…well, looking stupid. ☺

20. We want to avoid feeling like an imposter/fraud.

Once again, let's start with a definition so we all know what we are talking about. The imposter syndrome:

"Impostor syndrome (also known as impostor phenomenon, impostorism, fraud syndrome, or the impostor experience) is a psychological pattern in which an individual doubts their accomplishments and has a persistent internalized fear of being exposed as a 'fraud.'"

Now, many, many people suffer from it. It doesn't matter how educated you are, there's a voice that goes on in many people's heads that says, "But one of these days they're going to catch on that you aren't that smart."

The research indicates that 70% of us are afflicted by this complaint, and it is experienced by every different type of person. Valerie Young [105] has developed a few examples of where it is found most frequently:

> ➤ *"Perfectionists set extremely high expectations for themselves, and even if they meet 99% of their goals, they're going to feel like failures. Any small mistake will make them question their own competence.*
> ➤ *Experts feel the need to know every piece of information before they start a project and constantly look for new certifications or trainings to improve their skills. They won't apply for a job if they don't meet all the criteria in the posting, and they might be hesitant to ask a question in class or speak up in a meeting at work because they're afraid of looking stupid if they don't already know the answer.*
> ➤ *When the 'natural genius' has to struggle or work hard to accomplish something, he or she thinks this means they aren't good enough. They are used to skills coming easily, and when they have to put in effort, their brain tells them that's proof they're an impostor.*
> ➤ *'Soloists' feel they have to accomplish tasks on their own, and if they need to ask for help, they think that means they are a failure or a fraud.*
> ➤ *'Supermen' or 'superwomen' push themselves to work harder than those around them to prove that they're not impostors. They feel the need to succeed in all aspects of life – at work, as parents, as partners – and may feel stressed when they are not accomplishing something."*

She may be on to the something. Certainly, it would be reasonable to expect those "outliers" to be unsure from time to time, but I think it is much more common than that. I have spoken to many professionals who are excellent at what they do, and yet think that one day they will be "discovered" as not being very good.

And you? Ever had that feeling of being an imposter? Go on. Admit it. Most of us have. (What, me? Why would anyone read a book that I wrote? ☺)

Driving Force #3: Prediction

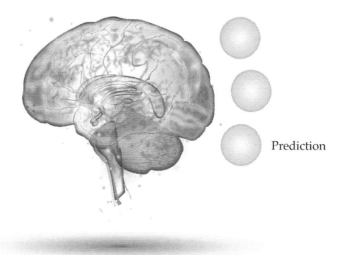

Prediction

Before I start to expand upon each of the facets under "Prediction," I want to give you a quick reminder. A reminder about the fact that the primary purpose for the brain is about prediction. Remember Medina's statement? ("...a problem-solving mechanism for survival...") That's all about prediction.

Some recent research by Bar [106] proposes:

> "... that the human brain is proactive in that it continuously generates predictions that generate the relevant future."

Remember, it is scanning for threats and rewards every $1/5^{th}$ second.

21. We want to have some degree of certainty about the future and be clear at work and in our social lives.

Do a Google or Google Scholar search, and you will find that there are many books, chapters, and papers devoted to the topics of certainty and clarity.

Certainty is of such importance to our brains that DiSalvo [107] devotes a complete section of his book to the issue.

DiSalvo states that not only do we "prefer certainty over ambiguity," but we crave it. In another paper, he reports on a study that shows our brains much prefer to know whether something will or won't happen than be uncertain. Even if the fact that, if it happens, it will result in a negative impact, we'd rather know than not know.

If our brains are placed in a state of uncertainty, then there is a release of cortisol, the efficacy of the PFC is reduced, and there is a tendency to rely more on the limbic system. Now, this is an unfortunate state of affairs since the PFC is the very device that helps make sense of what is going on, rationalize the situation, and think about what to do next!

Taking a look for a moment at the opposite of certainty, i.e., uncertainty, Milliken [108] talks about three types of uncertainty. This might be a way of gaining insight about certainty:

> ➤ *State uncertainty (What will the future environment look like?)*
> ➤ *Effect uncertainty (What do these events or trends mean?)*
> ➤ *Response uncertainty (What should we do about it?)*

Although Milliken was primarily addressing organizational strategies, I think that his simple list of three questions could be useful in helping to increase certainty in more personal cases. For the sake of more easily remembering the list, I think it could be further simplified to the following:

> ➤ *What?*
> ➤ *So what?*
> ➤ *Now what?*

One of the more modern tenets of great leadership is "to be vulnerable." In addition, many therapists and marriage counsellors suggest it as way of increasing the quality of a relationship. It's a state, however, that many people find difficult to attain, let alone adopt.

Being vulnerable is opening oneself up and allowing the possibility for anything to happen. Understanding that the brain craves certainty, we can start to understand why being vulnerable is so hard. It pushes against one of the very things that the brain seeks.

I introduced a term at the beginning of the book, VUCA (standing for volatility, uncertainty, change, and ambiguity), which will impact all of us to a greater and greater extent as we move forward. All of these four dynamics have a drastic impact on our brains. Our brains hate them.

I have said several times before in this book that we're all different. As you do some self-reflection, what is your need for certainty in the various aspects of your life? Are you sure?

22. We want to know what is expected of us in our work and social lives.

Which comes first? The chicken or the egg? We could ask the same of expectations and outcomes.

OK. That's an obtuse way of starting a paragraph, but I wanted to get your attention. Setting expectations happens to all of us, all of the time, although some of the times it might be at such a low level that we are not conscious of it. There's also a growing body of evidence that the act of setting expectations (reasonable ones – and we'll come back to that in the second book) has a significant impact on the likelihood of achieving those expectations.

An example of one of the higher levels of expectation setting is New Year's resolutions. Whether we achieve them or not is a different question. But, many of us realistically set out expectations of ourselves for the year. In the majority of cases, these are primarily oriented towards our private and social lives.

Another example of higher-level expectation setting is the periodic, and mostly dreaded, performance review in our working lives. Again, the fact that most of them don't work is not the subject of this particular facet. [109] Most organizations go through this immensely stressful and time-wasting process to set up descriptions of what outcomes or results are expected of us in the coming period.

At a much lower level, there is a growing body of evidence that inside our brains there is a constant expectation setting and review process going on. It seems to work like this:

When we are about to do something, our nonconscious brain sets up an expected outcome for that thing. Then we do it. The brain then compares the expected outcome with the actual outcome. If we "get it right," then we feel the impact of dopamine, and we give ourselves a little reward. If we "get it wrong," then we don't get the dopamine hit. At a neuronal level, we are constantly comparing expectations against reality. It seems that this applies to whether it is something we receive from the external world or something we do ourselves.

One last comment. When we don't meet the expectations of others or of ourselves, we feel that we have let them or ourselves, down. How many of you nod your head in agreement when someone says, "I am my own worst critic"?

Bottom line? We are driven by expectations. From others and from ourselves. How do you feel when your expectations are not met? How do you feel when you don't meet the expectations of others? Or your own?

23. We want to know how we will be measured and evaluated.

This facet follows on from expectations, the previous topic. Once we know what is expected of us, we want to understand the dimensions of how we will be measured. For some of us, this is really important. We don't want to even start on a project or activity without knowing how we will be measured. Or, for those tasks we set up for ourselves, the parallel question might be "How will I know if I have been successful?" At the other end of the scale, there are many people who will just jump right in without knowing what the success criteria look like.

How important is it to you to know how you will be measured and evaluated before you jump into an activity or task?

24. We want to know how we will be rewarded.

In the business world particularly, the follow-up question to how we are going to be measured is how we are going to be rewarded. It also happens in our private lives. "If you clean up your room [expectations] by noon [measurement] then we'll go to the movies [reward]."

Many compensation systems, whether they be incentive bonus schemes, sales commissions, stock options, salary increases, etc. are based upon the need to know how we will be rewarded. And, once again, it is not just about money. The rewards are often non-monetary. The unit of currency of the reward is important to establish upfront. We immediately get back to the issue of expectations. If my expectation is that I am rewarded in one currency, for example your time, and you give me another currency, for example money, then my expectations are not met.

I will pick up the issue of expectations, measurement, and evaluation, and reward in the second book when we talk about delegation, goal-setting, and performance management.

How important is it to you to know how you will be rewarded before you jump into an activity or task?

25. We want to have a high degree of autonomy, i.e., be in control of our own destiny, in our work and in our social lives.

According to *Wikipedia*, autonomy is derived from the Greek and, when translated, means "one who gives oneself one's own law." The *Oxford Learner's Dictionaries* online defines autonomy as "… the ability to act and make decisions without being controlled by anyone else." For our purposes here, we will use the following definition: "Autonomy is the perception of exerting control over one's environment – illusory or real." The sensation of having choices within any given situation feels rewarding. Let's face it, few of us likes to be told what to do.

In my presentations, I will often ask my audience that very same question. "Who likes to be told what to do?" Most of the time there are a few chuckles and off-color remarks and, of course, most people don't raise their hand. From time to time, there are a few people who do. When questioned further, however, there are a few trends among responses when people like being told what to do.

One instance in which people like being told what to do is when they are uncertain how to go about a task. It could be that they don't have the skill to do it or that they do have the skill but don't know how to get it done in this particular case. Then they are happy to be told what to do. This probably takes us back to the fact that the brain likes to be right, and if we go ahead without knowing what to do, we risk being wrong.

Another theme takes us back to certainty. As a general consensus, most people don't necessarily like being told what to do but they want some definition of what they should be focusing on, what will be expected of them, how they will be measured, and how they will be rewarded, facets which have already been covered.

Not wanting to be told what to do shows up in other ways as well. It often shows up when we give other people advice and goes something like this: "What you should do is… [*fill in the blank*]."*

In his book *Drive*, [110] Daniel Pink summarizes our need for autonomy as:

> ➢ autonomy over task (i.e., what people do)
> ➢ autonomy over time (i.e., when people do what they do)
> ➢ autonomy over team (i.e., who they do it with)
> ➢ autonomy over technique (i.e., how they do it)

Other research indicates that there is the need for autonomy over other areas, for example, autonomy over behavior.

---

* When I first arrived in the U.S., I met a female psychotherapist. One day, I made the mistake of using a suggestion to her that included the word "should." She suggested that I not use this terminology by saying, "Don't should on me, and I won't should on you." I have been very sensitive about "shoulding" on anyone ever since.

Other words that occur frequently in the facet of autonomy are control, freedom, and discretion. People who have a high need for autonomy will probably prefer things such as authority, responsibility, self-determination, independence. and individual decision-making.

When a high need for autonomy is combined with a low need to be part of a group, it can just make for a lone wolf character.

This issue of autonomy alone might be one of the fundamental nonconscious drivers of our behavior. When we are told what to do, even though we assent and agree at a social, superficial level, we resent being told what to do. Research indicates that we even might behave irrationally and sabotage our own efforts unless we have reached our own decisions as to what to do and how to do it. This has serious impacts in the coaching and mentoring environments.

Pink summarizes much of the research on needs and motivations as follows: [111]

> "Human beings have an innate inner drive to be autonomous, self-determined, and connected to one another."

If we take a deeper look into some of Pink's comments, we find that he expands on his theme:

> "… the main motivator is the freedom, challenge, and the purpose of the undertaking itself (p 76).
>
> The most successful people, the evidence shows, often aren't pursuing conventional notions of success. They're working hard and persisting through difficulties because of their desire to control their own lives, learn about the world, and accomplish something that endures.
>
> According to a raft of studies from self-determination theory, researchers, people oriented toward autonomy and intrinsic motivation, have higher self-esteem, better interpersonal relationships, and greater well-being than those that are extrinsically motivated."

He adds that autonomy appears to be "a human concept rather than a Western one."

Let us now look at our social and love lives rather than our work lives. Although it might seem like an unusual reference, Esther Perel [112] identifies the issue of autonomy as central to great relationships:

> "From the moment we can crawl, we navigate the treacherous paths of separation in an attempt to balance our fundamental urge for connection with the urge to experience our own agency (p 111)."

Perel points out that in a great relationship there needs to be a balance between on the one hand surrender and intimacy and, on the other hand, autonomy. She cites psychologist Janet Reibstein as saying that our current model of marriage, which stresses togetherness and honesty:

> "… is much better at spelling out the criteria for intimacy than those for autonomy."

The emphasis is on building closeness, not on sustaining individuality. My patients who adhere closely to this ethos of intimacy wind up feeling that their individual aspirations, or those of their partner, are no longer legitimate (p 191)."

Under this theory, people with a high need for autonomy might have a tough time sustaining close relationships.

What is your need for autonomy? At work? At home?

26. We want to make things happen in our work life and in our social life.

You've met that type of person. No sooner have you finished talking about a possible opportunity or goal or action than they run off and act upon it. They move to action without a second's thought, sometimes to the detriment of themselves and others around them. We need these people as they make things happen. Often, we wish they would think things through a little more.

To what degree do you jump in with both feet and make things happen?

27. We want to know what's going on.

It makes perfect sense from an evolutionary point of view. The more we knew about our surroundings – physical, contextual, and social – the greater the chance of our survival.

But, once again, you've met the type of person that has to be in on everything. They have to know everything that is going on. They have to be "in on things." On the positive side, they can be a fount of knowledge if you want to know what's going on in the organization. On the negative side, they can be seen as the hub of corporate gossip.

Often, they want to get invited to so many meetings that they rarely get any work of their own done. In the consulting business, we have an acronym for that kind of behavior. We call it FMS – fear of missing something.

To what degree do you have to know everything that is going on around you?

28. We want to be right and achieve some degree of perfectionism.

We have an intense desire (or maybe need?) to feel right. Ming Hsu et al [113] identified activation in the amygdalae when faced with ambiguity (or feeling less than certain) about which choice to make. For many people, the need to feel right translates into the need to "be right" which in turn can skew their subsequent thinking and decision-making.

The need to be right goes even further. It can affect the way we view subsequent information presented to us. Our confirmation bias will tend to "filter out" data that doesn't match our viewpoint. This becomes a vicious cycle where we become convinced that we are right as we reject data that indicates that we might be wrong. And, of course, we all deny that are doing so. ☺

As regards perfectionists, you've met them. The people who want everything to be just perfect. And anything that is the slightest degree away from perfect drives them nuts. They will enter into a room and straighten up the pictures on the wall if they are slightly crooked. They will straighten and sometimes rearrange the books on the bookshelf. They will ensure that all the cans in the pantry are aligned. They can drive some of us nuts.

On the other hand, you've met people at the other end of that spectrum. Those that don't seem to care about any degree of getting it "right" or even close to "perfect" at all. Any answer, or any result or any work product, will be fine no matter how it looks. They too can drive some of us nuts.

A balance in between is probably healthy. A regard for quality, without going crazy.

And all of this might come from that same dopamine brain dynamic that sets up expectations and judges actions against them.

What about you? Do you need to be right? All of the time or some of the time? Perfectionist?

29. We want no changes – keep things the same at work and in our social lives.

Once again, this makes complete sense from an evolutionary point of view. If you were trying to figure out how to survive then, if everything stayed the same, it would increase your chances. Makes sense.

The way our brains handle information reinforces the process. It works like this. For everything we can think about, the brain constructs a "mental model" or "schema." Whether it be a real thing like a car or a banana or a concept like an atom (I know atoms are real but most people have only ever conceived of them not seen one), the brain builds up a network of generalities about the object in question.

As new data about an object arrive, the brain qualifies it. Does this data match what I already know about the object? If it matches, then the brain adds it into its mental model or schema and feels good about it, getting a little hit of dopamine. If, however, the new data contradicts the mental model, the brain needs to make a choice. There are a number of options:

> Ignore It: This can happen at a nonconscious level. There is a body of research that demonstrates how our brains can just "not see" data that doesn't fit our mental models, even scientists' brains who you would think would have been trained out of such a mistake. It can also happen at a conscious level. We recognize that something doesn't fit, and we simply ignore it. There are many old adages illustrating this point, for example, "There's none so deaf as those that don't want to hear."

> Reject It: Confirmation bias and maybe other biases will tend to direct us to just toss it away, especially if we are in a rush, under pressure, or under some other form of stress.

> Generalize It: Turn it from the specific that might not work for your schema into something that is more general so that you can make it fit.

> Change It: We reinterpret the data so that it does fit. In that way, our brains can "accept" the new data.

> Think About It: From an energy point of view, this is a highly expensive process for the brain. It involves a conscious evaluation and a potential "rewiring" process. The brain tends to use it as a last resort.

But not for everybody. And not for some people in different situations. Some people get scared stiff at the thought of even a minor change. Yet others take change in their stride. Some people want to have no changes at work but are fine with changes at home. Some people are fine with changes at a macro level but resist at a micro level. Change their job, no problem, but change where the sugar is at home, and you have a fight on your hands.

There are even other people, who not only tolerate change, but actively seek it out.

What about you? When and where are you OK with change?

30. We want to understand what is going on and make sense of things at work and socially.

Once again, from a survival point of view this makes complete sense. If I wasn't aware of what was happening around me, didn't understand it, and couldn't make sense of it, then my chances of survival were reduced.

This sense-making is happening most if the time except, possibly, when we are asleep. We make sense of the world by interpreting the cues as we interact with our environment. As a result of the meaning we give to these stimuli and our interpretations of them over time, we build up experiences, beliefs, memories, attitudes, preferences, biases, etc. Most likely, we don't have complete information about everything so our brains "invent" or fill in the missing information. We refer to this process by the highly unscientific name of "MSU" – or "make stuff up." Very often, the process of MSU is at a nonconscious level. We're not aware of the fact that we are doing it. Most of the time, the narrative that we develop is unlikely to be the same narrative that someone else will develop even though we have experienced the same data. Or nearly the same.

The process of sense-making is driven by all of our background experiences. I will cover more of that in Section C, "Understanding Your Self."

We are all doing this all of the time. In times of change, however, we are likely to be driven to spend more of our time in making sense of what is going on.

While I was writing this book, I was working with the senior leaders of a large company that was going through some major changes. The industry was changing around them as a result of a variety of factors and their revenue was steadily decreasing. In response, the company had started off ten major change initiatives. When we tested which facets were ranked highest among the group of leaders, the need to make sense of what was going on consistently was ranked in the top three.

Back to you. How much of your mental energy is spent on sense-making both at work and at home? Too little? Too much? Just right?

31. We want things to be consistent.

To some degree, this is similar to the facet of not wanting change. There are elements of overlap, certainly. But it goes in a couple of slightly different directions.

We start out at birth desiring consistency. It appears that consistency is highly important to the social, emotional, and cognitive development of babies and young children. At a young age, this consistency comes from regularity, routines, and orderliness, in addition to setting and enforcing limits; these all contribute to a positive, consistent environment in our early stages of development.

Repeated experiences in a consistent environment help strengthen networks of connections in the brain. These connections form the foundation for the development of trust in others, self-esteem, behavior regulation, and many other abilities. [114]

Cialdini [115] suggests that "the desire for consistency is a central motivator of our behavior." He points out that not only do we desire consistency (and desire the appearance of consistency) but that it is such a powerful influence that it often causes us to act against our own best interests. Of course, this is one thing that will take us into the area of irrationality, which I will deal with later.

In addition, not only do we like to see consistency in others and in our experiences of others, but we like consistency in our environment and ourselves. With regard to ourselves, Cialdini writes:

> *"Most of the time we will be better off if our approach to things is well-laced with consistency. Without it, our lives would be difficult, erratic, and disjointed."*

As Cialdini states, most of the time being consistent is useful to us. It saves energy, thinking, and time. Furthermore, the personality trait of inconsistency is considered undesirable.

People with a high need for consistency will often use words like regularity, orderliness, stability, plans, rules and guidelines, compliance, and schedules and routines.

You? Your need for consistency? In others and in yourself? And what about what you claim you need in yourself, and how you actually behave? Are they consistent?

32. We want some ambiguity in work and social situations – but not too much.

First of all, let's look up some definitions:

That fount of all knowledge, *Wikipedia*, defines ambiguity as:

> *"Ambiguity is a type of meaning in which several interpretations are plausible. A common aspect of ambiguity is uncertainty. It is thus an attribute of any idea or statement whose intended meaning cannot be definitively resolved according to a rule or process with a finite number of steps. (The ambi-part of the term reflects an idea of 'two' as in 'two meanings.')"*

I am differentiating these facets from the facets concerning uncertainty. Uncertainty regards a lack of, or vague, information. Ambiguity is where we have information, but it can be interpreted in multiple ways or could lead us to multiple choices.

So, what does the brain do with ambiguity? As with uncertainty, it doesn't like it. There have been many studies regarding risk, uncertainty, and ambiguity and the brain, and a couple of trends seem to emerge.

Ambiguity is handled by neural networks in the brain similar to those that handle fear. [116] The type of risk associated with having uncertainty with known outcomes creates less activity in the brain than risk in which there is uncertainty with unknown outcomes. [117]

Bottom line? The brain dislikes uncertainty, risk, vagueness, and ambiguity. All of them. But it can tolerate small amounts of each, provided that they are in service of a larger, more certain, lower-risk, clearer, and more well-defined environment. What is your tolerance for vagueness and ambiguity?

33. We want some things to be spontaneous, but surprises at work and socially can scare us.

How many of us have worked for a boss who says that he/she can tolerate most things if they are not surprised? What about those of us who have arranged a well-meaning surprise for a friend, but the gesture backfired? When people say that they don't like surprises what they normally mean is that they don't like surprises which have a potential negative outcome, although that is not true for everyone. Some people don't even like positive surprises.

As we saw in our discussion of the four processes in the brain, surprise is one of the six fundamental emotions. We recognize the facial expressions of surprise although sometimes we confuse the facial expression of surprise on someone else's face with that of anger. [118]

From an evolutionary point of view, however, that confusion might have a good explanation. If something is a surprise to us, it might mean that our beliefs about the world are out of date and need updating. [119] The surprise/update construct processes engage different neural circuitry. [120] From a survival and prediction viewpoint, it would make evolutionary sense that surprise would elicit a similar reaction to fear. It would mean that we "needed to encode a new version of our environment."

And, for many people, the fear response happens instantaneously whether the surprise is a positive one or a negative one.

Finally, there are different neural circuits that are engaged depending on whether the surprise is a reward or a threat (punishment). [121]

There is much research going on at the amount about the brain mechanisms associated with surprise, and the picture is gradually becoming clearer. For example, studies have shown that surprise interrupts both our cognitive ability and our ability to take action [122] but also increases our perception and motivation, willingness to explore, and ability to learn. [123] Once again, from an evolutionary viewpoint, all of these make sense.

Surprise, surprise. What is your reaction to surprises? Love 'em or hate 'em?

34. We want to feel that we can take care of ourselves.

We have already discussed independence and autonomy together with their opposite, helplessness. The feeling that we can take care of ourselves is a sense that we can put the desire for independence and autonomy into action. (And here, by using the phrase "take care of ourselves," I am focusing on the ability to move things to action rather than the possible interpretation of taking care of our own health.)

There is a whole host of research in this field, all reaching similar conclusions, i.e., that helplessness, or a sense of not being able to take care of ourselves, has a major impact on all animals, ranging from mice to humans. One older study illustrates the overall point; it showed "students at greater risk of helplessness reporting significantly more procrastination, lower grade point averages, and more dysphoria" (unease or dissatisfaction). [124]

How do you view your own ability to take care of yourself? At work? At home?

35. We want to have some sense of tradition.

This facet can be treated lightly or in great depth. The depth can come from many sources, one of which is the future of tradition in an ever-increasing technologically-based world.

Let's start with the simple, slightly easier end of the scale. Tradition, convention, rituals, or whatever you wish to call them have seemingly had a place in our lives for a long time. Whether it be personal rituals (like always brushing your teeth before bed), family traditions (like dinner together on Friday evening), tribal "oral" traditions (like the passing on of tribal stories, myths, and legends), national traditions (like Thanksgiving and Bastille Day), religious traditions (like fish on Friday, baptisms, burials, Christmas, Diwali, or bah mitzvahs), or societal traditions (like marriage or military parades), or some mix of all of the above, they are prominent in all of our lives. Stag nights, bachelorette parties, baby showers, twenty-first birthday parties … you name it … the rituals are everywhere. They are often "rites of passage."

For some people, these rituals are very important and provide an "anchor" for their lives. The Friday night visit to the pub, for example. Other people are way less interested. I stated earlier that many of these facets interact with other facets. Consider the interaction between the need to belong to an in-group and rituals. Many groups have developed rituals as part of the "belonging" process. On the other hand, I suspect that people who don't have a strong need or desire to belong to a group might develop some personal rituals of their own, like a glass of champagne to start the evening off on a Friday night.

That's the easy part to identify. By the way, I am not saying that all of the rituals are easy to understand or that all of them are positive, just that it is easy to identify that they exist. Presumably, it is also easy to personally identify whether they are important to us as individuals.

The more difficult part is how technology will impact tradition, rites, and rituals moving forward. Will they become more important or less important? Another book will be required to explore this.

For you, how important are rituals? What do they mean to you? What if they weren't there?

36. We want to have some sense of conformity.

In some ways, this facet leads on from the prior one. Traditions, rites, and rituals imply some sense of conformity. And nonconformity, or lack of following tradition, etc., is often decried at family, religious, and societal levels.

Some of us get great comfort in conforming to what is required from us. Others get excitement from breaking the rules or going against what is "expected" of us.

Yet, we benefit greatly from conformity. How many of us (unless we were young and/or under the influence) have decided that it would be a good idea to drive on the wrong side of the road, used red as the "go" sign at crossroads, or deliberately connected the hot water pipe to the right-hand faucet? (And how many of you are now checking, at least in your mind) whether I have that piece of standardization correct?) We all benefit by adhering to standards. USB, HDMI, and iOS/Android operating systems have all become standards, and we conform to the standard. Or do we? Maybe we just conform until something better comes along.

So, some conformity is good. Just the concept of total conformity, to some of us, appears terrifying. Yet you want the bank clerk to treat the deposit you have put into your bank in exactly a pre-described way, i.e., credited to your account.

From an evolutionary perspective, conforming to the norms of the tribe you were in probably gave you a great advantage in terms of personal survival. If you didn't conform to social norms, then it is reasonable to assume that you increased your chances of being ostracized from the tribe, hence reducing your chances of survival.

What about what happens in the brain if you conform? There are, as you can imagine, many studies regarding compliance, conformity, and social norms. Cialdini (once again) and Goldstein offer an opinion. [125] They suggest that there are three reasons that we are guided be external influences:

> ➤ to form accurate perceptions of reality and react accordingly (prediction)
> ➤ to develop and preserve meaningful social relationships (participation)
> ➤ to maintain a favorable self-concept (participation)

And they add:

> "... the ways in which these goals interact with external forces to engender social influence processes that are subtle, indirect, and outside of awareness."

So, once again, we come back to the nonconscious guiding of our behavior. We conform way more often than we think. We are more influenced by people with whom we identify, i.e., our in-group. What are we non-consciously influenced about? All sorts of things, even by simply being told what is going on around us, including the energy usage of our neighbors and whether prior guests in our hotel room reused their towels. And there's lots more. Expert opinion. Celebrities. Racial bias. Majority behavior.

The degree to which we are influenced depends on a number of dynamics including positive affect and perspective taking. [126] If we decide to go along with the group and we believe the group to be wrong, there's a lot of brain activity goes on in the PFC as you can imagine. If we do decide to take a stand and go against the crowd, there's an increase in activity in our dear old friend, the amygdala. [127]

The bottom-line? You are probably being influenced to conform more than you believe. To what degree do you need conformity? To what degree do you conform to your needs?

37. We want to have some sense of harmony and stability at work and socially.

It can be reasonably assumed that social harmony and social stability would, from an evolutionary viewpoint, be advantageous from a survival point of view. This could be both as an individual and as a group. Politeness, "going along to get along," and "not rocking the social boat," would all seem to be great strategies when it comes to survival. We have already covered the need for independence or autonomy but the need for social harmony can be seen as the counterbalance of independence, i.e., interdependence. The need for group survival as well as individual survival.

The topic, once again, has been the subject of considerable research, most of which leads in the same direction as described above. One pair of researchers has recently added in the concept of "rejection avoidance" as being part of the overall process. [128]

The independence-interdependence spectrum clearly has a large cultural element to it. Using a great generalization, Western societies tend towards independence while Eastern societies tend towards interdependence so social harmony is likely to differ considerably across that spectrum.

Within that overall framework, there are large differences between what social harmony means in different countries and regions. This has been the subject of many training sessions and is even the topic of a variety of intelligences as exemplified by David Livermore's book called *Cultural Intelligence*. [129]

So, to what degree do you play along with social harmony? Do you find yourself biting your tongue? Is it important to you that other people adhere to the social norms? Or do you just ignore it and do what you will?

38. We want to be sure – we don't like feeling doubt.

Let's start this with a definition, once again, from that source of all wisdom, *Wikipedia*. It states:

> *"Doubt is a mental state in which the mind remains suspended between two or more contradictory propositions, unable to assent to any of them. Doubt on an emotional level is indecision between belief and disbelief. It may involve uncertainty, distrust, or lack of conviction on certain facts, actions, motives, or decisions. Doubt can result in delaying or rejecting relevant action out of concern for mistakes or missed opportunities."*

This may not be a perfect definition, but it gives us a starting point.

I probably don't have to point this out any more. Most brains dislike all of the things that describe doubt. Suspense between two propositions, indecision, uncertainty, distrust, etc. So, it is not surprising that doubt causes trouble for our brains. They want the opposite.

In addition, doubt requires conscious reasoning, i.e., the engagement of the PFC and that is energetically expensive. It's one of the reasons why, if you are doubtful about something, it keeps coming back in your head, and, after a while, you feel tired. You just want it resolved.

Some people find that they can live in this state while others really detest it. When they face doubt, it's almost as if they can't think of anything else.

How are you at living in doubt? Take it in your stride or worry wart it to death? I have no doubt that you'll find an answer to this one.

39. We want people to be authentic with us.

Have you ever been with someone who was smiling, and you just knew that their smile was not genuine? Or watched a celebrity or politician smile, and you just didn't believe them? Or heard someone say something, and you knew that it wasn't correct? And yet, when asked to explain how you knew those things, many of us have a hard time pinpointing what drove our certainty.

Authenticity. Our brains have evolved an acute sense of authenticity and are extremely good at picking up on the cues that indicate whether someone is being authentic with us. We pick up on clues that make us uncomfortable. Most of this is at a nonconscious level.

Let's go back to Dr. Gordon's book [130] where he lists a table called "Common Nonconscious Communication Cues Together with Their Likely Cause":

Pupil dilation	Interested and aroused
Pupil constriction	Disinterested
Natural extended gaze into someone's eyes	Sense of intimacy
Peering over your glasses at someone	Critical or judgmental
Crow's feet at the corner of the eye	Authentic smile
Mouth only smile	Inauthentic smile
Twisted smile	Sarcasm
Tight or pursed lips	Dislike the situation
Finger in or to the mouth	Sign of insecurity and need for reassurance
Hand on chin – index finger pointing to the cheek	Critical evaluation or disengagement
Holding hands in tent position	Confidence that you have the right answer
Shoulder shrug	Non-understanding or disinterested

As regards pupil dilation and constriction, there is a story about jade traders of old selling their wares. They would place a piece of jade in front of a potential client. The client would look at the jade. The trader would look at the client's eyes. If their pupils constricted, the trader went on to the next piece of jade. If their pupils dilated, there was no price reduction offered! Apocryphal or not, it makes the point.

Darwin (and the rest of us) are indebted to Monsieur Duchenne de Boulogne who studied the human face and smile, contributing insight regarding the authentic smile. I quote from Eckman et al [131] who quote from Duchenne:

> *"The emotion of frank joy is expressed on the face by the combined contraction of the zygomaticus major muscle and the orbicularis oculi. The first obeys the will, but the*

second is only put in play by the sweet emotions of the soul; the. . . fake joy, the deceitful laugh, cannot provoke the contraction of this latter muscle...The muscle around the eye does not obey the will; it is only brought into play by a true feeling, by an agreeable emotion. Its inertia, in smiling, unmasks a false friend."

None of these cues are pure black and white, and they are not perfect all of the time. But over time, our brains learn to pay attention. And some of them can be subtle and nuanced. For example, peering at someone in a critical way can be just a slight tilt of the head by a few degrees. But the recipient is fully aware!!

They can also be enhanced by other visual or verbal cues. Tight lips accompanied by monosyllabic answers gives a strong message.

The uncomfortableness arises when the verbal language is in conflict with the cue. Tight lips and monosyllabic answers are in alignment. But being told something while someone has their arms folded or looking slightly away from you or with their body turned slightly away from you will all be interpreted by the brain, at a nonconscious level, as inauthentic, whether you aware of it or not. You may just feel some degree of discomfort and may not know why. But your brain does.

To what degree do you pick up on these cues? When you do, what impact do they have on you? How impacted are you when you pick up on inauthenticity?

40. We want to minimize risk at work and in our social lives.

This is another example where, by now, there should be little or no reason to expand upon the brain's reaction to risk. The brain doesn't like anything which is unpredictable, and if something has risk attached to it, then, almost by definition, it is unpredictable. Or, more accurately, there can be several outcomes, each of which can be predicted, but which outcome will occur cannot be predicted exactly.

But, let's dig in one level deeper. What do we mean by risk? In the research, you will see reference to a number of different domains of risk, namely:

- ➢ Recreational risk
- ➢ Physical risk
- ➢ Emotional risk
- ➢ Social risk
- ➢ Financial or investment risk
- ➢ Intellectual risk
- ➢ Ethical risk
- ➢ Health risk
- ➢ Gambling

There seems to be a general sense that none of us has a trait-based, consistent approach to risk across all of these domains. [132] We might go paragliding on Saturday afternoon but not be willing to risk making a social gaffe on Saturday evening. We might love to perform with the local theater group but not be willing to take a risk in the stock market. We are a "complicated blend" in that we each have different levels of risk tolerance in each of the domains listed above. And this might change depending on whether we are at work or in our social lives.

In addition, there are a number of other variables that seem to impact our willingness to take risks based on who we are and the context of our lives. In general, men take more risk across all domains than do women, although the degree of difference varies by domain. In addition, men perceive the risk as less.

We tend to have less of a propensity for risk:

> ➢ as we grow older
> ➢ when we become parents
> ➢ when we want to have more children
> ➢ when we have an increased number of siblings

We tend to have a greater tolerance for risk:

> ➢ the further down the birth sequence we are
> ➢ as we see our life-expectancy reducing

But you might well ask, why do we enjoy some sense of risk? If our brains hated risk and avoided it all costs, then roller coasters wouldn't make any money, horror movies wouldn't be popular, Las Vegas wouldn't exist, and Halloween wouldn't be much fun.

There are at least a couple of theories on this. The first is that we have an underlying cost-benefit analysis that we run non-consciously. The theory suggests that our risk decisions are driven more by the perceived benefit of an activity to us and less by the perceived risk. [133]

The next theory is that it has been evolutionarily advantageous to explore. We increased our chances of survival if we explored new possibilities, found new sources of food, better places to live, new friends and allies, and different mating possibilities. Of course, there was risk associated with all of these opportunities.

Finally, on a more lighthearted note, one of my colleagues [134] uses the following advice when he is mentoring clients:

"Risk is the only legal, long-acting, performance-enhancing drug that we have."

In what domains are you comfortable with risk? And where do you avoid risk?

41. We want to be curious and learn.

In some ways, this is the other side of the coin, or the flip side, of the risk avoidance facet.

If we are curious, then we are likely to have to take risks in order to satisfy that curiosity.

Curiously, the depth of research on curiosity does not reflect the length of time that it has been studied. In 2015, researchers were still lamenting how little we know about the underpinnings of curiosity:

2012: "Despite the importance of curiosity and related behaviors, the topic has been largely neglected in human neuroscience; hence, little is known about the neurobiological mechanisms underlying curiosity." [135]

and

2015: "Curiosity is a basic element of our cognition, but its biological function, mechanisms, and neural underpinning remain poorly understood." [136]

So, what do we know? Well, we're not entirely ignorant. Psychologists have recognized the importance of curiosity, specifically in learning, and even more specifically in learning in child development.

A fairly recent article [137] identified that when we are curious about something, we are more likely to remember it when we learn about it. Obvious? Maybe. But what might not be so obvious is that if we are curious about something, we are also more likely to remember other, non-related aspects that we learned en route.

The study also found that there was increased activity in the hippocampus (learning and memory) when curiosity was more pronounced. In addition, they found that, in advance of learning the new information, there was increased activity in the hippocampus as if it were getting ready to learn. Further, they found activity in the reward circuits. In other words, if we are curious, we learn more overall and we feel good about it.

In addition, the study might have shed some light on curiosity as a motivator. It appears that the more curious someone is, the less need there is for external motivation.

And, as Mlodinov [138] points out, curiosity was/is a necessary factor for adaptation:

"A novelty-seeking (i.e., curious) organism might get injured exploring alien terrain or might face a predator, but an organism that avoids the unfamiliar at all costs might fail to discover sufficient food sources and starve."

and

"An unchanging environment offers those who have found a comfortable niche no urgent impetus to explore or innovate. But conditions do change, and animals have a better shot at survival if they have previously gathered information about new feeding sites, escape routes, hiding places, and so on."

Some researchers [139] have divided curiosity into two parts, namely not knowing something (information gap) and almost knowing something (anticipation of resolution). Both of these are impacted by time.

"When people did not expect to close their information gap soon (long time to resolution), not knowing affected the subjective experience of curiosity more strongly than when they expected to close their information gap quickly (short time to resolution). As such, people experienced less positive affect, more discomfort, and more annoyance with lack of information in a long than a short time to resolution situation. Moreover, when time in the long time to resolution setting passed, the anticipation of the resolution became stronger, positive affect increased, and discomfort and annoyance with lack of information decreased. Time is thus a key factor in the experience of curiosity.

It is also relatively easy to conceive of many different dimensions for curiosity. We each might be curious in one dimension but not in others. Here's a few examples, using curiosity with respect to different dimensions. A person might be intellectually curious but emotionally reluctant. Sexually curious but geographically anchored to the same place. Gastronomically curious but rarely reads anything outside of their normal genre.

You – where are you curious, and where do you stay in your shell?

42. We want to know that we are heard and our opinions count.

Have you ever been in a meeting when you were not invited to give your opinion about a topic on which you had some strong ideas? How about when you were able to proffer an opinion, but it didn't get air time, no one followed up on it, or, even worse, the idea got put down? Or your idea wasn't picked up at the time, yet when another person suggested the same thing, the idea was taken up and attributed to them.

I would love to report that these are rare occurrences, but, alas, as we all know, that is not the case. In my work with teams or groups, I have seen countless examples of all of these.

So, what went on in your brain the last time that happened to you? Well, it depends not only on how you feel about having your opinion not heard or not count but on how you score yourself in some other facets.

To start with, let's look at how you feel about your opinions. A recent coaching client was describing how he had primarily been brought up by his grandparents. As a child, he was continually told to be quiet as his opinion didn't count. As an adult, he always has an opinion. And if he senses that he hasn't been heard, it badly triggers him, and his reactions are unpredictable. Mostly, not good. Once he knows he has been heard, then he worries much less about whether his opinions are taken on board and/or implemented.

Consider how this facet interacts with some others, for example:

> ➢ Your need to feel equal to/better than others
> ➢ Your need to win or beat other people
> ➢ Your need to receive recognition from people who are important to you
> ➢ Your need to be valued and respected by others

If you score high on any of these facets, the impact of being triggered is likely to be significantly enhanced if you have a high need to have your voice heard.

What is your reaction to not having your opinions, thoughts, or ideas acknowledged?

43. We want to be able to "go with the flow" at work and in social situations.

We all have a natural style, essentially, the one we are born with. What we have when we are children doesn't just go away…it hangs around. "Show me the boy at seven years old, and I will show you the man!" has been variously attributed to Aristotle, St. Francis Xavier, and the Jesuits. And probably more people than that. I am putting my money on Aristotle! More recently in a longitudinal study, [140] the BBC followed fourteen children, from all walks of life in England, every seven years starting when they were seven. They found, with a few exceptions, that the adage is mostly true.

On the other hand, we add in aspects that are adaptive as we grow older. We have to in order to survive and thrive. Many of these additions are influenced by outside forces. Others are more internal. If we naturally shy away from social interactions, we may not thrive as a TV show host. But if "showing up" becomes part of our job, we can often adapt and "go along with it." The adaptation part is mostly about being flexible.

Some people have a hard time with adaptation and flexibility, only grudgingly moving off their standard behaviors by the minimal practical amount. You've met them. Other people seek out situations which will force them to change, seemingly working on the principle that they need the stimulation of adaptation in order to thrive. You've met them too.

Then there are the rest of us that are in the middle. Sometimes it's easy, and sometimes it's hard. Every time that we do adapt, the brain needs to go through its own internal workings. Being flexible and "going with the flow" means that the brain has to face all those things it doesn't like – life becomes unpredictable.

Where are you on the "going with the flow" spectrum? Nearer the "grudgingly" change end or the "seek out" change end?

44. We want to have commitment from others at work and from others in our social lives.

Commitment to what you do is the subject of many old adages and is the topic of many self-help books. "Say what you mean and mean what you say." "Put your money where your mouth is." We live in a world where we expect people to live up to their commitments. And if they let us down, we have a variety of reactions.

At the brain-based level, it can simply mean that we are faced with a potential threat of a change or a loss or something worse. If someone has failed to deliver on their commitment to us, then that might mean we are faced with the possibility of failing on a commitment to someone else – and all of the threats that might bring along with it.

At the psychological level, and probably applicable over a longer time frame, we go down the thinking process that we cannot "trust" this person again, especially if we start to see it as part of a pattern of behavior from that individual.

As part of the coaching work that I do, I am always on the lookout for people using the word "try." It is an indication that I need to peel back one more layer of the commitment onion. Are they really committed to the action they are espousing? Yoda suggested, "Do, or do not. There is no try." I will follow up the inclusion of "try" with an exercise where I ask them to demonstrate "trying." If you carry out the exercise, you will discover that Yoda is/was right. You either do or do not.

And do we hold ourselves to the same standard that we hold other people? For many of us, maybe most, we probably don't. For me, I will try and do better next time. Wait! I will do better next time. Thanks Yoda!

And you? To what degree do you need to have others deliver on their commitments? Do you let non-delivery against commitments slide or does it trigger you badly?

Driving Force #4: Purpose

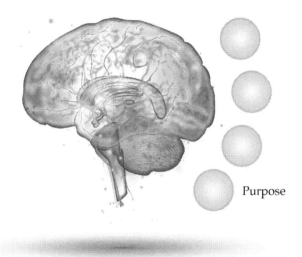

Purpose

Some General Comments about Purpose and Pleasure Domains

The facets that I described under Protection, Participation, and Prediction result primarily in triggers that will cause a sense of threat. For example, if a situation is ambiguous (Prediction), and I score ambiguity high, then I could easily get triggered and hence threatened by anything that is ambiguous.

And before we move on to Purpose and Pleasure, please remember that the brain does not deal with these until it feels safe, i.e., the threats from Protection, Participation, and Prediction have been significantly reduced or gone away.

The facets that I am about to describe for Purpose and Pleasure are slightly different. These facets are more descriptions of desired rewards – and if something stops me from getting that reward, I might feel triggered and hence threatened. For example, if living out my sense of purpose is important to me such that I rank it highly, if something happens that reduces the chance of me achieving my sense of purpose, then that might put my brain into a threat state.

So, let's look at them in more detail.

45. We want to achieve mastery in our fields and have an opportunity to practice it on a regular basis.

So, what do we mean by mastery? Pink [141] says it best:

"… the desire to get better and better at something that matters."

And that seems to sum up a loose subject very well. But why is it important?

Pink cites:

> *"A study of 11,000 industrial scientists and engineers working at companies in the United States found that the desire for intellectual challenge – that is, the urge to master something new – was the best predictor of productivity. Scientists motivated by this intrinsic desire filed significantly more patents than those whose main motivation was money, even controlling for the amount of effort each group expended."*

Some readers might say, "Well, that's OK for scientists, but what about the rest of us?" Wrzesniewski and Dutton [142] studied hospital cleaners, nurses, and hairdressers and found a parallel result. They found that by creating the opportunity for workers to craft their own roles to include "more absorbing challenges," employees reported increased satisfaction and boosted "their own views of their skills." There may be some element of "autonomy" at play here as well, but they write, "Even in low autonomy jobs, employees can create new domains for mastery."

Pink also provides us with the grandiose title of "The Three Laws of Mastery." I would call them descriptors, but I'll let you decide which you prefer. They are:

> ➢ Mastery is a Mindset: He bases this description on the work of Carol Dweck who differentiates between a "growth mindset" (constantly striving to understand more) and a "fixed mindset" (resting on what you already know). The mastery mindset is always about learning not just about performance.
> ➢ Mastery is a Pain: It takes a long time to approach mastery. Ten years. 10,000 hours. And it is not easy. It requires "perseverance and passion," and sometimes it's not much fun.
> ➢ Mastery is an Asymptote: For those readers who can't remember, "asymptote" means something that you can get very close to but cannot actually get there. Think about the person in a room who is told that he/she is to move halfway to the door every minute. They will never actually reach the door as they will only ever halve the gap between them and the door. The joy is in the pursuit. "The journey is the reward," as the old saying goes.

So, it's about learning all of the time, going on a pathway that may be difficult, and you never actually get there! Wow! Sign me up for some of that! Yet there are many, many people who choose that path.

Many years ago, I listened to Tim Gallwey give a presentation where he asked a group of tennis players what their goal was when they played tennis. Their first response was "To win, of course." Tim's response was "In that case, why don't you always play someone who is weaker than you?" Their second response was much more about the challenge of getting better: mastery.

So, I wonder about two questions. First, to what degree is the drive of mastery based upon the (more) Western paradigm of success for the individual. Or is it global in nature? Second, from an evolutionary perspective, I am intrigued by the degree to which the pursuit of mastery is a benefit mainly to the individual, or to the tribe. Did the pursuit of mastery by an individual have a concomitant benefit to the tribe?

Now, about you. At this stage of your life, what is your need for mastery?

46. We want to develop ourselves/self-actualize.

Ever since I learned about this concept, I have always thought of it as "Be the best that you can be."

Unfortunately, that phrase became co-opted for other purposes and, as a result, has begun to lose meaning for me.

But, if we once again turn to *Wikipedia*, we can get some guidance as to what the concept is all about:

> *"The term was originally introduced by the organismic theorist Kurt Goldstein for the motive to realize one's full potential. Expressing one's creativity, quest for spiritual enlightenment, pursuit of knowledge, and the desire to give to and/or positively transform society are examples of self-actualization. In Goldstein's view, it is the organism's master motive, the only real motive: 'the tendency to actualize itself as fully as possible is the basic drive... the drive of self-actualization.'"*

The concept is the top, or final, level of Maslow's hierarchy of needs, and, for many people, that is how they have come across the term.

In a recent article, Ordun and Akun [143] help us out by describing the psychological profile of "self-actualized people" as consisting of two dimensions:

> ➢ *"openness to experience (being aware of one's emotions, having insight, empathy, and healthy interpersonal relations)*
> ➢ *reference to self (being responsible for oneself, having a well-developed ethical understanding and self-esteem, expressing oneself cognitively and emotionally, and not being too much sensitive to other people's ideas, influences, and criticisms)."*

and later, they outline Maslow's definition of self-actualization as comprising the following parts:

> ➢ *"feeling trust with an open attitude*
> ➢ *choosing development instead of fear and doubt*
> ➢ *listening to one's sound inner voices; being honest to oneself*
> ➢ *taking necessary steps for being satisfied, not only focusing on ultimate goals but also discovering the process of self-actualization*
> ➢ *living peak experiences*
> ➢ *exploring one's secret psyche*
> ➢ *having courage to see and give up defense mechanisms"*

Taking all of those aspects into consideration, how important is self-actualization to you?

47. We want to have a Mission/Purpose and know that our lives have Meaning.

In his *Blue Zones* book, [144] Dan Buettner identifies "Purpose" as one of the nine factors for a long and happy life. His summary:

> *"The Okinawans call it* ikigai, *and the Nicoyans call it* plan de vida. *For both it translates to 'why I wake up in the morning.' In all the Blue Zones, people had*

119

something to live for beyond just work. Research has shown that knowing your purpose is worth up to seven years of extra life expectancy."

Pink [145] adds to this by expanding on his theme of mastery:

"Autonomous people working towards mastery perform at very high levels. But those who do so in the service of some greater objective can achieve even more. The most deeply motivated people – not to mention those who are most productive and satisfied – hitch their desires to a cause larger than themselves."

In his book *Start with Why,* [146] Simon Sinek makes a similar point. People want to get engaged with something that is bigger than them or bigger than the product of the company that they work for produces.

I have worked with many people over the decades, and many have not yet identified their greater Mission/Purpose even fairly late in life. The idea of having a greater purpose sounds good – but maybe a little soft and fluffy for some people, especially those without that overall "purpose." But, what does the science tell us?

The science definitely suggests that an overall purpose is good for us. Take a look at the conclusion of a 2010 study by Boyle et al, [147] for example:

"Conclusion: Greater purpose in life is associated with a reduced risk of Alzheimer's disease and mild cognitive impairment in community-dwelling older persons."

In more detail (I have removed some of the greater detail for clarity's sake):

"… adjusted for age, sex, and education, greater purpose in life was associated with a substantially reduced risk of Alzheimer's disease. Thus, a person with a high score on the purpose in life measure (90th percentile) was approximately 2.4 times more likely to remain free of Alzheimer's disease than was a person with a low score (10th percentile).

In subsequent models, purpose in life also was associated with a reduced risk of Mild Cognitive Impairment and a slower rate of cognitive decline."

So. There you have it. Purpose in life seems to equate not only to increased life expectancy, higher motivation, higher productivity, and greater life satisfaction but also to a significantly reduced chance of Alzheimer's disease, mild cognitive impairment, and cognitive decline. Sounds like a good idea to me. ☺

What about you? Do you know your life Mission and Purpose? If you do, how important is the pursuit of it to you?

48. We want to live in accordance with our core values and work with people/organizations that align with those values.

Let's start, as we have done several times in this section, by looking at a definition…in this case, what do we mean by core values? In this instance, however, we probably have to go down two tracks – organizational core values and personal core values.

Strangely enough, when doing the research for this portion of the book, I came across a useful outline of organizational core values in, of all places, The National Park Service. Here's how they describe organizational core values:

"The core values of an organization are those values we hold which form the foundation on which we perform work and conduct ourselves. We have an entire universe of values, but some of them are so primary, so important to us that throughout the changes in society, government, politics, and technology, they are STILL the core values we will abide by. In an ever-changing world, core values are constant. Core values are not descriptions of the work we do or the strategies we employ to accomplish our mission. The values underlie our work, how we interact with each other, and which strategies we employ to fulfill our mission. The core values are the basic elements of how we go about our work. They are the practices we use (or should be using) every day in everything we do.

They:

> *Govern personal relationships*
> *Guide business processes*
> *Clarify who we are*
> *Articulate what we stand for*
> *Help explain why we do business the way we do*
> *Guide us on how to teach*
> *Inform us on how to reward*
> *Guide us in making decisions*
> *Underpin the whole organization*
> *Require no external justification*
> *Essential tenets"*

That seemed to me a good, albeit long, explanation for a nonprofit organization. For profit organizations might add topics such as:

> *Educating clients and potential clients*
> *Assessing recruitment processes*
> *Increasing engagement and retention*
> *Fostering diversity*

But what about personal core values? I deal with this topic to a much greater degree in Section C, "Understanding Your Self." For many people, especially millennials, working for an organization whose values are aligned with their own is highly important. Personally speaking, I have left the employ of several organizations whose practiced values did not align with my own.

And I use the word "practiced" as a way to differentiate between what companies say they stand for and what they actually do when push comes to shove. Unfortunately, espoused values and values in practice are rarely the same.

Do you know what your own core values are? If so, do they align with the organization that you work for? If not, how important is that to you? If you don't know your own core values, is it important to find out what they are?

49. We want to express ourselves artistically.

It seems that Homo sapiens have had a long history of expressing ourselves through artistic endeavors. Yet, at least at first glance, it is not apparent that the adaptation required to develop the ability for such an artistic expression had any evolutionary advantage. And certainly, it appears to many people that this ability has been unevenly distributed to say the least. While some people are undoubtedly artistically gifted, others, like myself, struggle to achieve this same level of artistic ability. (In my case, the only examination I ever failed was an art exam!!!)

So, why is it important to us? Or at least to some of us? Again, let's spend a moment on some definitions on what we mean by "artistic expression." To do so, I am going to cite an article by Lomas [148] which gives us a good starting point for our discussion. He proposes a new field of study, "positive art," and, for his purpose, summarizes the areas of focus of artistic expression as visual art, music, literature, and drama

Other researchers add in sculpture, dance, poetry, and film although I suspect the latter had little to do with adaptive evolution. ☺

So, let's use those eight as our starting point. (I suspect that there will be many artists who will want to add to that definition; I will be happy to consider any expansion in the next edition.)

Lomas also provides us with some clues as to potential advantages of artistic expression:

> "Moreover, the paper identifies five main positive outcomes that are consistently found in the literature across all these forms: sense-making, enriching experience, aesthetic appreciation, entertainment, and bonding."

In her article, Zaidel [149] offers a summary of how art and the brain may have interacted, summarizing it into three theories:

> "1. The localized brain regions and pathways theory links art to multiple neural regions.
> 2. The display of art and its aesthetics theory is tied to the biological motivation of courtship signals and mate selection strategies in animals.
> 3. The evolutionary theory links the symbolic nature of art to critical pivotal brain changes in Homo sapiens, supporting increased development of language and hierarchical social grouping."

Just from these two sources, we can certainly start to see how some of these dynamics might have conferred some adaptive advantages. But what does art actually do to the brain? Bolwerk et al [150] provide us with some clues (again, I have removed some of the detail for the sake of clarity). Two groups of mid-sixties adults were each given 10-week long art assignments. One group was assigned the task of "actively producing art in an art class" while the other group "cognitively evaluated artwork at a museum."

> "We observed that the visual art production group showed greater spatial improvement in functional connectivity of PCC/preCUN to the frontal and parietal cortices than the cognitive art evaluation group. Moreover, the functional connectivity in the visual art production group was related to psychological resilience (i.e., stress resistance)."

So, it seems that it may be possible that "artistic expression" might also increase some level of brain functionality and help resist stress. Once again, sounds like a good idea.

What about you? How much of a need to do you have for artistic expression? Which of the eight items in our definition appeals to you? Would it be a good idea to add some form into your personal portfolio?

50. We want to explore and live out our spirituality.

Section B Part 4g of the book is devoted entirely to the impact of spirituality on our brain, our well-being, and our longevity so I will not spend much time on it here.

Suffice it to say, for some people this is one of the most important, if not the most important, facet of their lives. The thought of living without that spiritual component in their lives would be a major threat. Yet to many other people, it is of little or no importance. At least at the stage of their lives that they are at right now.

Do you have a desire for spirituality to be part of your life? How important is it to you?

51. We want to feel passionate about something.

In some ways, a passion can be akin to a mission, purpose, or meaning. Many writers and researchers treat the two as synonyms for the same thing, and for some people, it is the same thing. I wanted, however, to identify it as something different. By way of example, I might use myself. My purpose in life might be to teach people about their brains, and I am passionate about understanding as much as I can about the brain, but I am passionate about antiques and photography. Having spent much of the past three decades in and around Silicon Valley, there are many people who are passionate about being an entrepreneur...or passionate about technology...or passionate about the Forty-Niners.

And here by the way, in case it is not clear, I am not referring to the romantic or sexual version of passion but the "excitement about something" variety of passion.

Let's go back to Wikipedia, where we find the following definitions:

> *"Passion is a feeling of intense enthusiasm towards or compelling desire for someone or something. Passion can range from eager interest in or admiration for an idea, proposal, or cause; to enthusiastic enjoyment of an interest or activity; to strong attraction, excitement, or emotion towards a person. It is particularly used in the context of romance or sexual desire, though it generally implies a deeper or more encompassing emotion than that implied by the term lust.*

> *Denis Diderot describes passions as 'penchants, inclinations, desires, and aversions carried to a certain degree of intensity, combined with an indistinct sensation of pleasure or pain, occasioned or accompanied by some irregular movement of the blood and animal spirits.' They can be so strong as to inhibit all practice of personal freedom, a state in which the soul is in some sense rendered passive; whence the name passions. This inclination or so-called disposition of the soul is born of the opinion we hold that a great good or a great evil is contained in an object which in and of itself arouses passion."*

OK. I am not sure I feel of those different things about antiques and photography, but certainly the "compelling desire."

I also know people who don't have a passion in their lives.

In a recent blog post, [151] I found some descriptors about passion that didn't come from the scientific community but resonated with me. I thought I would share them. The author called them "the five intricate ideas of passion you need to take note of":

> ➢ *You need to go ALL IN with passion. Stop concentrating on stuff that puts your passion on the sidelines.*
> ➢ *Passion means getting out of your comfort zone. That means feeling fearful, weird, confused, unsure, etc. A better life definitely is waiting outside the zone.*
> ➢ *You still need to tweak passion with honesty. Be honest with yourself.*
> ➢ *Passion goes full circle. Do yourself a favor, and always listen to your heart. Don't stray too far from your passion even though you think you need to learn this and that other thing.*
> ➢ *And yet, passion must mix with reality. We can't escape how the world works with its various systems, cultures, and people. As much as you want to do what you love, reality kicks in now and then. This is especially true in business. If you want to create a business doing what you love, you need to find the convergence of your passion with what people are willing to pay for. My best advice is to keep learning and trying new things which can support your passion. But try it only once! Don't keep trying for the sake of it. If it's not fun anymore. It's time to let go.*

And for you? Do you have a passion? How important is to you in your life? What would it feel like if you found that you couldn't spend any more time on it?

52. We want a challenge.

Maybe that is a bold statement? Maybe not everyone wants a challenge? It can seem that way sometimes when we are trying to manage, teach, lead, coach …or whatever your role is. But let's look into it further. Why do we like to play puzzles? Sudoku? Crossword puzzles? It seems that across the globe there is a fascination with playing puzzles and games, especially now that many are available instantaneously at our smartphone-enabled fingertips.

As soon as we start looking into this almost obsession with challenge, we come across "The Winner Effect." One of the better descriptions of this is given by Sheely, [152] and I will use him extensively here:

> *"When an animal, be it fish or human, wins a contest, there is a large release of testosterone and dopamine into their brain. Over time, this changes their brain's structure and chemical makeup, making them smarter, more confident, and able to take on larger challenges than before."*

So, if we win at one of these puzzles, we get a hit of testosterone and dopamine which changes our brains and leads us to think that our chances are better next time. What if we lose?

> *"… testosterone is also a hormone released during competition. All competitors release it before a big game, and afterwards usually only the winners will get a boost while the losers' testosterone falls. This opposite effect with testosterone reduction is called the 'loser effect.' It makes the loser meek and timid over time, its submissiveness an evolutionary advantage preventing it from getting into future fights that could cost it its life since it has a history of losing."*

So, win or lose, the effect either drives us on or keeps us out of trouble. It's easy to see how all of these effects might have conferred an adaptive advantage from an evolutionary perspective.

What is your need for a challenge? Do you take on any challenge that is offered?

Or do you only take on challenges that you think you can be successful at?

53. We want to seek the truth.

Do we want to seek the truth? If we start with the basic level of our brains, we can legitimately ask whether truth-seeking is a useful adaptive process.

This topic is a subject of debate, and there are a number of eminent scientists that think maybe not. For example, Haselton et al [153] report on some comments from Pinker:

> "... the process of natural selection is not concerned with truth per se and in some instances even disfavors a truth-seeking mind. For example, there are many adaptive problems in which the best solution sacrifices costly truth-seeking in favor of fast approximations."

Haselton et al also report on comments from Churchland:

> "The principal function of nervous systems is ... to get the body parts where they should be in order that the organism may survive...Truth, whatever that is, definitely takes the hindmost."

They summarize by stating:

> "The idea that the primary function of the brain is to generate true beliefs and valid inferences is, of course, not entirely wrong. An organism that always made invalid judgments and false inferences could not be very successful. But this is quite different from claiming that the brain essentially strives for truth, as if it were evolutionarily optimized for arriving at truthful judgments and logical inference. From an evolutionary perspective, truth should matter only to the degree that it contributes to survival and reproductive success."

So, it seems that truth-seeking may not be a driving force at the brain level, but at the psychological and social levels, it is still probably a major driver for most people. Or at least some variant of the truth. We know that, in the absence of information, the brain "makes stuff up" (MSU). It fills in details that might never have been there in the first place.

In addition, our brains are constantly filtering out data that might go against our biases; we are often only receptive to the small amounts of data that does not pose a threat to our sense of psychological safety (confirmation bias and schema reinforcement). Hence, the brain's search for truth may in fact be the search for a specific truth that serves our current needs.

What about for you, the reader? Where do you stand on your search for the truth?

Driving Force #5: Pleasure

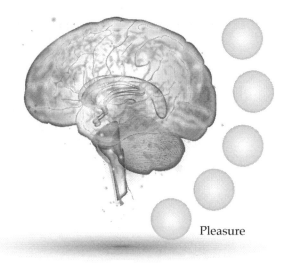

Pleasure

53. We want to experience joy and happiness.

Once again, I may be crazy to take on such huge topics and then summarize them into a couple of paragraphs. I am crazy! Nevertheless, let's "give it a go."

This time, if we refer to *Wikipedia* to start with, we get a welcome surprise …

"The word joy means a feeling of great pleasure and happiness."

It seems simple – joy and happiness are the same thing. Then we get the complication:

C. S. Lewis saw a clear distinction between joy, pleasure, and happiness: "I sometimes wonder whether all pleasures are not substitutes for joy," and, "I call it joy, which is here a technical term and must be sharply distinguished both from happiness and pleasure. Joy (in my sense) has indeed one characteristic and one only in common with them; the fact that anyone who has experienced it will want it again...I doubt whether anyone who has tasted it would ever, if both were in his power, exchange it for all the pleasures in the world. But then joy is never in our power, and pleasure often is."

For our purposes here, I choose to treat them the same. If we are seeking pleasure overall, how much of a drive is it for us to pursue happiness (or joy)?

Happiness is generally perceived to be one of the six basic emotions (along with surprise, fear, sadness, anger, and disgust/contempt). It has been suggested that maybe there are some sub-emotions of happiness that can be identified which might be useful in helping to explain what happiness is. Furthermore, it has been suggested that it might be easier to differentiate them through their associated vocal sounds rather than through the more traditional approach of using visual facial expressions. The five sub-emotions are achievement/triumph, amusement, contentment, pleasure, and relief. [154]

Maybe that helps us define what happiness is. Maybe not.

I was doing some consulting work for a company several years back when the founder started to talk about barbecuing – once again, hang in there, there is a valuable point to this. He had a brand new outdoor kitchen and, even more importantly, a brand new high-end barbecue. He was talking about cooking the perfect filet mignon (or maybe it was a New York strip steak) with friends and family and sharing a glass or two of wine. He was clearly reminiscing.

Then he stopped and drew a metaphoric parallel. He said that people didn't buy a Black & Decker drill because they want a drill. They buy it because they want a hole. He laughed. I don't want or need a barbecue...What I want is the joy of having a great steak and some great wine with my family and friends. The barbecue is the excuse. What we want in our lives is joy.

He went on to create a company whose primary mission was to help people experience "joyful living."

Some of us are very clear about what makes us happy. Some of us are clear, but, in fact, what we expect to make us happy doesn't. Some of us are less clear.

Now back to you. What gives you joy and happiness? Do you know? And if you do, how do you react if something gets in the way of you achieving them?

54. We want to experience sensual gratification.

One of the sub-emotions identified as part of happiness was pleasure, physical pleasure. Our drive for physical pleasure – sensual gratification, sex, or whatever you want to call it – comes from the brain not the genitals. In particular, it is driven by the hypothalamus which triggers off the process of hormone release that gives us the drive to want sensual gratification, and by the basal ganglia which is linked to the reward system so that we want to do it again. And, in some cases, again and again. ☺

For some people, it is a high drive. For others, less so. What about you?

55. We want instant gratification.

It has become evident over the past several decades that life has become more immediate in many, if not all, aspects. I am not going to fill space here by enumerating the myriad of ways that our lives have sped up. But this change of speed has changed our expectations. We expect overnight delivery as standard. We expect high-speed broadband. We expect our employees (and ourselves) to be available 24/7. We expect an instant response from our texts. This is happening in both our professional and personal lives.

I am not attempting to make a value judgment here although I have strong opinions about the dynamic and its impact. Rather, I am attempting to draw your attention to the fact that, more and more, it seems that we become unhappy if we are not instantly (or close to it) gratified.

How much are you driven by the need for instant gratification? How long can you wait for a response to a text that you have sent before you start to get antsy?

56. We want to experience stimulation and excitement.

There are a group of people that are known as "sensation seekers." Helen Fisher [155] calls them "explorers" and writes:

"And although they are not necessarily fond of risk, they are willing to take risks to enjoy new, intense, and exhilarating adventures...only explorers overwhelmingly agreed with the statement 'I find unpredictable situations exhilarating.'"

This characteristic of "unpredictable = exhilarating" clearly flies in the face of the part of the brain that requires certainty, clarity, consistency, and no change. Yet Fisher found that in a large sample, 26% of people were explorers (27.1% of men and 25.1% of women).

This group of people are:

"Intensely curious and unusually creative. They are restless, energetic, and spontaneous, often impulsive. They get bored easily when not absorbed in something that intrigues them."

How important is this to you? How many of these adjectives describe you?

57. We want to play.

It seems that many animals play. It also seems that the bigger the brains of the animal, the more they are likely to play. [156] Since human beings have relatively large brains for our body size, it would be reasonable, therefore, to assume that humans like to play.

In the beginning of his book on play, [157] Stuart Brown states:

"Neuroscientists, development biologists, psychologists, social scientists, and researchers from every point of the scientific compass now know that play is a profound biological process. It has evolved over eons in many animal species to promote survival. It shapes the brain and makes animals smarter and more adaptable. In higher animals, it fosters empathy and makes possible complex social groups. For us, play lies at the core of creativity and innovation.

Of all animal species, humans are the biggest players of all. We are built to play and built through play. When we play, we are engaged in the purest expression of our humanity, the truest expression of our individuality. Is it any wonder that often the times we feel most alive, those that make up our best memories are moments of play?"

and

"I have found that remembering what play is all about and making it part of our daily lives are probably the most important factors in being a fulfilled human being. The ability to play is critical not only to being happy but also to sustaining social relationships and being a creative, innovative person."

But what happens to play in our lives? At some point as we get older, we are made to feel guilty for playing. We are told that it is unproductive, a waste of time, even sinful.

And play, obviously, takes on a myriad of forms and takes on many dimensions. I am not sure what a spectrum of play would look like, but skydiving would seem to come close to one end of the play spectrum while stamp collecting might be at the other.

What are the ways in which you play? And how important is it to you?

58. We want to be loved.

I chose this "short" (I am being facetious here ☺) facet as the last one on the list, maybe for purely sentimental reasons. It seems appropriate. In some ways, I have addressed some of the issues of love in our need to be respected, recognized, and appreciated by people who are important to us. In addition, I include a section (Section B Part 4f) on the brain, love, and sex, which is focused towards what is going on in the brain. But the purpose of this facet is about something else. It's to bring to your attention the question of how important it is to you in general and in this stage of your life.

It's about what happens to us when we get what we want in the way of love and what happens if we don't get it or something gets in the way or we lose it.

How important is it to you?

Section B Part 2d. Your Personal Threat Context

Your Personal Threat Profile (which is the amalgamation of your responses to all of the facets described above) gives you your susceptibility to being triggered by certain types of events.

Your Personal Threat Context gives you your sensitivity to being triggered. Have you ever noticed that sometimes you are resilient to many things, and at other times the same thing that you handled perfectly well one day can send you over the edge the next day? One of the reasons for this is your Personal Threat Context. Some of the elements of your Threat Context are driven by day-to-day aspects, even hour by hour. Others are driven by longer term issues.

Before we look at the elements that comprise your Personal Threat Context, there are some general comments I would like to make. As I covered in Brain Principle #1, "Ancient Brains," all of our brains are subjected to all sorts of threats these days for which they are ill-equipped. For example, during the period of time that I was writing this book, I was driving through the state of Virginia and was stopped for speeding. I was given a ticket for driving at 84 miles per hour in a 70 limit. Judging by the number of police vehicles hidden on the Virginia highways, I guess that I am not the first person to be stopped for such an offense. ☺ I have been stopped before in other states (not many times I must add), so it didn't worry me unduly. At least it didn't until I started to receive letters from attorneys in Virginia telling me that I could get a jail sentence, a suspended license, international travel restrictions, a permanent criminal record…the list went on with all other sorts of doom and gloom. My normal positive outlook on life started to take a beating.

The point I am making here is not that it's OK to speed but that we all face threats in our everyday lives, and while they may not be immediately life-threatening like they were out on the Savannah many years ago, our brains don't know that. We are constantly bombarded with messages, many of them negative and threatening. In addition, we are all now living in what has become known as a VUCA environment. VUCA stands for Volatility, Uncertainty, Complexity and Ambiguity – any one of these dynamics can put our brains into a threat state.

So, your Personal Threat Context comprises those sensitivities that you have over and above those which are generally around us these days i.e. those aspects of your life that are, probably, out of your control, or over which you have little control.

Some of the areas that determine your Personal Threat Context are:

Degree of Control

The degree to which you perceive that you have control over what is going on around you. For example, you are leaving a job and going to a new one. Most of the time, there is a degree of stress involved, but people report a lot more stress when they have been let go for some reason rather than when they have chosen to leave. If there are more major events going on in your life, then many of them might have the potential to cause you stress. If you want to find a list, then simply do an Internet search for "life stress events."

In greater detail, when you look at the degree to which you have control, it is sometimes useful to categorize the situation or event by asking the following types of questions: How much control do I have over the situation? How much influence do I have over the situation? How much choice do I have over my responses? Is the situation one in which "It is what it is," namely, I have no control or influence over the situation and the sooner I learn to accept the situation, the better it will be?

When we take a look at stress management and associated strategies, I will outline a few that you might use when you have little or no control

Degree of Support

The amount of support you have surrounding whatever is causing you stress. Once again, let's take a look at an example. A supposedly positive one. If you have been given a promotion at work, what support are you receiving? From your new boss? From your peers? From your staff? From HR and other staff organizations? From your significant other? From family members and friends? The more support you experience (practically not theoretically), the greater the chances of reducing the degree of threat that you perceive.

Tiredness

How tired we are drastically impacts many of our brain's activities, including our ability to manage our stress. Even during a regular day when you have had a good night's sleep the previous night, stress will tend to take a greater toll at the end of the day than at the beginning. If you have a choice, deal with high stress activities in the morning rather than in the afternoon or evening.

In addition, our ability to deal with stress tends to be higher on Monday or Tuesday than it is on Friday.

Sleep

Lack of sleep can have a major impact on our Personal Threat Context. Once again, insufficient sleep can cause us to overreact to even the slightest situations that we might otherwise have handled perfectly. If you have had insufficient sleep on any given night and if you have control, defer even slightly potentially stressful tasks.

But, how little is insufficient? There are a number of schools of thought. One school of thought is that everyone is different. The right amount for one person might be insufficient for another. If you believe in this school, then discovering what is perfect for you is a very important. On the other hand, there is a school of thought that suggests that eight hours is required for us all and that without that we are at risk of suffering from sleep deprivation. Regardless of which school of thought you believe, most of the research suggests that we don't get enough sleep.

You can read more about sleep and the impact of lack of sleep in Part 4c of this section.

Positivity

As the Monty Python song suggests, "Always look on the bright side of life." "Count your blessings" has been a mantra for many years for many people. It turns out that your overall positivity, also known as positivity-negativity bias, tends to have a major impact on your overall reaction to stressors. The more you tend to have a positive outlook, the more you tend to be able to keep your threats and associated stress in check.

Normalization

This is about the degree of exposure you have to a particular situation, event, or sequence of events. When something is new to us, regardless of our Personal Threat Profile, the very fact that it is new can tend for it to become stressful. Once we have seen something for the third, fourth, fifth or hundredth time, then it becomes normalized, and our brain treats it in accordance with patterns that have been laid down. The first time your boss criticizes one of your ideas in public, it can cause a major issue. Once you come to expect that, then it becomes less of an issue. (Whether you should allow him/her to get away with it is another issue. ☺)

Information

The more information we have about what is going on, why, and how it fits into the overall picture of things, the less we are inclined to let it stress us. Unless, of course, the information you learn adds fuel to your stress fire. In general, the more information we have about any given situation, the less it ramps up our Personal Threat Context.

Training

The more we receive training about the issues that face us, the less likely we are to get triggered.

Other Stress

What else is going on in your life? To some degree this overlaps with the first of the Threat Context elements, but it is more focused on what is going on rather than whether you have control over it. If you are changing jobs, moving to a new city and/or state to do so, and getting married and attempting to lose weight all at the same time, then you might want to minimize any other changes in your life.

There are many "stress scale" tests that you can find on the Internet. Here are the topic areas from one that I downloaded from such a test set. [158]

Death of a spouse, divorce, marital separation, imprisonment, death of a close family member, personal injury or illness, marriage, dismissal from work, marital reconciliation, retirement, change in health of family member, pregnancy, sexual difficulties, gaining a new family member, business re-adjustment, change in financial state, change in frequency of arguments, major mortgage, foreclosure of mortgage or loan, change in responsibilities at work, child leaving home, trouble with in-laws, spouse starts or stops work, begin or end school, change in living conditions, revision of personal habits, trouble with boss, change in working hours or conditions, change in residence, change in schools, change in recreation, change in social activities, minor mortgage or loan, change in sleeping habits, change in number of family reunions, change in eating habits, and minor violation of law.

I am sure that there are many more, and you will be able to add some of your own.

Note that while it is clear that most of the events described will obviously cause stress to most of us, some events that are intended to be the opposite of stressful can be stressful for some people. For example, the same list describes "outstanding personal achievement, change in church activities, vacation, and Christmas" as potentially stressful.

Notes and References for "Understanding the Brain: Five Driving Forces":

[56] Gordon, E. (2012). Brain Revolution: Self, Relationships and Society. Brain Revolution Publications.

[57] Mann, A. (2018, January 15). Why We Need Best Friends at Work. Retrieved December 13, 2018, from www.gallup.com

[58] Duhigg, C. (2016, February 25). What Google Learned From Its Quest to Build the Perfect Team. New York Times Magazine.

[59] Naomi I. Eisenberger and Matthew D. Lieberman (2004) op cit

[60] Chester, D. S., & DeWall, C. N. (2017). Combating the sting of rejection with the pleasure of revenge: A new look at how emotion shapes aggression. Journal of Personality and Social Psychology, 112(3), 413–430. http://doi.org/10.1037/pspi0000080

[61] Dieker, N. (2017, October 24). How Important Is Financial Security to Happiness? Retrieved December 13, 2018, from www.thebillfold.com

[62] Buettner, D. (2017). The Blue Zones of Happiness: Lessons From the World's Happiest People. National Geographic.

[63] Singh-Manoux, A., Adler, N., & Marmot, M. (2003). Subjective social status: its determinants and its association with measures of ill-health in the Whitehall II study. Social Science and Medicine, 56(6), 1321–1333. http://doi.org/10.1016/S0277-9536(02)00131-4>

[64] Kahneman, D. & Tversky, A. (1984). "Choices, Values, and Frames". American Psychologist. 39 (4): 341–350. doi:10.1037/0003-066x.39.4.341.

[65] Dassen, F. C. M., Jansen, A., Nederkoorn, C., & Houben, K. (2016). Focus on the future: Episodic future thinking reduces discount rate and snacking. Appetite, 96(c), 327–332. http://doi.org/10.1016/j.appet.2015.09.032

[66] Dassen et al (2016) op cit

[67] Berry, M. S., Sweeney, M. M., Morath, J., Odum, A. L., & Jordan, K. E. (2014). The Nature of Impulsivity: Visual Exposure to Natural Environments Decreases Impulsive Decision-Making in a Delay Discounting Task. Plos One, 9(5), e97915–7. http://doi.org/10.1371/journal.pone.0097915

[68] Anokhin, A. P., Grant, J. D., Mulligan, R. C., & Heath, A. C. (2015). The Genetics of Impulsivity: Evidence for the Heritability of Delay Discounting. Biological Psychiatry, 77(10), 887–894. http://doi.org/10.1016/j.biopsych.2014.10.022

[69] Brosnan, S. F., & de Waal, F. B. M. (2003). Monkeys reject unequal pay. Nature, 425(6955), 297–299. http://doi.org/10.1038/nature01963

[70] Brosnan, S. F., & de Waal, F. B. M. (2012). Fairness in Animals: Where to from Here? Social Justice Research, 25(3), 336–351. http://doi.org/10.1007/s11211-012-0165-8

[71] Singer, T., Seymour, B., O'Doherty, J. P., Stephan, K. E., Dolan, R. J., & Frith, C. D. (2006). Empathic neural responses are modulated by the perceived fairness of others. Nature, 439(7075), 466–469. http://doi.org/10.1038/nature04271

[72] Andreoni, J., Aydm, D., Barton, B., Bernheim, B. D., & Naecker, J. (2016, March 22). When Fair Isn't Fair: Sophisticated Time Inconsistency in Social Preferences. Retrieved August 31, 2018, from https://docplayer.net/64596999-When-fair-isn-t-fair-sophisticated-time-inconsistency-in-social-preferences.html

[73] Gilles Le Garrec, Fairness, social norms and the cultural demand for redistribution, Sciences Po OFCE Working Paper, n°20, 2017-09-20. Downloaded from URL : www.ofce.sciences-po.fr/pdf/dtravail/WP2017-20.pdf

[74] Killen, M., Elenbaas, L., & Rutland, A. (2016). Balancing the Fair Treatment of Others while Preserving Group Identity and Autonomy. Human Development, 58(4-5), 253–272. http://doi.org/10.1159/000444151

[75] van den Bos, K., & Lind, E. A. (2016). The Psychology of Own Versus Others' Treatment: Self-Oriented and Other-Oriented Effects on Perceptions of Procedural Justice. Personality and Social Psychology Bulletin, 27(10), 1324–1333. http://doi.org/10.1177/01461672012710008

[76] Gottman, J. M. (2014). Principia Amoris: The New Science of Love. Routledge.

[77] Huber, Machteld; Knottnerus, J. André; Green, Lawrence; Horst, Henriëtte van der; Jadad, Alejandro R.; Kromhout, Daan; Leonard, Brian; Lorig, Kate; Loureiro, Maria Isabel (2011). "How should we define health?". BMJ. 343: d4163. doi:10.1136/bmj.d4163.

[78] https://study.com/academy/lesson/what-is-physical-health-definition-components-examples.html

[79] Williams, et al (2008) op cit

[80] Krienen, F. M., Tu, P. C., & Buckner, R. L. (2010). Clan Mentality: Evidence That the Medial Prefrontal Cortex Responds to Close Others. Journal of Neuroscience, 30(41), 13906–13915. http://doi.org/10.1523/JNEUROSCI.2180-10.2010

[81] Zak, Paul J (2017). Neuroscience of Trust. Harvard Business Review, 1-11

[82] Milanov, M., Rubin, M., & Paolini, S. (2014). Different types of in-group identification. Psicologia Sociale, 3, 205–232.

[83] Milanov, M., Rubin, M., & Paolini, S. (2014). Different types of in-group identification. Psicologia Sociale, 3, 205–232.

[84] https://www.forbes.com/sites/insertcoin/2018/02/24/shiny-dragonite-is-here-and-pokemon-gos-community-day-is-your-best-shot-at-him/#2604ad462b5a

[85] Berger, J. (2017). Invisible Influence: The Hidden Forces that Shape Behavior. Simon & Schuster.

[86] www.humansynergistics.com

[87] Kashdan, T. B., DeWall, C. N., Masten, C. L., Pond, R. S., Powell, C., Combs, D., et al. (2014). Who Is Most Vulnerable to Social Rejection? The Toxic Combination of Low Self-Esteem and Lack of Negative Emotion Differentiation on Neural Responses to Rejection. Plos One, 9(3), e90651–8. http://doi.org/10.1371/journal.pone.0090651

[88] Somerville, L. H., Kelley, W. M., & Heatherton, T. F. (2010). Self-esteem Modulates Medial Prefrontal Cortical Responses to Evaluative Social Feedback. Cerebral Cortex, 20(12), 3005–3013. http://doi.org/10.1093/cercor/bhq049

[89] Zannas, A. S., & West, A. E. (2014). Epigenetics and the regulation of stress vulnerability and resilience. Neuroscience, 264, 157–170. http://doi.org/10.1016/j.neuroscience.2013.12.003

[90] Bajaj, B., Robins, R. W., & Pande, N. (2016). Mediating role of self-esteem on the relationship between mindfulness, anxiety, and depression. Personality and Individual Differences, 96(C), 127–131. http://doi.org/10.1016/j.paid.2016.02.085

[91] Chavez, R. S., & Heatherton, T. F. (2015). Multimodal frontostriatal connectivity underlies individual differences in self-esteem. Social Cognitive and Affective Neuroscience, 10(3), 364–370. http://doi.org/10.1093/scan/nsu063

[92] Agroskin, D., Klackj, J., & Jonas, E. (2014). The Self-Liking Brain: A VBM Study on the Structural Substrate of Self-Esteem. Plos One, 1–13. http://doi.org/10.1371/journal.pone.00

[93] Huston, M. (2017, December). Why We Compete. The Atlantic.

[94] Taylor, C. (1992). Multiculturalism and The Politics of Recognition: An Essay by Charles Taylor. Princeton University Press.

[95] https://www.naeyc.org/resources/pubs/yc/may2017/caring-relationships-heart-early-brain-development

[96] Burklund, L. J., Eisenberger, N. I., & Lieberman, M. D. (2008). The face of rejection: Rejection sensitivity moderates dorsal anterior cingulate activity to disapproving facial expressions. Social Neuroscience, 2(3-4), 238–253.

[97] Owen, D., & Davidson, J. (2009). Hubris syndrome: An acquired personality disorder? A study of US Presidents and UK Prime Ministers over the last 100 years. Brain, 132(5), 1396–1406. http://doi.org/10.1093/brain/awp008

[98] "Napoleon complex" is a theorised complex occurring in people of short stature. It is characterized by overly-aggressive or domineering social behavior and carries the implication that such behavior is compensatory for the subject's stature.

[99] Utevsky, A. V., & Platt, M. L. (2014). Status and the Brain. PLoS Biology, 12(9), e1001941–4. http://doi.org/10.1371/journal.pbio.1001941

[100] Hu, J., Blue, P. R., Yu, H., Gong, X., Xiang, Y., Jiang, C., & Zhou, X. (2015). Social status modulates the neural response to unfairness. Social Cognitive and Affective Neuroscience, 11(1), 1–10. http://doi.org/10.1093/scan/nsv086

[101] Hu, J., Blue, P. R., Yu, H., Gong, X., Xiang, Y., Jiang, C., & Zhou, X. (2015). Social status modulates the neural response to unfairness. Social Cognitive and Affective Neuroscience, 11(1), 1–10. http://doi.org/10.1093/scan/nsv086

[102] Schulman, D. (2002, November 1). The Biology of Benevolence. Psychology Today.

[103] https://www.lifehack.org/522064/the-benefits-benevolence

[104] https://www.brainpickings.org/2015/06/16/how-adam-smith-can-change-your-life/

[105] Abrams, A. (2018, June 20). Yes, Impostor Syndrome Is Real. Here's How to Deal With It. Time.

[106] Bar, M. (2009). The proactive brain: memory for predictions. Philosophical Transactions of the Royal Society B: Biological Sciences, 364(1521), 1235–1243. http://doi.org/10.1098/rstb.2008.0310

[107] DiSalvio, D. (2011). What Makes Your Brain Happy and Why You Should Do the Opposite. Prometheus Books.

[108] Milliken, F. J. (1987). Three Types of Perceived Uncertainty About the Environment: State, Effect, and Response Uncertainty. The Academy of Management Review, 12(1), 133–143.

[109] Dixon, P., Rock, D., & Ochsner, K. N. (2010). Turn the 360 around. NeuroLeadership, 3.

[110] Pink, D. (2011). Drive. Riverhead Books.

[111] Pink, D. (2011). Drive. Riverhead Books. p 71

[112] Perel, E. (2017). Mating in Captivity: Unlocking Erotic Intelligence. Harper Paperbacks.

[113] Hsu, M., Bhatt, M., Adolphs, R., Trane, D., & Camerer, C. F. (2005). Neural Systems Responding to Degrees of Uncertainty in Human Decision-Making. Science, 310(5754), 1680–1683. http://doi.org/10.1126/science.1115327

[114] http://www.bbbgeorgia.org/consist.php

[115] Cialdini, R. B. (2008). Influence: Science and Practice. Allyn and Bacon.

[116] Wang, S., Yu, R., Tyszka, J. M., Zhen, S., Kovach, C., Sun, S., et al. (2017). The human amygdala parametrically encodes the intensity of specific facial emotions and their categorical ambiguity. Nature Communications, 8, 1–13. http://doi.org/10.1038/ncomms14821

[117] Wang, L., Zheng, J., Huang, S., & Sun, H. (2015). P300 and Decision Making under Risk and Ambiguity. Computational Intelligence and Neuroscience, 2015(1), 1–7. http://doi.org/10.1155/2015/108417

[118] Zhao, K., Zhao, J., Zhang, M., Cui, Q., & Fu, X. (2017). Neural Responses to Rapid Facial Expressions of Fear and Surprise. Frontiers in Psychology, 8, 169–8. http://doi.org/10.3389/fpsyg.2017.00761

[119] Nour, M. M., Dahoun, T., Schwartenbeck, P., Adams, R. A., Fitzgerald, T. H. B., Coello, C., et al. (2018). Dopaminergic basis fore signaling belief updates, but not surprise, and the link to paranoia. Pnas.

[120] O'Reilly, J. X., Schuffelgen, U., Cuell, S. F., Behrens, T. E. J., Mars, R. B., & Rushworth, M. F. S. (2013). Dissociable effects of surprise and model update in parietal and anterior cingulate cortex. Pnas, 1–10. http://doi.org/10.1073/pnas.1305373110/-/DCSupplemental

[121] Murty, V. P., LaBar, K. S., & Adcock, R. A. (2016). Distinct medial temporal networks encode surprise during motivation by reward versus punishment. Neurobiology of Learning and Memory, 134, 55–64. http://doi.org/10.1016/j.nlm.2016.01.018

[122] Wessel, J. R., Jenkinson, N., Brittain, J.-S., Voets, S. H. E. M., Aziz, T. Z., & Aron, A. R. (2016). Surprise disrupts cognition via a fronto-basal ganglia suppressive mechanism. Nature Communications, 7, 1–10. http://doi.org/10.1038/ncomms11195

[123] Schomaker, J., & Meeter, M. (2015). Short- and long-lasting consequences of novelty, deviance and surprise on brain and cognition. Neuroscience & Biobehavioral Reviews, 1–12. http://doi.org/10.1016/j.neubiorev.2015.05.002

[124] McKean, K. J. (1994). Using multiple risk factors to assess the behavioral, cognitive, and affective effects of learned helplessness. Journal of Psychology, 128(2), 177.

[125] Cialdini, R. B., & Goldstein, N. J. (2004). Social Influence: Compliance and Conformity. Annual Review of Psychology, 55(1), 591–621. http://doi.org/10.1146/annurev.psych.55.090902.142015

[126] Stallen, M., Smidts, A., & Sanfey, A. G. (2013). Peer influence: neural mechanisms underlying in-group conformity. Frontiers in Human Neuroscience, 7, 1–7. http://doi.org/10.3389/fnhum.2013.00050/abstract

[127] Berns, G. S., Chappelow, J., Zink, C. F., Pagnoni, G., Martin-Skurski, M. E., & Richards, J. (2005). Neurobiological Correlates of Social Conformity and Independence During Mental Rotation. Biological Psychiatry (Vol. 58, pp. 245–253).

[128] Hashimoto, H., & Yamagashi, T. (2013). Two faces of interdependence: Harmony seeking and rejection avoidance. Asian Journal of Social Psychology, 16(2).

[129] Livermore, D. (2009). Cultural Intelligence: Improving Your CQ to Engage Our Multicultural World (Youth, Family, and Culture). Baker Academic.

[130] Gordon, E. (2012). Brain Revolution: Self, Relationships and Society. Brain Revolution Publications.

[131] Ekman, P., Davidson, R. J., & Friesen, W. V. (1990). The Duchenne Smile: Emotional Expression and Brain Physiology II. Journal of Personality and Social Psychology, 58(2), 342–353.

[132] Hanoch, Y., Johnson, J. G., & Wike, A. (2006). Domain Specificity in Experimental Measures and Participant Recruitment. Psychological Science, 17(4), 300–304.

[133] Hanoch, Y et al (2006) op cit

[134] Peter Johnson, MD, Private Conversation

[135] Jepma, M., Verdonschot, R. G., van Steenbergen, H., Rombouts, S. A. R. B., & Nieuwenhuis, S. (2012). Neural mechanisms underlying the induction and relief of perceptual curiosity. Frontiers in Behavioral Neuroscience, 6, 1–9. http://doi.org/10.3389/fnbeh.2012.00005/abstract

[136] Kidd, C., & Hayden, B. Y. (2015). The Psychology and Neuroscience of Curiosity. Neuron, 88(3), 449–460. http://doi.org/10.1016/j.neuron.2015.09.010

[137] Gruber, M. J., Gelman, B. D., & Ranganath, C. (2014). States of Curiosity Modulate Hippocampus-Dependent Learning via the Dopaminergic Circuit. Neuron, 84(2), 486–496. http://doi.org/10.1016/j.neuron.2014.08.060

[138] Mlodinow, L. (2018). Elastic: Flexible Thinking in a Time of Change. Pantheon.

[139] Noordewier, M. K., & van Dijk, E. (2016). Curiosity and time: from not knowing to almost knowing. Basic and Applied Social Psychology (Vol. 38, pp. 411–421).

[140] BBC Seven-Up series – available via YouTube

[141] Pink, D. (2011). Drive. Riverhead Books.p 109

[142] Wrzesniewski, A., & Dutton, J. E. (2001). Crafting a Job: Revisioning Employees as Active Crafters of their work. Academy of Management Review, 26(2), 179–201.

[143] Ordun, G., & Akün, F. A. (2017). Self Actualization, Self Efficacy and Emotional Intelligence of Undergraduate Students. Journal of Advanced Management Science, 5(3), 170–175. http://doi.org/10.18178/joams.5.3.170-175

[144] Buettner, D. (2012). The Blue Zones: 9 Lessons for Living Longer From the People Who've Lived the Longest. National Geographic.

[145] Pink, D. (2011). Drive. Riverhead Books.

[146] Sinek, S. (2018). Start with Why: How Great Leaders Inspire Everyone to Take Action. Simon Sinek.

[147] Boyle, P. A., Buchman, A. S., Barnes, L. L., & Bennett, D. A. (2010). Effect of a Purpose in Life on Risk of Incident Alzheimer Disease and Mild Cognitive Impairment in Community-Dwelling Older Persons. Archives of General Psychiatry, 67(3), 304–310.

[148] Lomas, T. (2016). Positive art: Artistic expression and appreciation as an exemplary vehicle for flourishing. Review of General Psychology, 20(2), 171-182.

[149] Zaidel, D. W. (2010). Art and brain: insights from neuropsychology, biology and evolution. Journal of Anatomy, 216(2), 177–183. http://doi.org/10.1111/j.1469-7580.2009.01099.x

[150] Bolwerk, A., Mack-Andrick, J., Lang, F. R., Dörfler, A., & Maihöfner, C. (2014). How Art Changes Your Brain: Differential Effects of Visual Art Production and Cognitive Art Evaluation on Functional Brain Connectivity. Plos One, 9(7), 1–8. http://doi.org/10.1371/journal.pone.0101035

[151] https://www.pickthebrain.com/blog/5-reasons-passion-means-everything/

[152] Sheeley, E. (n.d.). The Winner Effect: How Success Affects Brain Chemistry. Retrieved December 13, 2018, from www.gamification.co

[153] Haselton, M., Bryant, G. A., Wilke, A., Frederick, D., & Galperin, A. (2009). Adaptive rationality: An evolutionary perspective on cognitive bias. Social Cognition, 27(5), 733–763.

[154] Sauter, D. A., & Scott, S. K. (2007). More than one kind of happiness: Can we recognize vocal expressions of different positive states? Motivation and Emotion, 31(3), 192–199. http://doi.org/10.1007/s11031-007-9065-x

[155] Fisher, H. (2010). Why Him? Why Her?: How to Find and Keep Lasting Love. Holt Paperbacks.P 45

[156] Iwaniuk, A. N., Nelson, J. E., & Pellis, S. M. (2001). Do Big-Brained Animals Play More? Comparitive Analyses of Play and Relative Brain Size in Mammals. Journal of Comparitive Psychology, 115(1), 29–41.

[157] Brown, S. (2010). Play: How it Shapes the Brain, Opens the Imagination, and Invigorates the Soul. Avery.

[158] https://www.health24.com/Mental-Health/Stress/Stress-management/41-major-life-stressors-20120721 - downloaded Feb 13, 2018

Section B Part 3: Facts and Myths About the Brain*

Over the past ten years or so, I have spent a lot of time teaching people about their brains, and many things have become clear to me. One thing that is very clear is that there is a strong pop culture associated with neuroscience and the brain; there is a fascination that borders on a morbid curiosity. As a result, there are a lot of myths, tall tales, and untruths that have become infused with the real neuroscience to the point where some of these myths etc. have become pervasive and have become seen as "facts." People use the Internet for their research, and some of what they find is misleading at best and plain wrong at worst. I thought it was important to cover some of the more "popular" myths that I have heard over the years.

In this chapter, I will cover some of the myths and will address some facts. Hopefully I will introduce you to some facts about the brain that you are not aware of and explain some aspects that you might not know. These are in no particular order.

One last word. As I started writing this chapter, I expected there to be a handful of myths, maybe as many as ten or so. As I asked around and did the research, I was very surprised at how many there are out there. My guess is that you, the reader, have heard others.

Myth 1: We only use 10% of our brain. (False.)

Most of us have heard this one. Many of us were told when we younger that we only use 10% of our brains. There's no other way of saying it, but this is just not true. Maybe we should call it "a bold-faced lie." In fact, we probably use most of our brains most of the time. Whether we use them as effectively as we could, is a different question! There are probably many reasons why this myth has taken hold so that many people, even to this day, still believe it to be true. Sad to say, in a recent study, about two-thirds of students in high school in America still believe that we only use 10% of our brains. What might be even worse is that half of the teachers that were polled in the study still thought that it was true. Unfortunately, this myth was made even popular by the movie *Lucy*, released in 2015.

In his book *We Are Our Brains*, Swaab [159] makes the following highly pointed statement:

> *"Take the myth that we use only 10 per cent of our brains. You might well be forgiven for thinking this is the case of certain people, but I haven't the faintest idea what prompted this crazy theory."*

Let's take a moment and think about this myth and speculate how it may have arisen. First, from an evolutionary point of view, it doesn't make any sense to carry anything "extra" around. It would go against the ability to survive using the basic fight or flight principle. Second, it is highly energy consuming to produce a brain during fetal and child development. There would be no reason to produce "extra." It would not make evolutionary sense. Third, to maintain the brain, with its high cost of energy consumption, through adulthood again just doesn't make sense. Finally, we know

---

* I have developed this list from a variety of sources and, in some cases, have used the wording as it stands. I have cited references where I have them. If I have failed to cite something, or failed to cite correctly, then please let me know, and I will correct it in the next edition.

from research that even simple tasks require a lot of the brain power available to us and damage to even a small part can have major negative consequences. Neuroscientists haven't yet discovered a part of the brain that can be damaged and yet have no effect on our functioning. So, it makes sense that we wouldn't have extra real estate in the brain just hanging in the wings waiting to be used.

The genesis for this myth probably came from the 1800s when William James, who was one of the most preeminent psychologists of the time, stated that most of us don't use our full potential. That's it! And my guess is that he is right. Many of us don't live up to our full potential.

It is likely that the myth was further propagated in the early days of imaging when researchers were using chemical stains when looking at images of the brains. The stains were effective in only about 10% of the neurons that were stained; this led many scientists to conclude that this 10% were the only active brain cells. So, the 10% number caught on and spread like wildfire.

While at any given moment not all of the brain cells are firing at the same time, research shows that most of the brain is active over a twenty-four-hour period. Even during sleep, areas like the PFC and the somatosensory cortex are active. Even when you are relaxing and it seems to you that your brain is on idle, your default mode starts to rapidly get engaged. If you were to image the brain at that time, you would see a tremendous amount of activity even though you are apparently at rest.

There is some shred of evidence that we might have some brain reserves. Autopsy studies show that many people have physical signs of Alzheimer's disease (such as amyloid plaques among neurons) in their brains even though they are not obviously impaired. Apparently, we can lose some brain tissue and still function pretty well.

So, if the 10% number is a myth, what percentage do we actually use? The truth is that we use all of it. There's no "spare" neural matter or real estate laying around just waiting for a job to do. This has been confirmed by thousands of brain scans where you can see activity coursing through the brain even when people are not asked to think about something specific.

Conclusion: This 10% notion has been completely debunked by scientific research. Please don't spread it any further.

Myth 2: The brain is at rest when we are asleep. (False.)

Counter to what you might intuitively expect, some parts of the brain are more active in sleep than awake.

Brain scans show activity in the brain when it is asleep versus when it is awake. The scans show an increase in blood flow and cerebral spinal fluid when the brain is asleep. Cerebral spinal fluid is the liquid in the brain which helps clean things out and nourishes the brain. It flows faster when the brain is asleep than when it is awake; it is clearing toxins and other nasty things that accumulate during the day. So, when we are asleep, the brain is more active in doing some of these housekeeping activities.

There have been many studies done that show when we are asleep, we have a tremendous amount of activity going on, particularly when we are dreaming, i.e., during REM sleep. Dreaming seems to reactivate brain networks that have been used during the day. Although it is still a hypothesis and has some controversy surrounding it, there is a theory that when we are asleep, the brain is triaging everything that happened during the day and making sense of it. There is good evidence that sleep, and more particularly dreaming, stabilizes our memories. During brain imaging studies, we see the brain regions that are active during dreaming and memory improvement the following day. There is some more recent evidence that creativity is increased with dreaming.

Our brain may need to dream in order to review the 11,000,000 bits of information per second that it is being constantly bombarded with. Sleep may be the point where the brain has a chance to sift through all of that data and to sort out what makes sense and doesn't make sense from a survival and evolutionary perspective. What was threatening, what was rewarding, and what do I need to remember? If I encountered someone or something during the day that was threatening, I might need to remember exactly what that person looked like and what their voice sounded like and where I saw them. Part of what dreaming is about may be to cement those memories.

In addition, think of this. We assess the cues that are facing us every $1/5^{th}$ second and "declare" them as a threat, reward, or neutral. Assuming that we are awake for 16 hours a day, this gives us 288,000 such events to evaluate. Maybe during sleep, we are reviewing all of these and integrating them into our memories. Maybe we just throw away the neutral ones. After all, they would be of little value in maximizing our chance of survival. Maybe we just review the ones that have a positive or negative valence associated with them? There is some evidence that when we are under stress, we only recall and memorize the negative ones. This would make sense from an evolutionary point of view.

Conclusion: The notion that our brain is at rest when we sleep has, therefore, been debunked. In fact, it may be the exact opposite! It may be even more busy that when we are awake.

Myth 3: The left brain/right brain dichotomy. (True and False.)

There is a commonly held belief that there is an absolute distinction between the left (logical) brain and the right (emotional) brain. The belief is that there are specific actions and behaviors that are attributed to the left brain as opposed to the right brain. The belief goes further; it promotes the idea that people are either left-brained or right-brained. And then this half-truth became distorted. Over the past thirty years, there has been a proposition that there are four quadrants to the brain based on the fact that there are two sides and a rear and a front. (This theory seems to have ignored the fact that the triune brain theory suggests three layers of the brain which would make six areas of the brain to take into account.)

Not so fast! It is true that the brain is physically divided into two connected hemispheres. Where the old belief breaks down is that we no longer believe the one-to-one relationship between each side of the brain and a set of functions. Rather, higher level functions of the brain seem to recruit a number of neural networks working together in a highly interconnected fashion across both hemispheres.

Once again, let's dig into how this myth arose. It probably arose from the Nobel Prize-winning research done by Roger Sperry in the 1960s. Sperry studied patients with epilepsy who were treated with a surgical procedure that cut the corpus callosum, effectively splitting the brain's two hemispheres. Once cut, the two halves couldn't communicate any more. Sperry and his colleagues did a number of studies looking at which parts of the brain were involved with math, drawing, and other functions.

So far, so good. Then the pop culture (and many authors) took over and created the notion that personalities and other unique attributes are determined by either one side of the brain or the other. The bottom line is that neither the neuroscience community nor the data support fully this notion of left brain orientation or right brain orientation. We have many, many brain scans that show there is no preferential use of the left brain versus the right brain. There are some activities that seem to be located in specific areas of the brain which have degree of specialization. For example, speech is thought largely to be a function of the left brain, but the right hemisphere is also involved. It is thought to add the emotional component of speech.

Conclusion: Is the myth disproven? Not entirely. The physical split is certainly true. But we now believe that there is much more networking and interconnections between the two sides, and many of the fundamental processes of the brain are spread over both sides.

Myth 4: We are stuck with what we have. (False.)

This myth refers to the idea that we have a whole set of neurons that are created at birth, and they grow, and we learn and develop our brains. And that's it. We used to believe that once we were into our late teens, then our brains were fully formed and no new brain cells could be made; we also used to think that with any damage or trauma to the brain, we would lose neurons, lose functionality, and none of it could be regained.

There are at least three aspects showing that we are not stuck with what we have.

First, the brain is changing all of the time. We refer to it as self-directed neuroplasticity. It is always happening. When we change a habit, for example, or learn something new, we create new neural pathways. So, we are not stuck with what we have. We are continually creating new connections such that our brains are different after these experiences.

Next, we also know that the brain is capable of neurogenesis. To cite from Wikipedia, "Neurogenesis is the process of birth of neurons whereby neurons are generated from neural stem cells. Contrary to popular belief, neurogenesis continuously occurs in specific regions in the adult brain." That means we create new cells in certain parts of the brain, most notably in parts of the hippocampus.

Third, certain areas of the brain can be reused and recruited for another function.

In some ways, we could also include our ability to change our mindset under this heading. What is someone capable of, and what they can achieve in life? What they can achieve intellectually or emotionally? Is it fixed and there is nothing they can do about it, or is it completely open? A fixed approach assumes that there is some genetic predetermination or that you have reached a personal ceiling in a given aspect of your life. More and more as we look at the research, we're finding that this just isn't the case. We are able, in many cases, to direct our own lives and create what we want.

Conclusion: Are we stuck with what we have? No. It's a myth.

Myth 5: The male brain and the female brain are different. (True and False.)

When I am teaching about the brain, this is one of the myths that comes up all of the time. There are always questions that arise. Do men and women differ in their memory? What about mathematics ability? Surely, we differ in the way we reason and how empathetic we are. People always want to know what the gender differences are. This is partly because culture tells us that men's brains and women's brains just are not the same. It is true that male and female hormones affect brain development differently. It is also true that brain imaging studies have found differences in the way that men and women feel pain or make social decisions or cope with stress.

Some gender differences have been found in some research. For example, in one study, women showed greater nonverbal engagement whereas men disengaged faster and showed face-saving techniques, such as pretending to be uninterested. The researchers concluded that women seek to regain a sense of belonging whereas men are more interested in regaining self-esteem. [160]

In a fairly recent article, [161] Tarlaci asks the question "Is there a difference between the active brain regions of men and women when they are in love? In the article, he answers his own question using results from other researchers. The results:

> "In men, greater activity was seen in the right dorsal insula, associated with penile tumescence, the region for seeing beautiful faces, and the visual integration area. In women, the regions for attention, memory, and emotion showed greater activity. [162] From this we can understand that men fall in love with women and their faces in a way that includes sexual arousal, while women are more interested in the romantic aspect of love – that is, they fall in love with love itself!" [163]

The extent to which all of these differences, however, are genetic (i.e., nature vs. nurture) is really unknown at this stage of our knowledge. For the most part, male and female brains are extremely similar, and there is much research to demonstrate that there are greater similarities of structure and function between the brains of the two genders than there are differences.

Ah yes, the cynics reply, but what about mathematics? That's a dead giveaway, isn't it?

A study done a few years back and reported in the *Psychological Bulletin* looked at almost a half a million boys and girls from sixty-nine different countries. What was found, contrary to popular belief, is that there was almost no gap in mathematics ability between boys and girls. This debunks the myth that is commonplace across many cultures that boys are better at mathematics than girls.

In some recent research on the Internet, I came across some statements about how ridiculous this gender difference narrative is. When I went back to verify the source, the site was no longer available so if any reader identifies it (or you are the author) then please let me know. I cite it in its entirety as I think it sums up the situation way better than I could.

> "Some of the sloppiest, shoddiest, most biased, least reproducible, worst designed, and most over-interpreted research in the history of science purports to provide biological explanations for differences between men and women. Eminent neuroscientists once claimed that head size, spinal ganglia, or brain stem structures were responsible for

women's inability to think creatively, vote logically, or practice medicine. Today the theories are a bit more sophisticated: men supposedly have more specialized brain hemispheres, women more elaborate emotion circuits. Though there are some differences (minor and uncorrelated with any particular ability) between male and female brains, the main problem with looking for correlations with behavior is that sex differences in cognition are massively exaggerated.

Women are thought to outperform men on tests of empathy. They do – unless test subjects are told that men are particularly good at the test, in which case men perform as well as or better than women. The same pattern holds in reverse for tests of spatial reasoning. Whenever stereotypes are brought to mind, even by something as simple as asking test subjects to check a box next to their gender, sex differences are exaggerated. Women college students told that a test is something women usually do poorly on, do poorly. Women college students told that a test is something college students usually do well on, do well. Across countries – and across time – the more prevalent the belief is that men are better than women in math, the greater the difference in girls' and boys' math scores. And that's not because girls in Iceland have more specialized brain hemispheres than do girls in Italy."

Conclusion: There are some minor differences, but in general, female and male brains are very similar. The myth of major gender differences in the brain is not supported by the research.

Myth 6: The brain feels pain. (False.)

When people hit their head, or get a concussion or someone gets a traumatic injury to the brain, they feel pain. Head injuries are very painful. There is an assumption that the actual brain tissue can feel pain. That assumption is incorrect. The human brain is the only organ in the body that doesn't have nerves which can sense pain. This is in spite of the fact that the brain is this huge focus or center of command for the entire nervous system. It doesn't feel pain. Pain in the head or around the brain is sensed by the meninges. The meninges is the thick, fibrous outer covering of the brain which protects the brain, and it *can* feel pain.

If a person has something pierce their skull and go into the brain, then it is the head and the meninges that feel the pain – the sensory receptors that lie outside of the brain. When surgeons perform neurosurgery, they anaesthetize the skin and the meninges, but their patients are frequently awake. When the brain is being manipulated, the patient can't feel it and experiences no pain. Many times, the patients are awake because the surgeon needs to ensure in the process that they are not affecting any critical areas of the brain like speech or anything like that.

Conclusion: The brain in and of itself cannot feel pain. It's the rest of the head and the surroundings that feel the pain.

Myth 7: Women are better at multi-tasking than men. (It depends.)

OK. I normally attempt to answer much more definitively than that. It depends? What sort of answer is that? Well, it's the closest I can come to reporting on what I read in the scientific research. The research is all over the map.

But let's pull this myth apart. First of all, we're going to have to talk about what we mean by "multi-tasking." Let's start at the very basic neuronal level. The brain is handling 11,000,000 bits of information per second for most, if not all, of our waking day. In handling all of that data, it is parallel processing. It is handling data from all of the senses most, if not all, of the time. So strictly speaking, it is indeed multi-tasking. It is able to listen, feel, see, touch, etc. all at the same time. It is often said that the brain is only capable of doing one thing at a time, but strictly speaking that's not true.

However, that is not what most of us mean by multi-tasking. Most of the time when we refer to multi-tasking, we are referring to the ability to cognitively and consciously focus on two or more tasks in parallel. However, even that definition does not help us much.

The research indicates that there are many factors that need to be considered in looking at multi-tasking. Gender is just one of them. Age seems to play a part. The impact of technology seems to play a part. What is being attended to seems to play a part. The impact of extraversion and introversion seems to play a part. The time frame that is being examined seems to play a part. The list goes on. I suspect that there is a lot of research going on, some good and some not so good, in this domain. To illustrate the point, one of the pieces of research in a peer reviewed journal consisted of only twenty-seven subjects. Trying to deduce or prove theories from that small of a sample is crazy.

To help our understanding of multi-tasking, let's take a look for a moment at the time frame issue. The time frame over which we are making our focused decisions comes into play as we dig deeper. At one end of the spectrum, the long-term end, we could call the balance of a professor's life as "multi-tasking" between publishing and teaching.* That is clearly not what most of us think of as multi-tasking.

At the other end of the spectrum, there has been a lot of research on the impact of performance when the research participants are forced to do what is called multi-task interference. This is where the participants in the research are tasked to do one thing and then a second task which interferes with their ability to concentrate on the first task. This is multi-tasking for the PFC, which has the primary responsibility for determining what to focus on. It would be great if neuroscientists could all agree on something, and to some extent they do. Most agree that multi-tasking in this context results in lower performance. But once again there is a difference of opinion as regards the impact of gender. Some say that women perform better, some say that the impact is equal for both genders, and others say that men perform better, especially when it comes to spatial issues. OK. That really doesn't help.

Some research suggests that the rapid changing of tasks is taxing for everyone. In terms of a timescale, this would be for minute to minute tasks rather than second or sub second tasks. For example, writing a list, answering the phone, listening to the dog bark, and attending to the kids. Anecdotally, it has come into common parlance that women are better at this than men. The research simply says that it is hard for everyone and that women are as equally frustrated by it as men are.

Conclusion: It isn't clear. That's the best we can say at this moment.

Myth 8: We are good at observing what is going on. (False, big time.)

We are not passive recipients of external information that enters our brain through our sensory organs. Instead, we actively search for patterns (like a Dalmatian dog that suddenly appears in a field of black and white dots), turn ambiguous scenes into ones that fit our expectations (it's a vase; it's a face), and completely miss details we aren't

---

* Trust me – there are research publications out there to that effect!

expecting. In one famous psychology experiment, participants are asked to focus on a basketball being passed between different teams and count the number of passes that are made. Half way through the process a guy in a gorilla suit is hulking around among the ball throwers. About half of all viewers do not notice the guy in the gorilla suit. They stare in disbelief when the video is played back to them.

But wait. It gets worse. Even when people know about the guy in the gorilla suit, they miss other important things. Like the fact that the curtains behind the players change color and that one of the players leaves completely.

In another experiment, an experimenter portrays the fact that he is lost. He walks over to a passerby and asks him to help, handing him a map. At that moment, two of the experimenter's colleagues walk between the experimenter and the passerby with a door…which hides the fact that the experimenter switches with another person. And the passerby, continuing to explain the best way for the person to walk to his destination, completely misses the fact that he is now talking to a different person.

So, our ability to consciously register our surroundings and what is happening there is severely in question.

We have a limited ability to pay attention (which is why talking on a cellphone while driving can be as dangerous as drunk driving) and plenty of biases about what we expect or want to see. Our perception of the world isn't just "bottom-up," built of objective observations layered together in a logical way. It's "top-down," driven by expectations and interpretations.

Conclusion: Our brains are terrible at accurately recording what is going on.

Myth 9: Our brains are good at remembering things. (False, big time.)

OK. So, if we're not good at seeing and observing things accurately, how are we at recall? We all have memories that feel as vivid and accurate as a snapshot, usually of some shocking, dramatic event – the assassination of President Kennedy, the explosion of the space shuttle Challenger, the attacks of September 11, 2001. People claim that they remember exactly where they were, what they were doing, who they were with, what they saw or heard. But several clever experiments have tested people's memory immediately after a tragedy and again several months or years later. The test subjects tend to be confident that their memories are accurate and say the "flashbulb memories" are more vivid than other memories. Vivid they may be, but the memories decay over time just as other memories do. People forget important details and add incorrect ones with no awareness that they're recreating a muddled scene in their minds rather than calling up a perfect, photographic reproduction.

"Flashbulb memories" are NOT as precise, detailed, and persistent as we claim them to be.

Conclusion: Sorry to say that once again our brains aren't as good as we think they are.

Myth 10: We have five senses. (False.)

OK. You might consider this is a trick. Sure, sight, hearing, touch, taste, and smell are the big ones. They get all the limelight and the attention. But we have many other ways of sensing the world and our place in it.

Here's a list created by my good friend and colleague, Dr. Susan Larson Kidd:

1. Visual – the sense of seeing and use of visual input processing (Sight)
2. Auditory – the sense of hearing and use of sounds (Hearing)
3. Tactile – sensation derived from touch to the skin, including pressure (Touch)
4. Gustatory – sensations of taste including sourness, sweetness, bitterness, and saltiness; and textures of food with oral tactile sensations (Taste)
5. Olfactory – the sense of smell and use of processing for regulations (Smell)

   Here's the additions that most people don't think about:

6. Proprioception – sensations derived from muscles and joints, especially from resistance to movement; so, your brain knows where each part of the body is and how it is moving at any given time (Body Positioning)
7. Vestibular – sensation derived from stimulation to the mechanism in the inner ear that occurs through movement and position of the head, including your relationship to gravity, acceleration, and deceleration (Balance)
8. Interoception – body sensations such as temperature, respiration, urogenital sensations, and pain (Internal Senses)
9. Time sense – your brain's natural ability to help your body with daily, monthly, and seasonal cycles such as sleepiness, alertness, hunger, and thirst, daily peristalsis, menstrual cycles, and seasonal changes; known also as circadian rhythms (Time)

We think we're pretty clever with our nine senses, but compared with other species, humans are missing out. Bats and dolphins use sonar to find prey; some birds and insects see ultraviolet light; snakes detect the heat of warm-blooded prey; rats, cats, seals, and other whiskered creatures use their "vibrissae" to judge spatial relations or detect movements; sharks sense electrical fields in the water; birds, turtles, and even bacteria orient to the earth's magnetic field lines.

By the way, have you seen the taste map of the tongue, the diagram showing that different regions are sensitive to salty, sweet, sour, or bitter flavors? It's also a myth. Receptors for the four tastes are spread throughout most of the tongue.

Conclusion: Nine senses not five.

Myth 11: We know what will make us happy. (Mostly false.)

In most cases, we haven't a clue. We routinely overestimate how happy something will make us whether it's a birthday, free pizza, a new car, a victory for our favorite sports team or political candidate, winning the lottery, or raising children. Money does make people happier, but only to a point – poor people are less happy than the middle class, but the middle class are just as happy as the rich. We overestimate the pleasures of solitude and leisure and underestimate how much happiness we get from social relationships.

On the flip side, the things we dread don't make us as unhappy as expected. Monday mornings aren't as unpleasant as people predict. Seemingly unendurable tragedies – paralysis, the death of a loved one – cause grief and despair, but the unhappiness doesn't last as long as people think it will. People are remarkably resilient.

Conclusion: Being happy and sad are not as predictable as you think.

Myth 12: Our brains are good at making rational decisions. (False.)

As we covered in the section on irrationality, there are many factors that influence how we make decisions. We think we're making our decisions consciously and rationally, yet time after time we can show through research and field tests that many of our decisions are not made rationally.

Conclusion: Sorry guys.

Myth 13: Change is difficult. (True and False.)

This is both true and false as it depends upon what is changing, who we are talking about, and what change we are talking about. If we are talking about the brain, then the brain changes easily. If you have reached this part of the book, then we have probably laid down some new neural connections in your brain. If we are talking about changing our opinions, behaviors, habits, biases, etc. then that's a whole different matter.

As you will have learned reading about the 5 P's, some people are very open to change whereas others will resist change. But even the people who are very open to change often have some aspects about their life in which they resist change. They may be delighted to take a different job or change a process that they use at work, but ask them to change the side of the bed that they sleep on, and they draw the line.

Conclusion: For some people, definitely true. Others, not so much. For yet others, definitely not true. Remember the "sensation seekers?"

Myth 14: Millions of our brain cells die off every day. (False.)

As the brain develops during childhood, it creates more connections than necessary. During our lifetime, then, the brain will remove, or "prune," the unnecessary connections in order to ensure that there is maximum efficiency. But these are more about the connections rather than the cells themselves.

There's an old adage (at least "old" in the neuroscience realm) of "Use it or lose it." Indeed, that does appear to be true. If certain skills, aspects, attributes, etc. are not exercised, then they will become less facile.

Certainly, brain cells do die off. For all sorts of reasons. But not to the degree that you need to worry about. That is, unless you are abusing your brain. At the time of writing this book, there is a mental health website that has "A list of things that kill brain cells." [164] It includes, in some detail, activities such as head trauma, health conditions, drugs, environmental issues, chemicals, psychological issues, and some miscellaneous activities. It also has a list of common myths about things that have been maligned as causing cells to die off but are harmless.

Conclusion: Yes, we do lose cells. But not millions every day. That's an exaggeration.

Myth 15: Your IQ is fixed. (False.)

IQ is a score intended to quantify how smart you are; the tests for IQ have been the subject of much scientific research and much debate. Scientists do believe that genetics and environment are significant influences on IQ but also that cognitive training such as cognitive skills training and logic skills training can improve overall IQ.

Furthermore, it was originally thought that your IQ was a predictor of your success. We now know that not only are there many different types of intelligence, [165] but there are many, many other factors to take into account with regard to life success if indeed it is predictable.

Conclusion: No, your IQ is not fixed.

Myth 16: IQ is the best measure of our intelligence. (False.)

There are many different types of intelligence. IQ is one, but only one, measure, and there are others that might be just as useful, depending on your role.

For example, in the past couple of decades, the concept of emotional intelligence has taken root in our national psyche.

Conclusion: IQ is just one measure. There are many more.

Myth 17: The bigger your brain, the smarter you are. (Probably False.)

When I first started the research for this book, I wrote that this myth was false. Then I read some more recent research which indicated that there is a correlation. In one or two studies, IQ did have some slight relationship to brain size. But I am skeptical of the studies. They may have correlation, but causation might be a different issue.

In addition, a recent study showed that bigger brains are smarter – but not much smarter.

Conclusion: Bigger brains might be a little smarter, but not much.

Myth 18: It's all downhill after 40. (Mostly False.)

It's true, some cognitive skills do decline as you get older. Children are better at learning new languages than adults – and never play a game of concentration against a 10-year-old unless you're prepared to be humiliated. Young adults are faster than older adults to judge whether two objects are the same or different. They can more easily memorize a list of random words, and they are faster to count backward by sevens.

But plenty of mental skills improve with age. Vocabulary, for instance – older people know more words and understand subtle linguistic distinctions. Given a biographical sketch of a stranger, they're better judges of character. They score higher on tests of social wisdom such as how to settle a conflict. And people get better and better over time at regulating their own emotions and finding meaning in their lives.

Conclusion: It depends on what you mean by downhill.

Myth 19: The brain is hardwired like a computer. (True and False.)

This is one of the most enduring legacies of the old "brains are electrical circuits" metaphor. There's some truth to it, as with many metaphors: the brain is organized in a standard way with certain bits specialized to take on certain tasks, and those bits are connected along predictable neural pathways (sort of like wires) and communicate in part by releasing ions (pulses of electricity).

But one of the biggest discoveries in neuroscience in the past few decades is that the brain is remarkably plastic. In blind people, parts of the brain that normally process sight are instead devoted to hearing. Someone practicing a new skill, like learning to play the violin, "rewires" parts of the brain that are responsible for fine motor control. People with brain injuries can recruit other parts of the brain to compensate for the lost tissue.

We speak of the brain's processing speed, its storage capacity, its parallel circuits, inputs, and outputs. The metaphor fails at pretty much every level: the brain doesn't have a set memory capacity that is waiting to be filled up; it doesn't perform computations in the way a computer does; and even basic visual perception isn't a passive receiving of inputs because we actively interpret, anticipate, and pay attention to different elements of the visual world.

There's a long history of likening the brain to whatever technology is the most advanced, impressive, and vaguely mysterious. Descartes compared the brain to a hydraulic machine. Freud likened emotions to pressure building up in a steam engine. The brain later resembled a telephone switchboard and then an electrical circuit before evolving into a computer; lately it's turning into a web browser or the Internet. These metaphors linger in clichés: emotions put the brain "under pressure" and some behaviors are thought to be "hardwired."

Conclusion: While some parts of the brain are hardwired, most of it isn't. It's an incredibly complex mish-mash of neural networks – with the Internet probably being the best metaphor.

Myth 20: Autism [166]

While Autism is clearly not a myth, there are several tall tales and misunderstandings that surround it. Here are a few that I discovered:

> 1: Autism is caused by a poor mother child relationship (a myth mostly restricted to the French speaking European community).
> 2: Autism is a rare condition and it is impossible to treat.
> 3: People with autism cannot speak.
> 4: People with autism have no empathy.

Final comment:

There are many, many more similar myths – some fairly outrageous. For fun, I have included some more in Appendix C, "Some Items in More Detail."

Notes and References for "Understanding the Brain: Facts and Myths":

[159] Swaab, D. F. (2014). We Are Our Brains: A Neurobiography of the Brain, from the Womb to Alzheimer's. (J. Hedley-Prole, Trans.) (1st ed.). Spiegel & Grau.

[160] Williams, K. D. & Zadro, L. (2001). Ostracism. In M. R. Leary (Ed.), Interpersonal rejection. (pp. 21-53). New York, NY: Oxford University Press.

[161] Tarlacı, S. (2012). The Brain in Love: Has Neuroscience Stolen the Secret of Love? NeuroQuantology, 10(4), 1–13. http://doi.org/10.14704/nq.2012.10.4.581

[162] Ortigue S, Bianchi-Demicheli F, Patel N, Frum C, Lewis JW. Neuroimaging of love: fMRI meta-analysis evidence toward new perspectives in sexual medicine. J Sex Med 2010; 7(11):3541-52.

[163] Marazziti, D., & Cassano, G. B. (2003). The neurobiology of attraction. Journal of Endocrinological Investigation, 26, 58–60.

[164] https://mentalhealthdaily.com/2014/03/01/list-of-things-that-kill-brain-cells-the-death-of-neurons/

[165] Gardner, H. (2006). Multiple Intelligences: New Horizons in Theory and Practice. Basic Books.

[166] Hadjlkhanl, N. (2014). Scientifically deconstructing some of the myths regarding autism. Swiss Archives of Neurology and Psychiatry, 165(8), 272–276.

Section B Part 4: The Brain – Care and Feeding

As I have said earlier, there is currently a vast amount of research activity being carried out about the brain and its interactions with various other aspects of our bodies and our lives.

The purpose of this section is to give you an overview of some of the areas that are currently being researched and that have an impact on our overall brain health. Each of the topic areas deserves a book in its own right but, unfortunately, that would take a while. ☺

a. The Brain and the Gut

Researchers have reached the conclusion that there is a significant interaction between the gut and the brain, and that this interaction happens through multiple channels in both directions. Research shows that a) the brain, specifically what we think and feel, influences the gut and b) what is happening in our gut can influence our brain, specifically our mood.

A couple of more facts upon which to base the discussion.

First, there is a collection of about 100 million nerve cells that are buried in the digestive system all the way from top to bottom. Literally. From your esophagus to your rectum. These nerve cells seem to have two roles – to control your digestive processes and to communicate with the brain in your head.

Inside your gut there are trillions (maybe 100 trillion) of bacteria, with a thousand or so different species. Researchers have estimated their total weight at between one and three pounds! They are exploring links between these bacteria and issues such as autism, anxiety, and depression.

I think most readers will be aware of the surge of interest in probiotics, and these have been the subject of much research. Some research has shown that an increase in certain carbohydrates that provide nutrition for the bacteria has the effect of reducing the impact of stress on the recipients and increasing their positivity and calmness.

And a recent article has suggested that these bacteria might have an influence on our motor skills and diseases associated with motor skills.

It has become clear that there is an interaction, but the mechanisms behind the interactions are not yet clear. It is also not clear which comes first...do problems with our gut cause us to have mental health issues or did the mental health issues cause us to have gut problems, or maybe even both?

In a recent article, [167] *Science News* outlines the research from a number of researchers exploring the possibility that there is a link between the neurodegenerative disease, Parkinson's disease, and what may be going on in our gut. They outline one theory:

> "... *suggests that substances swallowed or sniffed set off an inflammatory reaction that alters the gut microbiome. In turn, alpha-synuclein may become misfolded and travel along the vagus nerve, from the lining of the gut, causing nerve cell death.*"

In a 2015 article [168], Svensson et al report:

"The research has presented strong evidence that Parkinson's disease begins in the gastrointestinal tract and spreads via the vagus nerve to the brain."

And in a more recent article, [169] Friedland and Chapman:

"It has become apparent that the intestinal microbiota orchestrates important aspects of our metabolism, immunity, and development. Recent work has demonstrated that the microbiota also influences brain function in healthy and diseased individuals. Of great interest are reports that intestinal bacteria play a role in the pathogenic cascade of both Parkinson and Alzheimer diseases."

The editor warns us though:

"Scientists need to test the idea to see if the gut is really involved in the disease (the phase of many efforts now) and then figure out if a treatment can be devised. That research process typically takes decades, and the odds of failure are far higher than the odds of delivering a headline-worthy breakthrough."

There's one more issue at play here. That is the issue of the "leaky gut." There is some debate in medical literature about this topic, and it is difficult to identify exactly what is fact, what is opinion, and what is something else. The proponents of "Leaky Gut Syndrome" ask the question "What happens when some of the stuff that's supposed to stay in your digestive tract gets into the blood stream?"

Well, the bottom line is that it's not good. First, let's take a quick look at what leaky gut is. The definition appears to be "increased permeability of the small intestine." The impact is that bacteria and partially digested food particles get into the blood stream when they shouldn't. This "leakage" has been associated with many diseases including, among others, arthritis, allergies, depression, eczema, hives, psoriasis, and chronic fatigue syndrome. In response to these bacteria and food particles, the body starts to generate antibodies.

It also seems that some of these unwanted substances (bacteria, partially digested food particles, and antibodies) can cross the blood-brain barrier and go into the brain. Not good. [170]

Watch this space. I suspect that there would be a lot more to write definitively about if I was writing on this subject in a couple of years.

b. The Brain, Heart, and Lungs

It has been known for a long time that there is an interaction between the heart and the brain. Darwin [171] made mention of it in 1872. Monks who have been practicing deep breathing and meditation have probably intuitively known of the positive interaction between the heart and the lungs and the brain for thousands of years. We're just now starting to understand the underlying mechanisms for these positive interactions.

In a recent paper, Jerath et al [172] describe the effects of voluntary deep breathing as follows:

"[Voluntary deep breathing] has been shown to contribute to a physiologic response characterized by the presence of decreased oxygen consumption, decreased heart rate, and decreased blood pressure, as well as increased theta wave amplitude in EEG

recordings, increased parasympathetic activity accompanied by the experience of alertness and reinvigoration."

In other and perhaps more understandable words, deep breathing decreases things if they need to be decreased and increases things that need to be increased. The net results? If you are feeling tense, then deep breathing will relax you and make you better able to deal with stress or cues that are likely to trigger you. Deep breathing will decrease a racing heart, increase your heart rate variability (HRV), and make you generally feel more awake and in control.

Heart rate variability? It turns out that this might be one of the more important measures of how we are doing under stress. What is it? Simple. It's the variation in the time between each heartbeat. Simple, but with a huge impact. The lower your heart rate variability, the more stress seems to be having an impact on you. The higher your heart rate variability, the calmer you are, and the more you are able to deal with stress.

Deep breathing increases your heart rate variability. Even two minutes of deep breathing has a positive effect on your ability to deal with stress for the next hour or so. Ten minutes in the morning can set you up for the day. Doing this three or four times a week for six weeks will alter your overall threshold for dealing with stress. Meditation has a similar effect. [173]

c. The Brain and Sleep*

Over the past couple of thousand years, there has been a lot of research on sleep and sleep deprivation. This has been done by people ranging from philosophers to scientists. What is the purpose of sleep? Why is it necessary? What actually happens during sleep? What are dreams, and why do we have them? Our understanding of sleep has changed drastically, and there are still multiple schools of thought on the subject. In recent decades, there has been a whole bunch of research on the impact of sleep on the brain.

I am just going to pick out a few aspects to focus on; I am leaving out some important topics such as the impact of technology on sleep, the impact of dreams, the impact of age, and the impact of the quality of sleep rather than quantity. Probably many other factors too!

In summary, what the research shows is as follows:

The purpose of sleep seems to be:

> ➢ To help us organize and consolidate memories from the day.
> ➢ To clean out the residue and by-products from the activities of the brain during the day.

We know this about sleep:

> ➢ Sleep is directly linked into our circadian rhythms. Sleep is crucial for childhood health and development.

The impacts of not getting enough sleep or lacking sleep are the following (A) :

---

* National Geographic (August 2018) has an extremely good article on "The Science of Sleep." I have leveraged many of its summaries. I strongly recommend reading it.

➤ Decrease our ability to make good decisions
➤ Decrease our problem-solving ability
➤ Decrease our general cognitive abilities in general
➤ Decrease our ability for self-control
➤ Decrease our abilities to deal with stress
➤ Decrease our "mood"
➤ Increase our irritability
➤ Increase our negativity
➤ Increase our chances of traffic and machine-related accidents

In addition to the above, chronic lack of sleep seems to (B) :

➤ Increase our susceptibility to long-term cognitive issues (e.g., Alzheimer's disease)
➤ Increase our risk of depression
➤ Increase our risk of psychosis
➤ Increase our risk of strokes
➤ Increase our likelihood of obesity
➤ Increase our risk of diabetes
➤ Increase our risk of cardiovascular disease

Extreme sleep deprivation leads to:

➤ A combination of all of A and B above!
➤ Impaired ability for decision making specifically involving [174] the unexpected, innovation, revising plans, competing distractions, and effective communication.

These results should worry us all. If you take nothing else from reading this book, then you might want to heed this: find out the amount of sleep you need and develop personal strategies for getting that amount!

What is the right amount of sleep?

While there is some debate as to how much sleep is the ideal amount, there seems to be a general sense from the research that, on average, we all aren't getting enough of it.

There does seem to be a reasonable consensus on two sleep "breakpoints." The average amount of sleep required by the "normal" adult is 7 hours. Less than 7 hours, on an occasional basis, seems to lead to the issues identified in A and B above. Less than 7 hours on a regular basis seems to lead to C above.

What Happens During Sleep?

"On a good night, we cycle four or five times through several stages of sleep, each with distinct qualities and purpose – a serpentine, surreal descent into an alternative world."

What about childhood sleep?

"Sleep is crucial for childhood health and development; it is when most hormone and infection-fighting proteins are released. Poor sleep in kids has been linked to diabetes, obesity, and learning disabilities." [175]

There is a growing interest in research concerning the link between sleep and Alzheimer's disease. For example, a study [176] performed by the Wisconsin Registry for Alzheimer's Prevention found that in a subjective self-report of poor sleep quality, more sleep problems and a daytime tendency to sleepiness were associated with a greater likelihood of Alzheimer's disease. The conclusion that this study reached was that effective strategies exist for improving sleep, and therefore, this approach could be an early intervention to attenuate the onset of Alzheimer's disease.

Science News reports [177]:

> *"... while the new research is compelling, plenty of gaps remain. There's not enough evidence yet to know the degree to which sleep might make a difference in the disease, and study results are not consistent."*

> *"A 2017 analysis combined results of 27 studies that looked at the relationship between sleep and cognitive problems, including Alzheimer's disease. Overall, poor sleepers appeared to have a 68 percent higher risk or these disorders than those who were rested, researchers reported..."*

What is still up for grabs, however, as was pointed out in the article in *Science News*, is that the relationship is unclear. Which comes first? Does a propensity for Alzheimer's disease cause poor sleep or does poor sleep increases the chances of developing Alzheimer's disease?

One theory (and hence the title of the *Science News* article) is that sleep is part of a cycle that "cleans" out the brain, like the wash and rinse cycle in our washing machines. The supposition is that during the day, waste products develop in the brain. Sleep enables a process of cleansing to occur. When we have inefficient or insufficient sleep, that cleaning process is interrupted, and the waste is not removed. In chronic cases, these waste products contribute to a "plaque-like" build up, which in turn causes the subsequent cognitive disease.

d. The Brain and Food

Aka: The Brain and Diet, Taste, and Eating Socially ☺

The first thing I want to say here is that this is a huge subject and truly deserves several books in its own right. I urge you to go on to Google Scholar and search "diet and the brain" or "brain and taste" ... or any such combination, and you will have enough articles to read to last a lifetime. Of necessity, I will only just be scratching the surface of these topics.

And you don't have to scratch very far to get to the conclusion. Our diets impact the brain to an extremely large degree! Probably way more than any of us give it credit for. Ignore it at your peril. And the impact is in two aspects. First, the wrong diet can impair our cognitive abilities, both in the short-term and the long-term. The second is that the wrong diet seems to drastically increase our risk of some kind of disease to the brain.

In general, it seems that the Western diet negatively impacts the brain through two important issues, sugar intake and high-fat content.

Let's start with the latter. In a paper published in 2011, Simopoulos [178] describes the change in our diet and our genes over the past 40,000 years. Look at this:

"Whereas major changes have taken place in our diet over the past 10,000 years since the beginning of the Agricultural Revolution, our genes have not changed. The spontaneous mutation rate for nuclear DNA is estimated at 0.5% per million years. Therefore, over the past 10,000 years, there has been time for very little change in our genes, perhaps 0.005%. In fact, our genes today are very similar to the genes of our ancestors during the Paleolithic period 40,000 years ago, at which time our genetic profile was established. Genetically speaking, humans today live in a nutritional environment that differs from that for which our genetic constitution was selected. Studies on the evolutionary aspects of diet indicate that major changes have taken place in our diet, particularly in the type and amount of essential fatty acids and in the antioxidant content of foods."

He starts off by outlining a major difference; we probably used to have a diet that had a ratio of 1:1 of Omega-6 and Omega-3. Nowadays, our Western diets have a ratio of somewhere between 10 and 25:1. That's a multiplication factor, not a percentage. This indicates a significant shortage of Omega-3, which is a source of important factors for brain health and possibly other behavioral aspects.

He goes into more detail about the failures of our current diet:

"Today industrialized societies are characterized by:

> *an increase in energy intake and decrease in energy expenditure*
> *an increase in saturated fat, omega-6 fatty acids, and trans-fatty acids, and a decrease in omega-3 fatty acid intake*
> *a decrease in complex carbohydrates and fiber intake*
> *an increase in cereal grains and a decrease in fruits and vegetables intake*
> *a decrease in protein, antioxidants, vitamin D, and calcium intake."*

In a more recent paper, Noble et al continue the theme [179]:

"Substantial evidence has linked consumption of a Western diet (WD), defined here as diets consisting of both high levels of fat (35-60% total kcal) and added sugars, with cognitive dysfunction."

They then go on to cite fifteen references to prove their point!

Then they add:

"The hippocampus, a brain region associated with the control of certain learning and memory processes, is particularly vulnerable to the deleterious effects of WD intake."

And continue by saying:

"The mechanisms through which WD consumption impacts the brain are not completely understood; however, emerging research has implicated the gut-brain axis as playing a critical role. The gut microbiome (the collective genome of microbes residing in the gastrointestinal tract) has a substantial impact on brain function. Moreover, the gut microbiome is profoundly affected by dietary factors."

So, back to the gut and the microbiome again! See Section B Part 4a!

There are plenty more articles on how bad our current diets are. Here are two articles whose titles illustrate the situation:

> *Damaging effects of a high-fat diet to the brain and cognition: A review of proposed mechanisms* [180]
> *Cognitive impairment following high fat diet consumption is associated with brain inflammation (20ʷ)* [181]

So, what would a good diet be? There seems to be a general conclusion leaning towards the Mediterranean diet. This diet is exemplified by olive oil, fish, fruits, and vegetables.

There is plenty of research which confirms the advantages of a Mediterranean-based approach, with these being a few recent titles. Don't worry if you don't understand all of the words. You'll get the overall message.

> *Mediterranean diet and preserved brain structural connectivity in older subjects* [182]
> *The effect of the Mediterranean diet on plasma brain-derived neurotrophic factor (BDNF) levels* [183]
> *The Mediterranean diet and healthy brain aging: Innovations from nutritional cognitive neuroscience* [184]

Now to the second issue. Sugar. There is plenty of evidence that the increase of sugars, etc. has negatively impacted our overall health, especially with regard to diabetes. But, how about sugar, insulin, and the brain?

Pretty much the same. Don't do it! The bottom line is that, in addition to its physical effects on the body, excessive sugar impacts cognitive ability, increases the risk of diseases of the brain, and acts like addictive drugs. I'll use the same approach as I did for fat; I will simply list the titles of some recent papers. Once again, don't worry about all of the words. It's the overall message that is important.

> *A high-fat, refined sugar diet reduces hippocampal brain-derived neurotrophic factor, neuronal plasticity, and learning* [185]
> *Excessive sugar intake alters binding to dopamine and mu-opioid receptors in the brain* [186]
> *Opiate-like effects of sugar on gene expression in reward areas of the rat brain* [187]
> *Long-term consumption of sugar sweetened beverage during the growth period promotes social aggression in adult mice with proinflammatory responses in the brain* [188]
> *Excessive sugar consumption may be a difficult habit to break: A view from the brain and body* [189]

The take away from all of that? Eat a better diet!

But before we leave the topic of diet, I need to address one other issue: alcohol. As you can imagine, there have been plenty of studies, good and bad, on this subject. As soon as one starts to pull back the layers of the alcohol onion, as it were, life gets very complex, very quickly. With a lot of controversy.

It seems that there are three main areas under question:

> The impact of fetal alcohol, i.e., drinking while pregnant

> ➤ The impact of alcohol on the developing, i.e., teenage brain
> ➤ The impact of alcohol on the adult brain

Let's deal with the easiest one first. Fetal alcohol. The bottom line is described in this abstract: [190]

> *"The most profound effects of prenatal alcohol exposure are on the developing brain and the cognitive and behavioral effects that ensue. Alcohol exposure affects brain development via numerous pathways at all stages from neurogenesis to myelination. Behaviors as diverse as executive functioning to motor control are affected."*

i.e., Yes, you do impact an infant's brain if you drink alcohol when pregnant.

OK. That was easy. Now for the next one. The teenage brain. And this is where some of the controversy starts. The questions center around:

> ➤ To what degree does alcohol impact the teenage brain?
> ➤ Can their brains recover?
> ➤ What about binge drinking?

There seems to be little doubt that alcohol does impact the teenage brain and not in good ways. Let's take a look at a couple of studies. Squeglia and Gray [191] have the following to say:

> *"After substance use is initiated, alcohol and marijuana use are associated with poorer cognitive functioning on tests of verbal memory, visuospatial functioning, psychomotor speed, working memory, attention, cognitive control, and overall IQ. Heavy alcohol use during adolescence is related to accelerated decreases in gray matter and attenuated increases in white matter volume, as well as increased brain activation during tasks of inhibition and working memory, relative to controls."*

Spas and Wayandt [192] seem to be in full agreement:

> *"This review synthesizes structural and functional neuroimaging studies on alcohol and executive functions. Results suggest that alcohol is associated with both acute and long-term impairment in executive functions. Finally, this review suggests that neuroimaging techniques reveal that alcohol is an especially harmful neuroteratogen which compromises executive functions in adolescence."*

(Neuroteratogen is a fancy way of saying something that interferes with behavior and neural activity.)

As regards recovery...it seems that there aren't enough reliable studies to draw specific conclusions.

Binge drinking? As you would expect, it seems to have the same set of effects as "normal" drinking, but research has shown some gender differences: [193]

> *"Females may be more vulnerable to the neurotoxic effects of heavy alcohol use during adolescence while males may be more resilient to the deleterious effects of binge drinking."*

Now. How about adults?

This is where the controversies can really be found. A couple of decades ago, the predominant theory was that while excessive drinking was bad, moderate drinking was OK. In fact, it was beneficial to one's health. Let's leave aside the fact that wishful thinking and confirmation bias probably had something to do with the wide adoption of this theory. ☺

More recent studies have shown that even moderate drinking has negative effects on the brain. Anyone who has imbibed knows that there are immediate (or acute) effects on our brains and our behavior. fMRI studies are now showing which networks are involved. One recent study outlined "five independent critical brain circuits" that are significantly affected by alcohol. [194] The study goes on to add that "Alcohol leads to dysfunction of cognitive control, causing behavioral disinhibition" which seems to me to be patently obvious!!!

So that's about the immediate effect. What about consumption over time? What impact does that have on the brain? Let's look at a 2017 study published in the *British Medical Journal*: [195]

> *"Higher alcohol consumption over the 30-year follow-up was associated with increased odds of hippocampal atrophy in a dose dependent fashion. While those consuming over 30 units a week were at the highest risk compared with abstainers, even those drinking moderately had three times the odds of right sided hippocampal atrophy. There was no protective effect of light drinking over abstinence. Higher alcohol use was also associated with differences in corpus callosum microstructure and faster decline in lexical fluency."*

For those of us that like a glass or two of wine with dinner, this is bad news. "No protective effect of light drinking over abstinence." I think I'll go and drown my sorrows. ☺

Up until this point, I have treated each of these topics separately. Professor Charles Spence would be appalled. Why do I say this, and who is Charles Spence? He is head of the cross-modal research laboratory at Oxford University and, as his title suggests, he studies the interaction between our senses. Here's a quick clip from a recent interview: [196]

> *"We all think that we taste food in our mouths, and yet that's an illusion in the sense that most of what you are tasting, the fruity, the floral, the meaty, the herbal, the burnt or the smoky, are actually being decoded by our nostrils, but our brain is doing this wonderful job of ventriloquizing the information that I get from my nose and making me believe as if it's coming from my mouth."*

Spence is a prolific researcher who looks at, among many other subjects, all aspects of the gustatory experience. What else is going on around you while you are eating. Where you are. Who you are with. The music and other sounds that are surrounding you. The shape of the plate. Where the food is located on the plate. It all gets integrated in the brain to give you a holistic experience.

One of Spence's experiments was to change the sound associated with eating various substances, for example chips (or crisps in the UK). They found that as soon as you change the sound associated with the food, you change the perception of the crispness, the crunchiness, or the freshness of the food.

Another experiment was to use an odorless red dye to change the color of a white wine to make it look red. Even the wine experts are then "fooled" into thinking that they can taste all of the aromas and flavors of what they would expect in a red wine.

This all adds up into a much larger concept. How we experience the taste of our food is not just about the ingredients. Here's another clip:

"A lot about what's going on is created by the atmosphere in which we eat and drink...the mood you're in, the people you're with, gives you the social aspects of dining...no one has ever had the perfect meal while they are fighting with their partner.

That great meal you had on holiday (vacation) and you cannot capture when you get back home is because you were relaxed when you were on holiday, you're less stressed, you're with your family – all of these things come together to enhance the experience and make it something truly memorable."

He introduces the concept of the "Provencale Rose Paradox."

"If you are from northern Europe, you go for your holiday to the Mediterranean, you're sitting somewhere by the side of the sea, sipping that rose wine, looking into your lover's eyes, the sun's setting, you can hear the sounds of the sea, the smell of the salty air – it's all there. And that tastes like the best glass of wine you've ever had. So, you bring back a bottle or two ... and you are disappointed."

So, what's the practical application of all this? Spence carried out another experiment in a dining room. [197] Diners were served the same menu, but the visual presentation of the ingredients on the plate was varied. Look at the results:

"... diners were willing to pay significantly more for the appetizer (a salad) when arranged in an artistically-inspired manner.

The main course was liked more and considered more artistic when the various elements were presented in the center of the plate, rather than placed off to one side. The participants also reported being willing to pay significantly more for the centered than for the offset plating. These results are consistent with the claim that people 'eat first with their eyes.'"

In the case of the appetizer, it was 44% more, and in the case of the main course, it was 32% more. Not trivial. And I am willing to bet that if we could get to the question of conscious or nonconscious behavior, we would find that it was all nonconscious.

Dan Buettner's "Nine Lessons for Living Longer," include three that are diet-oriented. Here's his summaries:

"Hara hachi bu – the 2,500-year-old Confucian mantra spoken before meals on Okinawa – reminds people to stop eating when their stomachs are 80 percent full. The 20 percent gap between not being hungry and feeling full could be the difference between losing weight and gaining it. People in the Blue Zones eat their smallest meal in the late afternoon or early evening, and they don't eat any more the rest of the day."

"Beans, including fava, black, soy, and lentils, are cornerstone of most Blue Zone diets. Meat – mostly pork – is eaten on average only five times per month and in a serving of three to four ounces, about the size of a deck of cards."

"People in all Blue Zones (even some Adventists) drink alcohol moderately and regularly. Moderate drinkers outlive nondrinkers. The trick is to drink one or two

glasses per day with friends and/or with food. And no, you can't save up all week and have 14 drinks on Saturday."

Finally, a brief note on social impacts. If you decide that you want to change your diet, don't forget that we are more likely to eat what is eaten by the people we hang out with. [198] Higgs and Thomson say it so well that I will use the abstract from their paper:

> *"Eating behavior is strongly influenced by social context. We eat differently when we are with other people compared with when we eat alone. Our dietary choices also tend to converge with those of our close social connections. One reason for this is that conforming to the behavior of others is adaptive, and we find it rewarding. Norms of appropriate eating are set by the behavior of other people but also shared cultural expectations and environmental cues. We are more likely to follow an eating norm if it is perceived to be relevant based on social comparison. Relevant norms are set by similar others and those with whom we identify. If a norm is relevant then there may be matching of behavior to the norm, but this will depend on other factors, such as how much attention is paid to the norm, how concerned we are about social acceptance, and the presence of other competing norms such as personal norms and consumption stereotypes. Norm matching involves processes such as synchronization of eating actions, consumption monitoring, and altered food preferences. There is emerging evidence that social eating norms may play a role in the development and maintenance of obesity. Social eating norms constitute a novel target for interventions to encourage healthier eating."*

In other words, if you want to change your diet, pay attention not only to what you are eating but who you are eating with. You will also see that your own Personal Threat Profile will affect to what degree you are socially influenced by the people that you eat with. Similarly, and this is REALLY obvious, if you want to reduce the amount of alcohol you consume, avoid parties and going to bars with your friends!!!

e. The Brain and Exercise

In many ways, this section could be simply. Very simple. It can be summarized in one word. *Exercise*! (That's a suggestion not an order. We know that the brain doesn't like being told what to do. But it's a very strong suggestion.)

The rest of this section will mainly be material to support that suggestion; but, in addition to the pure physical benefits of exercise, let's talk about why exercise is good for the brain. There is a deluge of papers that support exercise-brain health hypothesis and I cite just a few. The following are some of the findings of these papers.

- ➢ Exercise can improve a number of aspects of cognition and performance in children, adolescents, and adults. [199] [200] [201]
- ➢ Exercise appears to increase our chance of "successful aging." [202] [203] [204]
- ➢ There's some evidence that exercise can reverse some of the negative effects of a bad diet. [205]
- ➢ Exercise appears to stave off the impact of a variety of diseases. [206] [207]

So, this is all well and good. But what type of exercise and for how long? Even a single aerobic bout [208] seems to have some effect, although regular sessions are recommended for maximum effect. Intense resistance exercise seems to have an additional effect. [209]

On the other hand, in his *Blue Zones*, [210] Dan Buettner identifies "moving naturally" as one of the nine factors for a long and happy life. His summary:

> "The world's longest-lived people don't pump iron, run marathons, or join gyms. Instead, they live in environments that constantly nudge them into moving. They grow gardens and don't have mechanical conveniences for house and yard work. Every trip to work, to a friend's house, or to church occasions a walk."

So, where does that leave us? Strict regimes at the gym or gentler approaches at home? I can't answer that. What I can conclude is that exercise is important – getting it is probably more important than how you get it.

f. The Brain, Love, and Sex

When I thought about writing about the topic of the brain, love, and sex, I knew it could be a difficult proposition. I thought the difficulties would not lie in the topic itself but would be associated with the audacity of attempting to write about a topic which has been the subject of so many great books, music, songs, etc. over the past several thousand years. And yes, it has been the subject of scientific research for a long time too, dating back to Aristotle, if not before. Both love and sex!

I thought I would start my research on the topic of "love and the brain" then move on to "sex and the brain." I thought that in order to tackle the topics, I would simply start off with a definition of love. That sounds easy, but it actually turned out to be quite difficult. I never did find one that was useful.

The topic of "the brain and love" was relatively easy, and you will see the results of my brief research below. The topic of "sex and the brain" was much harder. This was mainly because of two reasons. First, there's some controversy about sex and orgasm, which results in some researchers having a proclivity for spending a lot of time and literature columns in refuting and repudiating other researcher's publications. And second, there is still controversy about the female orgasm and how and why it fits into the evolutionary picture.

I want to start with a paragraph from Daniel Amen [211] since he sums it all up so well:

> "Even though it feels genital, the vast majority of love and sex occurs in the brain. Your brain decides who is attractive to you, how to get a date, how well you do on that date, what to do with the feelings that develop, how long those feelings last, when to commit, and how well you do as a partner and a parent. Your brain helps you be enthusiastic in the bedroom or drains you of desire and passion. Your brain helps you process and learn from a break-up or makes you more vulnerable to depression or obsession. When the brain works right, it helps you be thoughtful, playful, romantic, intimate, committed, and loving with your partner. When the brain is dysfunctional, it causes you to be impulsive, distracted, addicted, unfaithful, angry, and even hateful, thus ruining your chances for continued intimacy and love."

In some ways, there's not a lot more to say, is there?

Sukel [212] describes some research done by Helen Fisher and others. They proposed a theory of three separate but intersecting brain systems which covered lust, romantic love and long-term attachment. This three-layered structure seems to have become the de facto standard. Sukel goes on to report some conversations that she had with Fisher:

164

"These brain systems often work together, but I think it's fair to say they often don't work together too .... one might feel deep attachment for one partner, be in romantic love with another partner, and then be sexually attracted to many others."

Oops. That throws a spanner (wrench) in the works.

Fisher [213] et al studied 17 people who were "intensely in love" – and proposed that romantic love is a:

"...behavioral 'attraction system' associated with dopaminergic reward pathways in the brain."

They also studied 15 people who had been rejected in love – and found that there was increased brain activity:

"... in related regions of the reward system associated with monetary gambling for uncertain large gains and losses, and in regions of the lateral orbitofrontal cortex associated with theory of mind, obsessive/compulsive behaviors, and controlling anger."

They go on to explain:

"The sex drive evolved to motivate individuals to seek a range of mating partners; attraction evolved to motivate individuals to prefer and pursue specific partners; and attachment evolved to motivate individuals to remain together long enough to complete species-specific parenting duties. These three behavioral repertoires appear to be based on brain systems that are largely distinct yet interrelated, and they interact in specific ways to orchestrate reproduction, using both hormones and monoamines."

Another way of describing this is in an article by Tarlaci [214] where he states:

"In brief, when people in love see their beloved, they fall into an ocean of dopamine in the reward pathways in their subcortical structures."

Not only is there an increase in the reward networks, but there is a decrease of activity in some of the areas of the PFC. Tarlaci again:

"The prefrontal region in humans is the most important region for visualization, intention, and decision-making and logical deduction. It is the source of logic and adherence to social rules, morality, and respect. The reduction in the activity of this region in people in love results in a weakening or loss of its functions. This is possible because the brain regions responsible for logic, and the rules of social morality have stopped working properly."

Tarlaci also states:

"When you're in love, the rules of logic aren't applied. Love comes in, and sense goes out the window. It is for this reason that people in love tend to take stupid and illogical risks. In the case of an impossible love, they are not persuaded by people trying to make them see sense."

So, who are we attracted by? If we return to the work of Dr. Evian Gordon, he has several paragraphs that address the cues that are associated with this attraction process. I quote these paragraphs in their entirety:

"We are still driven by the innate motivation to find a partner who is sexually attractive, has good genes to pass on to our offspring, will stick around until the children are grown up, and will be able to look after us materially and socially.

Face, body shape, and smell are key sexual cues. Both sexes tune in to body beauty reflected in symmetry, which is the key marker of genetic health quality and physical health.

Males non-consciously pick up cues from female body structure, such as a waist that is about 70% the size of the hips (which has evolutionary child-bearing significance), a childlike face, small nose, and full lips and cheeks (which tap into a protective need), smooth skin, and a flat stomach (which indicates that the female is not pregnant and is available to impregnate).

Cues to a female that a male has good genes to pass on to offspring are physical strength, attractiveness, symmetry, the smell of pheromones, and deep voice indicative of high testosterone. Females also tune into cues that a male is likely to be loyal and has sufficient resources to provide for her until any children are independent. These cues are related to traits such as endurance, empathy, sensitivity, and altruism. Connectedness and security markers range from sensual attentiveness after orgasm to financial generosity."

Is this "romantic love dynamic" universal? It appears so. Xu [215] et al found:

"… that midbrain dopamine-rich reward/motivation systems were activated by early stage romantic love in Chinese participants, as found by other studies."

and Tarlaci [216] reports:

"Scientifically speaking, love probably made its appearance with Neanderthals between 350 and 30 thousand years ago."

and

"If love started with the Neanderthals, anthropological studies have shown that today, 147 out of 166 societies in the world have a word for love or at least the concept of love, while for the other nineteen, it has been suggested that not enough questions of the right kind have been asked to discover whether it exists or not. For this reason, love is accepted as a universal or near universal feeling."

Before we leave the subject of the brain and love, I thought I would report on what appears to me to be the driest definition of romantic love that I discovered: [217]

"Romantic love could be considered as a collection of activities associated with the acquisition and retention of emotions needed to survive and reproduce. These emotions change the individual's behavioral strategies in a way that will increase the likelihood of achieving these goals. Love may be defined as an emergent property of an ancient cocktail of neuropeptides and neurotransmitters. It appears that lust, attachment, and attraction appear to be distinct but intertwined processes in the brain each mediated by its own neurotransmitters and circuits. These circuits feed on and reinforce each other. Sexual craving is mediated by testosterone and estrogen and has the amygdala as an important center. Attraction is mediated by hormones of stress and reward including dopamine, norepinephrine cortisol, and the serotonergic system and has the nucleus accumbens, the ventral tegmental area, as key mediators."

So, there you have it. From the brain's perspective:

> *"Love may be defined as an emergent property of an ancient cocktail of neuropeptides and neurotransmitters."*

Try saying that when you propose to your future fiancé or fiancée. ☺

OK. I think we're all convinced that love has a huge impact on the brain, or maybe the other way around.

But what about sex? What's going on in the brain during sex? And, again you probably won't be surprised to learn that there's a lot of research going on here. And probably a lot of volunteers willing to participate in the research. ☺

In 2016, the difficulties and controversies were well summarized in the abstract of a chapter written by Levin: [218]

> *"The human female orgasm bestows the greatest pleasure without recourse to drugs. Despite numerous studies, there are many aspects of the activity that are poorly understood. These include its neurophysiology and pharmacology, while even its typology, induction, and function(s) are contentious issues. It can be induced by a variety of agencies that include genital and non-genital sites and even by exercise. While there are similarities with the male orgasm, there are a few differences, the major one being that women can have repeated multiple orgasms while males cannot. Despite current speculative claims in the literature, it does not mediate or facilitate sperm transport through its uterine contractions. Brain imaging that measures cerebral regional blood flow has revealed that there is no single orgasm center, but rather specific areas are either activated, inhibited, or unaffected during orgasm. However, no consensus has yet been achieved due to experimental procedural differences and data handling by researchers."*

In addition, it's easy to see the relationship between male ejaculation, usually linked with orgasm, and the survival and continuation of the species. It is less easy to see the relationship between female orgasm and species survival – there does not seem to be such a direct relationship. [219]

Bottom line: There's a lot going on. And the brain is the most important organ in both love and sex.

g. Spirituality and the Brain

This topic is as daunting to tackle as was love and sex, maybe more so. As I outlined at the beginning of this section, the purpose of these different perspectives is simply to highlight the fact that the brain is impacted by many different aspects. Whether you call it spirituality, religion, or your own word or phrase for it, this is one such aspect.

One of the first things I discovered in my research was that I was not alone in my trepidation. Here's an extract from a 2013 study:

> *"However, discussions about spirituality remain somewhat taboo in British society."* [220]

and

"As this topic (religion and health) continues to push into the mainstream of medical and population health research – it is already less marginal and less obscure than it was even 7 years ago – a tacit narrative has taken root which evinces a widespread lack of awareness of the parameters of this field. This includes misperceptions about where this field came from, how much research has been done, and the breadth and depth of this work." (221)

That theme is repeated in some of the literature – there is much research out there, but you have to look for it.

A caveat in advance. With this writing, I am not intending to persuade anyone to become religious or spiritual or to change their minds if they already are. Neither am I proselytizing any specific spiritual, religious, or philosophical approach.

In summary, there is research to indicate that having a faith-based approach to life increases people's sense of their subjective well-being, which includes measures such as life-span, mental health, and happiness. I think it is best summed up by two of Dan Buettner's books: (222) (223)

With regard to living longer:

"All but 5 of the 263 centenarians we interviewed belonged to a faith-based community. Denomination doesn't seem to matter. Research shows that attending faith-based services four times per month will add 4 to 14 years of life expectancy."

And with regard to happiness:

"In most countries, religious people are happier than nonreligious people. A 2015 study by the London School of Economics and Erasmus University Medical Center in the Netherlands found that participants who went to services in a church, mosque, or synagogue regularly experienced a more significant mental health boost than those who engaged in other social activities."

His advice?

"If you're religious, attend services regularly. If you're not, take the time to visit a half dozen places of worship to see if any resonate. If organized religion just isn't your thing, look for groups in your area with whom you might share and practice your spiritual beliefs. Whatever you believe in, engaging regularly in a spiritual practice can influence your life in a deep, sustained, and positive way."

While there are notable exceptions, (224) these overall conclusions seem to be borne out across different faiths, across different countries and regions, across different sexual orientations, (225) across different ethnic groups, (226) and across different age groups. (227)

This is not a scientific review, but it would seem reasonable to assume, at the very least, the conclusions have wide applicability.

So, it seems that, amongst other things, mental health is improved by having and practicing religious or spiritual beliefs. But what is actually going on in the brain? And are the positive outcomes simply a result of some other aspect, for example, having respect from others, being part of an in-group, having self-respect, etc.?

As soon as we start down the neuroscientific path to investigate spirituality and the brain, we instantly run against a whole host of issues with regard to the scientific process. The difficulty of doing this research is well articulated by Newberg, [228] who appears to be one of the giants in this field. The scientific side of the equation is becoming more understood, exact, and measurable year by year. The subjective reporting on the spirituality side, however, remains difficult to define and quantify, for example:

"If someone defines spiritual as a feeling of 'awe' and another as a feeling of 'oneness,' what types of questions should be used to assess and measure spirituality?"

In addition, some of the studies focus on the practice of meditation and measure its impact on the brain, regardless of whether the practice is, in fact, linked with spirituality.

With all of that said, it does seem that there are some correlations between the brain and spirituality. I include a few examples of what some of the research suggests:

Miller et al [229] report:

"Importance of religion or spirituality, but not frequency of attendance, was associated with thicker cortices in the left and right parietal and occipital regions, the mesial frontal lobe of the right hemisphere, and the cuneus and precuneus in the left hemisphere."

Urgesi et al [230] found:

"… that selective damage to left and right inferior posterior parietal regions induced a specific increase of self-transcendence (a predisposition of human beings toward spiritual feeling, thinking, and behaviors)."

Holbrook et al [231] suggest:

"Spirituality involves a feeling of profound personal connection to a sacred reality (e.g., God) and is often characterized by experiences of comfort and peace. The neuropeptide oxytocin appears to be a plausible biological mediator of such spiritual experiences, as oxytocin is closely linked with social affiliation, intimacy, and stress-attenuation."

Van Elk and Aleman [232] discuss:

" … four different brain mechanisms that play a key role in religion and spirituality: temporal brain areas are associated with religious visions and ecstatic experiences; multisensory brain areas and the default mode network are involved in self transcendent experiences; the Theory of Mind network is associated with prayer experiences and over-attribution of intentionality; top-down mechanisms instantiated in the anterior cingulate cortex and the medial prefrontal cortex could be involved in acquiring and maintaining intuitive supernatural beliefs."

Finally, as further proof that the interaction of spirituality and the brain is a topic worth investigating, it now has its own "neuro" label, neurotheology:

"Basically, in the study of neurotheology, we are trying to understand the relationships among the different areas and functions of the brain and how they help us or restrict us in terms of engaging the spiritual side of ourselves." [233]

and

"Neurotheology, also known as 'spiritual neuroscience,' is an emerging field of study that seeks to understand the relationship between the brain science and religion. Scholars in this field strive up front to explain the neurological ground for spiritual experiences such as 'the perception that time, fear, or self-consciousness have dissolved; spiritual awe; oneness with the universe.' There has been a recent considerable interest in neurotheology worldwide. Neurotheology is multidisciplinary in nature and includes the fields of theology, religious studies, religious experience and practice, philosophy, cognitive science, neuroscience, psychology, and anthropology." [234]

h. Attitude and the Brain

I think it probably goes without saying that it is easier to have a great attitude if you are happy. So, that is one of the aspects of this section – happiness. Another aspect that I hear reported all of the time when I discuss attitude is positivity. A third aspect and one that has come to the fore more recently, is having a growth versus a fixed mindset.

In his book *The Blue Zones of Happiness,* [235] Dan Buettner identifies the nine aspects of happiness:

1. *Love someone – the right partner determines 90% of your happiness or lack thereof*
2. *Have an inner circle of friends*
3. *Engage in the outside world*
4. *Learn to be likeable*
5. *Move naturally – a daily dose of physical activity – weave it into your day*
6. *Look forward – focus on meaningful things, set goals and monitor progress*
7. *Sleep seven plus hours*
8. *Shape your surroundings – home, workplace, finances, social network, and inner life*
9. *Belong to a social group or community that suits you*

There's a couple of others that he adds in when he addresses practices, namely:

10. *Focus on the happiness of others*
11. *Make a best friend at work*
12. *Monitor your health*

I have loved the research that I have done for this book – it has made me very happy. But there were a few surprises. When I started to research happiness, I thought that I would pick up an old favorite, Austin's book *Zen and the Brain*; the surprise was that there was no entry for "happiness" in the table of contents. Neither was there an entry for "happiness" in the index. What about joy? Nope. No entry there either. Seems like I was striking out.

So, I thought that I would go to another tried and true favorite, Frederickson's *Positivity.* [236] No real luck there either. There is an entry for "happiness" in the index, in fact several, but she turns away from the word:

"You have noticed that the term happiness is not in my top ten. I avoid this term because I feel it's murky and overused...that same feeling is often better described by another, more specific term, like joy, gratitude, or love, depending on the exact circumstances."

Then she introduces ten forms of positivity:

"joy, gratitude, serenity, interest, hope, pride, amusement, inspiration, awe, and love."

So maybe, in our quest for how attitude affects the brain, it might be more helpful to look at the more detailed aspects that Fredrickson offers. She continues by suggesting that we each look at every one of these ten forms of positivity and make our own personalized portfolio for each of them.

Let's examine some of the science behind Frederickson's approach by looking at a dozen of her findings, all of which have solid research behind them:

> *"Positivity calls forth more possibilities from within us than we typically see – and certainly more than we see under the influence of negativity.*
> *Positivity (in the form of amusement or serenity) produced more possibilities than negativity (in the form of anger or fear).*
> *When people are injected with positivity, their outlook expands. They see the big picture. When we inject them with neutrality or negativity, their peripheral vision shrinks.*
> *Quite literally, then, positivity changes our outlook on life. It expands your world view. You take more in.*
> *The researchers learned that when people felt positive, their performance on the two tasks changed in tandem: the broader the scope of their visual attention, the more creative they became on the verbal task.*
> *Students do better on standardized tests when they enter them having self-generated a positive emotion.*
> *The evidence shows that simply imagining a joyful memory or receiving a small kindness can make a difference in the ease with which people locate creative and optimal solutions to the problems they face on a daily basis.*
> *They found that managers with greater positivity were more accurate and careful in making their decisions and were more effective interpersonally.*
> *… managers with greater positivity infect their work groups with greater positivity as well, which in turn produces better coordination among team members and reduces the effort needed to get their work done.*
> *Negotiators who strategically displayed positivity were more likely to gain concessions, close deals, and incorporate future business relationships into the contracts they forged.*
> *… people who enjoyed more positivity in their lives were more able to cope with adversity in an open-minded way.*
> *As our positivity grows, so does our trust in others, and vice versa."*

Her list of the positive impacts of positivity goes on. And the effects seem to be universal. Ordinary people, students, managers, negotiators – anyone, it seems, is more effective when they adopt a positive attitude. What's not to like?

Let's now move on to the subject of mindsets.

I have heard this quote attributed to many people, but the general consensus is that it comes from Henry Ford:

"Whether you think you can or think you can't, you are right."

This really sums up the work being done on mindsets. Carol Dweck [237] has spent a great deal of time, energy, and research on this topic. Here's a few things that she has to say:

"For twenty years, my research has shown that the view you adopt for yourself profoundly affects the way you lead your life."

and

"Believing that your qualities are carved in stone – the fixed mindset – creates an urgency to prove yourself over and over."

And she contrasts that with:

"This growth mindset is based on the belief that your basic qualities are things that you can cultivate through your efforts. Although people may differ in every which way – in their initial talents and aptitudes, interests, or temperaments – everyone can change and grow through application and experience."

These approaches all seem, to some degree, to be based upon common sense, although the degree to which attitude affects these issues may have come as a surprise. What about the brain? Let's take a look at three recent discoveries:

"Using a large behavioral sample of 240 children, we found that positive attitude toward math uniquely predicted math achievement, even after we accounted for multiple other cognitive-affective factors...In both cohorts, we found that positive attitude was associated with increased engagement of the hippocampal learning-memory system. [238]

More frequent experiences of positive emotions assist adolescents in avoiding emotional dysfunction and depression [239] *– but not too much positivity.*

Daily positive events may serve a protective role against inflammation. [240]

So, overall, we're left with a strong impression that attitude has a drastic impact on the brain, and, most importantly, a positive attitude has not only a positive impact on the brain but on many aspects of our lives.

i. The Brain and Family

Here I am using the concept of "family" in the widest of interpretations. Family, friends, loved ones, and a close social "tribe."

The research tends to lean in two distinct directions – the positive impact of having an ongoing, supportive "family" and the negative impact of growing up in a dysfunctional family or a family in poverty.

Let's look at the second of these two first. The negative impacts of growing up in a dysfunctional family are huge. It is summed up well by an article on *Harvard University's Center on the Developing Child* website, [241] and I reproduce it in full:

"The future of any society depends on its ability to foster the healthy development of the next generation. Extensive research on the biology of stress now shows that healthy development can be derailed by excessive or prolonged activation of stress response systems in the body and brain. Such toxic stress can have damaging effects on learning, behavior, and health across the lifespan.

Learning how to cope with adversity is an important part of healthy child development. When we are threatened, our bodies prepare us to respond by increasing our heart rate, blood pressure, and stress hormones, such as cortisol. When a young child's stress response systems are activated within an environment of supportive relationships with adults, these physiological effects are buffered and brought back down to baseline. The result is the development of healthy stress response systems. However, if the stress response is extreme and long-lasting, and buffering relationships are unavailable to the child, the result can be damaged, weakened systems and brain architecture, with lifelong repercussions.

It's important to distinguish among three kinds of responses to stress: positive, tolerable, and toxic. As described below, these three terms refer to the stress response systems' effects on the body, not to the stressful event or experience itself:

> *Positive stress response is a normal and essential part of healthy development, characterized by brief increases in heart rate and mild elevations in hormone levels. Some situations that might trigger a positive stress response are the first day with a new caregiver or receiving an injected immunization.*

> *Tolerable stress response activates the body's alert systems to a greater degree as a result of more severe, longer-lasting difficulties, such as the loss of a loved one, a natural disaster, or a frightening injury. If the activation is time-limited and buffered by relationships with adults who help the child adapt, the brain and other organs recover from what might otherwise be damaging effects.*

> *Toxic stress response can occur when a child experiences strong, frequent, and/or prolonged adversity – such as physical or emotional abuse, chronic neglect, caregiver substance abuse or mental illness, exposure to violence, and/or the accumulated burdens of family economic hardship – without adequate adult support. This kind of prolonged activation of the stress response systems can disrupt the development of brain architecture and other organ systems, and increase the risk for stress-related disease and cognitive impairment, well into the adult years.*

When toxic stress response occurs continually, or is triggered by multiple sources, it can have a cumulative toll on an individual's physical and mental health – for a lifetime. The more adverse experiences in childhood, the greater the likelihood of developmental delays and later health problems, including heart disease, diabetes, substance abuse, and depression. Research also indicates that supportive, responsive relationships with caring adults as early in life as possible can prevent or reverse the damaging effects of toxic stress response."

That's on the dysfunctional family side of the equation. There's much research supporting the correlation between poverty and brain development. A couple of examples:

"... data indicate that income relates most strongly to brain structure among the most disadvantaged children.

Specifically, among children from lower income families, small differences in income were associated with relatively large differences in surface area, whereas, among children from higher income families, similar income increments were associated with smaller differences in surface area. These relationships were most prominent in regions supporting language, reading, executive functions, and spatial skills." [242]

and

"Infants from low-income families had lower volumes of gray matter, tissue critical for processing of information, and execution of actions. These differences were found for both the frontal and parietal lobes. No differences were detected in white matter, temporal lobe volumes, or occipital lobe volumes. In addition, differences in brain growth were found to vary with socioeconomic status (SES), with children from lower-income households having slower trajectories of growth during infancy and early childhood. Volumetric differences were associated with the emergence of disruptive behavioral problems. [243]

Not that it's our choice, but being born into a poor dysfunctional family does not set the brain up for a good life.

On a happier note, Dan Buettner's "Nine Lessons for Living Longer" [244] include two lessons that are family-oriented. Here are two summaries from him:

"Successful centenarians in the Blue Zones put their families first. They keep aging parents and grandparents nearby or in the home, which also lowers the disease and mortality rates of their children. They commit to a life partner (which can add up to three years of life expectancy), and they invest in their children with time and love, which makes the children more likely to be caretakers when the time comes."

"The world's longest-lived people choose, or were born into, social circles that support healthy behaviors. Okinawans create moai – groups of five friends that commit to each other for life. Research shows that smoking, obesity, happiness, and loneliness are contagious. By contrast, the social networks of long-lived people favorably shape their health behaviors."

Conclusion: Friends and family are desperately important from minute one.

j. The Brain and Meditation/Mindfulness

A mindfulness wave has swept across many fields of our lives over the past decade.

The Western world in particular has become engulfed with new discoveries about the wonders of meditation and mindfulness. In 2016, even *Time* magazine took the topic on board and published a magazine focused on mindfulness. Since then, they have published a number of sister books. You know that when something has come to the attention of *Time*, then it has become mainstream ☺

A cursory look at the literature will quickly result in a number of related words: contemplation, enquiry, awareness, consciousness, and so on. I am sure that there are many more. Several authors and practitioners have come to the fore, and their work has guided much of the thinking.

In addition, many conferences are held on the practices, and many consulting firms, large and small, offer advice on how to bring mindful practices into organizations.

It is worth remembering, however, that these two practices have been around for centuries, if not thousands, of years in many philosophies and religions. It appears that, in this field, science may be doing the catch-up. ☺

When I have spoken to people about mindfulness during my travels, everyone has their own interpretation of what it is; in many cases, there is an immediate link with yoga, and frequently, people associate it directly with meditation. So, in order for us to all get on the same page, let's take a deeper dive by, once again, looking at a couple of definitions using our trusty source, *Wikipedia*:

First, meditation. What is it, how long has it been around, and what is it used for?

> *"Meditation is a practice where an individual uses a technique, such as focusing their mind on a particular object, thought, or activity, to achieve a mentally clear and emotionally calm state."*

> *"Meditation has been practiced since antiquity in numerous religious traditions and beliefs. Since the 19th century, it has spread from its origins to other cultures where it is commonly practiced in private and business life."*

> *"Meditation may be used with the aim of reducing stress, anxiety, depression, and pain, and increasing peace, perception, self-concept, and well-being. Meditation is under research to define its possible health (psychological, neurological, and cardiovascular) and other effects."*

Then, mindfulness.

> *"Mindfulness is the psychological process of bringing one's attention to experiences occurring in the present moment, which one can develop through the practice of meditation and through other training."*

Once again, useful definitions, but not overly helpful.

Let's try a different approach. Jon Kabat-Zinn, one of the leading researchers, practitioners, and authors in the field, helps us by describing "Seven attitudinal factors (that) constitute the major pillars of mindfulness …": [245]

- ➤ *Non-judging*
- ➤ *Patience*
- ➤ *A beginner's mind*
- ➤ *Trust*
- ➤ *Non-striving*
- ➤ *Acceptance*
- ➤ *Letting-go*

In her 2016 "White Paper," [246] Rinske Gotink also assists us in our understanding by providing a summary of the skills that are trained in Jon Kabat-Zinn's Mindfulness-Based Stress Reduction course: (the layout is mine for clarity)

> *"… participants are trained in noticing what happens internally: from awareness of bodily sensations to changes in emotional state to eventually being able to observe one's own thought processes.*

> *Five main skills are taught:*

> - ➤ *observing (noticing or attending to thoughts, feelings, perceptions, or sensations)*
> - ➤ *describing or labelling observations with words (for instance 'an itch,' 'anger,' or 'memory')*
> - ➤ *non-reactivity to inner experiences ('I see the anger but I do not have to go with it')*
> - ➤ *non-judging of experiences ('It is okay that there is anger')*

> ➤ *acting with awareness"*

I think we are starting to get a sense of what mindfulness is about. But meditation? Maybe not so much; we'll return to it later. In the meantime, let's see if we can see what impact these practices have on the brain. I'll start with a paper by Gotink et al: [247]

"...to systematically review the evidence of the effect of secular mindfulness techniques on function and structure of the brain. Based on areas known from traditional meditation neuroimaging results, we aimed to explore a neuronal explanation of the stress-reducing effects of the 8-week Mindfulness Based Stress Reduction (MBSR) and Mindfulness Based Cognitive Therapy (MBCT) program."

Bottom line? They found that mindfulness programs do in fact change the function and structure of the brain. In more detail:

"The prefrontal cortex, the cingulate cortex, and hippocampus showed increased activity, connectivity, and volume in stressed, anxious, and healthy participants. Additionally, the amygdala showed decreased functional activity, improved functional connectivity with the prefrontal cortex, and earlier deactivation after exposure to emotional stimuli."

What does this mean? Important parts of the brain get better, the amygdala shows less activity, and a greater degree of interaction with the PFC. (Remember – these are the two parts that are in a constant struggle.)

The paper also indicates a positive impact that mindfulness programs have on cardiovascular issues, but those are outside the realm of this book no matter how interesting.

Mindfulness has been shown to have positive impacts in the areas of perception, body awareness, pain tolerance, emotion regulation, introspection, complex thinking, and sense of self.

How about programs that just focus on meditation? There are many studies that indicate that these programs also have a positive impact on the brain; here are a few examples:

Cotier et al [248] found that even only an eight-week meditation program was of value:

"Overall, this study provides further support for short-term meditation as a potentially beneficial method of mental training for the elderly that warrants further investigation."

Lazar et al [249] monitored brain activity during meditation:

"The results indicate that the practice of meditation activates neural structures involved in attention and control of the autonomic nervous system."

Kang et al [250] examined the differences between experienced meditators and "meditation-naive volunteers" and noted:

"A convergent line of neuroscientific evidence suggests that meditation alters the functional and structural plasticity of distributed neural processes underlying attention and emotion.

Moreover, in the region adjacent to the medial prefrontal cortex, both higher fractional anisotropy values and greater cortical thickness were observed. Our findings suggest that long-term meditators have structural differences in both gray and white matter."

Vestergaard-Poulsen et al [251] compared experienced mixed-sex meditators with a group of people with no meditation history and found:

"Extensive practice involving sustained attention can lead to changes in brain structure. Here, we report evidence of structural differences in the lower brainstem of participants engaged in the long-term practice of meditation."

and they add:

"This could account for some of the cardiorespiratory parasympathetic effects and traits, as well as the cognitive, emotional, and immunoreactive impact reported in several studies of different meditation practices."

I could go on. There are plenty more. As I warned the reader at the beginning of the book, however, we are still in the early stages of research in this field. There are still some researchers who are saying that it is too early to jump to conclusions, some saying that there might be correlation but no causation, and yet others saying that it looks like there is causation, but we don't yet know why and how.

If I were a gambling man, I think I would place my bet on the fact that there is likely to be some strong relationship. Meditation certainly looks like it has added value and is very unlikely to be found to be harmful or have negative side effects.

k. The Brain and Music

I thought this one would be easy. And it was, in a way. A Google Scholar search of "music and the brain" only produced 83,000 papers! On the other hand, there is so much research that it is difficult to know where to start and how to organize the results. I know that this will be one of the sections that will be revised and expanded in the next edition.

What can be said with relative certainty is that music, in all its forms, is ubiquitous. Habibi and Damasio [252] summarize the impact of this all-pervasiveness well:

"The ease with which music leads to feelings, the predictability with which it does so, the fact that human beings of many cultures actively seek and consume music, and the evidence that early humans engaged in music practices, lead us to hypothesize that music has long had a consistent relation to the neural devices of human life regulation."

The research tends to cover three areas, although I have not seen it broken out this way: playing an instrument (e.g., learning the violin), playing the instrument with others (e.g., singing in a choir or playing in a band), and listening to music.

Let's take some examples, in that order.

What happens to the brain when we learn to play a musical instrument? We can break this down into two areas. What happens to the brain directly and what other "halo" effects are there?

As regards the impact to the brain, there is much evidence that supports the fact that there are changes to two areas of the brain – not surprisingly, to "gestural motor activity and auditory perception" and "growing evidence that learning music has more general effects on brain plasticity." [253]

From the point of view of "halo" effects, yes there are some, but there is also some debate as to their magnitude and significance. In a meta-study (i.e., a study of studies) of music training for children, Gordon et al [254] reported:

> "Results supported the hypothesis that music training leads to gains in phonological awareness and reading fluency skills."

Another study [255] suggests that:

> "… adolescents with music training have better school grades, are more conscientious, open, and ambitious."

Hallam, in one of the more deeply researched articles, [256] strongly suggests that there are positive correlations between music training for children and a variety of positive side effects, especially if begun before the age of seven. These side effects cover positive contributions to:

- *Aural perception and language skills*
- *The development of literacy skills*
- *Aural and visual memory*
- *Spatial reasoning and mathematical performance*
- *Intellectual development*
- *Executive functioning and self-regulation*
- *Creativity*
- *Music and personality*
- *Educational motivation and reengagement of the disaffected*
- *Social cohesion and inclusion*
- *Prosocial behavior and team work*
- *Empathy and emotional intelligence*
- *Psychological well-being*
- *Personal development and self-beliefs*
- *Health*

Wow! A pretty impressive list. Great bang for the buck. In the interest, however, of full disclosure, I need to mention a word of caution. The article was:

> "Published in Great Britain in 2015 on behalf of the Music Education Council by the International Music Education Research Centre (iMerc), Department of Culture, Communication and Media, UCL Institute of Education, University College London"

While there is no reason to suspect anything other than perfect research, we just might want to take a step back before getting too excited.

What about older adults? I am afraid there are mixed results. One study [257] said that, although the older (60-85 age range) adults became significantly better at music, this did not translate to either physiological stress management or general self-efficacy skills.

Some studies [258] [259] that seem to be in support of beneficial side effects to studying music seem to hedge their bets even more so than normal scientific "shyness."

> *"We conclude that musical engagement may be a useful cognitive training to promote cognitive enhancement."*

and

> *"… the article concludes by arguing for further research to contribute to the growing body of evidence placing music learning at the center of healthy aging agendas."*

So, it seems that there probably are probably some positive side effects, but it is less clear that that is the case.

How about playing music with others?

Once again, I turn to Hallam [260] who provides a long list of research articles that support the positive aspects of social cohesion, inclusion, prosocial behavior, and team work, by citing two of her summaries:

> *"Group music making clearly has the potential to promote social cohesion and support inclusion. Making music with others creates bonds which are not easily created in other ways. This process may also lead participating individuals to become more tolerant and accepting of others and increase their beliefs in social ethics."*

> *"Making music with others in small and large groups requires team work, particularly when music is to be performed. Team work relies on participating individuals supporting each other and developing trust and respect. Group music making provides an ideal vehicle for developing prosocial, team working skills."*

Reading Hallam's work made me think about the possible uses of music-making in the topics of team development and overcoming bias. This possibility needs more thought.

Finally, listening to music. Why is it so rewarding? Why are so many feelings and passions generated? Why are there tears associated with the positive emotions that it generates?

I mentioned earlier that there have been several surprises in my research. One of these was when I discovered that there was an emotional scale specifically developed for measuring the impact of music – the Geneva Emotional Music Scale or GEMS. [261] Another surprise took place a few moments later. There was no *Wikipedia* entry for it!☺

The GEMS [262] currently contains 45 labels that were consistently chosen for describing musically evoked emotive states. These states can be grouped into nine different categories (below), which in turn condense into three "super factors" (sublimity, vitality, and unease). The nine categories are wonder, transcendence, tenderness, nostalgia, peacefulness, energy, joyful activation, tension and sadness.
Zentner, the author of the GEMS, states:

> *"…the variety of emotions uncovered in his work has little in common with those defined by basic emotion theory."*

His general comments are that there is no doubt that music elicits emotion, but that:

> ➤ *"Musical emotions are less common than we might think.*
> ➤ *Musical emotions are harder to trigger in a lab situation than is generally recognized by researchers because they emerge from the combination of a variety of factors (including the structure of the music, the performance of the music, the state of the listener, and the context of the listening situation).*
> ➤ *Musical emotions are typically more a blend of complex emotions as opposed to easily characterized basic emotions (such as 'happiness' or 'sadness')."*

So, we now have some descriptors to describe the music that moves us. In a recent article, Baltes and Miu correlated a positive mood after listening to Puccini's "Madame Butterfly," with an increase in sublimity and vitality and a decrease in unease. [263]

Koelsch, [264] as have many other researchers, steps one pace further into the brain to explain:

> *"Functional neuroimaging studies on music and emotion show that music can modulate activity in brain structures that are known to be crucially involved in emotion, such as the amygdala, nucleus accumbens, hypothalamus, hippocampus, insula, cingulate cortex, and orbitofrontal cortex."*

Salimpoor et al [265] attempt to give us a neurobiological explanation of why we are moved by using the understanding of the brain's desire and ability to do pattern recognition, anticipation, and reward:

> *"At a fundamental level, listening to music involves tracking a series of sound events over time. Because humans are experts in pattern recognition, temporal predictions are constantly generated, creating a sense of anticipation. We summarize how complex cognitive abilities and cortical processes integrate with fundamental subcortical reward and motivation systems in the brain to give rise to musical pleasure."*

This might explain Bach's work, the attraction of fugues, and the novelty of jazz when it cannot be so well anticipated.

I cannot leave the topic of music without mentioning the work being done by William Henshall, formerly of the 1990s-pop band, Londonbeat. Will, whom, in the interest of full disclosure, I have met on one occasion, was a rock musician who became fascinated with neuroscience. He became intrigued as to whether music can help us focus, and if so, who does it help, and what type of music best helps? He has formed a company [266] that has developed a number of algorithms for fine-tuning the music you listen to while working in order to increase your productivity.

l. Training Your Brain

Over the past decade or so, there has been a profusion of brain training exercises, or games, available over the Internet and a wide range of claims as to what they can do to your brain.

There has been almost as many papers written claiming the advantages of using these exercises and games and an equal number of papers debunking their use.

For every paper that offers a "scientific proof" that the exercises are useful, there's another paper that "proves" they are not.

This apparent dichotomy is summed up nicely in the opening summary of the paper by Simons et al, "Do 'Brain Training' Programs Work?": [267]

> "*In 2014, two groups of scientists published open letters on the efficacy of brain training interventions, or "brain games," for improving cognition. The first letter, a consensus statement from an international group of more than 70 scientists, claimed that brain games do not provide a scientifically-grounded way to improve cognitive functioning or to stave off cognitive decline. Several months later, an international group of 133 scientists and practitioners countered that the literature is replete with demonstrations of the benefits of brain training for a wide variety of cognitive and everyday activities. How could two teams of scientists examine the same literature and come to conflicting 'consensus' views about the effectiveness of brain training?*"

So, what are we to believe? And if we do believe, is it real, or is it simply the placebo effect?

My belief is that it comes down to this. The wildest statements at both ends of the spectrum of claims are probably untrue. On the other hand, brain training exercises are probably better for the brain than doing nothing. And it is unlikely to be doing your brain any harm.

Let's start out with the simplest claims. There's been some claims that doing crosswords, numbers games, and Sudoku is good for the brain. Maybe they are. Certainly, practicing crosswords, numbers games, and Sudoku will probably make you better at crosswords, numbers games, and Sudoku! Will this help your ability to solve quadratic equations? Probably not. But if you enjoy it, it makes you feel good, and you don't attach any major expectations for mental-health benefits, then go ahead. The fact that you are exercising your brain won't be doing it any harm.

One of the problems, however, is that we tend to like, and hence do, the things we are already good at or reasonably good at. That would be like having great biceps and constantly exercising those because it is easier, and less painful, to work on those muscles rather than on the other muscle groups that need work.

On the other hand, the brain feels rewarded when it is successful. Working on something that you're already good at makes the brain feel good. And that's not a bad thing. It may set you up for tackling something that you are less good at.

What about the research? Let's take a look at the summary of what Simons et al [268] had to say about the results of their meta-analysis of the research:

> "*... we find extensive evidence that brain training interventions improve performance on the trained tasks, less evidence that such interventions improve performance on closely related tasks, and little evidence that training enhances performance on distantly related tasks or that training improves everyday cognitive performance.*"

So, if you want to improve, for example, your mental flexibility, then doing brain training exercises focused on that attribute will probably help, but that is unlikely to help much in other related attributes, such as memory.

They also stated that they found that most of the studies about brain training exercises had "major shortcomings in design or analysis."

What about the training exercises themselves? What are the attributes of the brain that can be trained?

As far as I can see, it's all over the map. Memory, focus, attention, concentration, mental flexibility, resilience, positivity, problem-solving, decision-making, vocabulary, mental agility, verbal fluency, stress management, self-regulation, empathy, creativity – the list truly does go on. The list covers many of the things that I cover in this and the second book.

A Google search will give you many places to try out some of the brain training exercises. Just be aware of any outrageous claims.

m. The Brain and Technology

There's a lot of interest and opinion about the impact of social media on our societies, our personal and private lives, our health, and, of particular interest for this book, our brains.

As I researched this section, I was reminded of a journalistic article I recall from many years ago. Apocryphal or not, I don't know, but the story goes something like this: The journalist was writing an article on strategic thinking and long-term planning. He asked the chairman of Sony Corporation what he thought the impact of the French Revolution was. After some moments of thought, the chairman replied, "It's too early to tell."

And that's what I sense about the impact of technology on our lives, our health, and our brains. It's way too early to tell, despite all of the doom and gloom on the one hand and the self-congratulatory cheers on the other.

In some ways, we are living through the world's largest ever social experiment. Except that it didn't start off with a research question to be answered, there was never any review by an ethics committee, and there really are too many confounds to be able to isolate the impact of any one of them and, therefore, develop a reasonable study methodology. If I were a social scientist, I would be very excited but would also be wanting to pull my hair out. ☺

I quickly realized that, at best, in this edition I might be able to point out some of the research that has been done to date. On the downside, the rate at which technology is bombarding us is such that it is difficult to keep up, let alone find good longitudinal studies. And the developments are in such wide-ranging fields. Let's identify a few:

- ➢ *Mobile devices, e.g., smartphones, iPads, and laptops*
- ➢ *Alexa and other smart speaker devices*
- ➢ *Wearables, especially watches and fitness monitors*
- ➢ *Big data and its uses*
- ➢ *Social media, its pervasiveness, use, and misuse*
- ➢ *Cryptocurrencies*
- ➢ *Online retail and delivery*
- ➢ *Internet everywhere*
- ➢ *24/7/365 real-time news*
- ➢ *Video streaming*
- ➢ *Online gaming*
- ➢ *Online learning*

> ➤ *Drone usage*
> ➤ *Internet of Things*
> ➤ *Driverless vehicles*
> ➤ *Artificial Intelligence*
> ➤ *RPA (Robotic Process Automation)*
> ➤ *Digital natives*
> ➤ *Post-truth, misinformation, and fake news*
> ➤ *???*

The list, literally and figuratively, does go on. I predict that I will get many queries as to why I didn't include such-and-such topic in my list. And such queries would be reasonable, so start them, and keep them coming.

At the macro-level, it's complicated. It is also complicated at the micro-level. Let's jump into the deep end for a moment to illustrate just how complicated. It is illustrated by a very recent paper [269] investigating the relationship between Passive Social Media Use (PSMU) and depression. The authors of this paper report the following:

> *"More time spent on PSMU was associated with higher levels on interest loss, concentration problems, fatigue, and loneliness."*

> *"Fatigue and loneliness predicted PSMU over time, but PSMU predicted neither depression symptoms nor stress"*

Then they state:

> *"It is unclear, however, if PSMU causes depression symptoms or vice versa."*

Not too helpful but a good illustration of the complexities and difficulties of current research.

In his canary-in-the-mine book, [270] Carr warns us that the Internet is causing us to be less curious, less investigative, and shallower in our thinking and is concerned about where it all might lead to. I suspect that, had they been able to, skeptics might have published a book voicing concerns about the Gutenburg press. ☺ (As an aside did you know that his full name was Johannes Gensfleisch zur Laden zum Gutenberg … wouldn't you want a name like that?)

To do this whole subject justice, I would need several books, but to keep it manageable and readable, I'll take a look at just three aspects of technology – social media, smartphones, and Robotic Process Automation*and, in each aspect, see if we can find positive, neutral, negative, and mixed impacts.

First, the use of social media.

In higher education [271]:

> *"Facebook was indeed perceived as an innovative and effective tool in a student-centered learning environment that enriched students' educational experiences, increasing the relevance of the subject matter and encouraging students to collaborate effectively with their peers and faculty. From the perspective of the educator, the use of Facebook in a*

---

* By way of full disclosure, at the time of writing, my wife has a full-time role in one of the major companies in this field; consequently, I have a high interest in the progress of the field.

team-based pedagogy setting significantly enhanced the teaching and learning process as it allowed the educator to tap into the digital learning styles of the students and provided innovative ways of involving and motivating students in the learning process."

OK. I think we can clearly put that in the positive column.

In another study [272] of a proprietary application of a social networking site, Leonardi suggests a positive outcome – he refers to it as "communication visibility." It's the implicit metaknowledge that users gain over time about who knows what and who are they communicating with. The advantage of this is:

"...that enhanced metaknowledge can lead to more innovative products and services and less knowledge duplication if employees learn to work in new ways. By learning vicariously rather than through experience, workers can more effectively recombine existing ideas into new ideas and avoid duplicating work."

Again, a positive result, albeit with limited application.

As regards social connectedness, this ends up in the mixed column: [273]

"Mixed findings are reported regarding the role that social media plays in fostering social connectedness, which suggests that young people may experience both positive and negative psychological outcomes."

"On one hand, they elevate the ease in which individuals may form and create online groups and communities, but on the other, they can create a source of alienation and ostracism."

A 2016 study [274] laments the fact that adolescents are engaging in the use of social media and signing legal documents before the executive portions of their brains are fully formed. An entry on the negative side!

The "like" icon has become widely understood and has become very powerful. It has added to the general dynamic of "peer pressure" in adolescence as indicated by these three comments from this study: [275]

"Adolescents were more likely to like photos depicted with many likes and refrain from liking photos with few likes – indicating the influence of virtual peer endorsement, a finding that held for both neutral photos and photos of risky behavior (e.g., smoking and drinking)."

"Viewing photographs with many (vs. few) likes was associated with greater activity in neural regions implicated in reward processing, social cognition, and attention."

"Furthermore, when adolescents viewed risky (vs. non-risky) photographs, activation in the cognitive control network decreased."

This probably goes into the neutral or mixed columns.

Let's now turn to smartphones and their usage. It is clear that there are innumerable advantages to smartphones, far beyond even the hyperbole that Steve Jobs used when he first introduced the iPhone. Those advantages are not in doubt. What I intend here is to look into the more unexpected areas where these devices are having impacts on our brains.

Our first study [276] reports that smartphone usage may have an overall detrimental effect:

> *"One potential consequence of the accessibility of smartphone technology is that the general disinclination and/or inability to engage analytic thinking may now be applicable not only to reliance on intuitive and heuristic thinking but also to no thinking at all."*

And,

> *"Across three studies, we find that those who think more intuitively and less analytically when given reasoning problems were more likely to rely on their smartphones (i.e., extended mind) for information in their everyday lives."*

Depending on your viewpoint about technological progress and its interaction with society, that result would probably be viewed as negative by many people.

It has been some years since Linda Stone introduced the concept of "continual partial attention" with regard to phones. The idea is that all the while your phone is switched on, part of your brain is continually asking the nonconscious questions of "Do I have a voicemail, email, text message, etc.?". The hypothesis is that this background attention and thinking process consumes cognitive resources. The University of Texas has been doing some research on this and has discovered that the phones need to be turned off, and, better yet, placed out of sight in another room.

Ward et al [277] have discovered:

> *"Results from two experiments indicate that even when people are successful at maintaining sustained attention – as when avoiding the temptation to check their phones – the mere presence of these devices reduces available cognitive capacity. Moreover, these cognitive costs are highest for those highest in smartphone dependence."*

Another checkmark in the negative column.

Finally, Robotic Process Automation. This technology has been flying under the radar for some time now, yet it brings with it the possibility of huge impacts on a wide range of people. Admittedly, this will be more from a social than a brain aspect, but I thought it important to include.

First of all, this may be the first of the technologies that requires specific introduction and definition. The formal definition is:

> *"Robotic Process Automation (RPA) is an umbrella term for tools that operate on the user interface of other computer systems in the way a human would do."* [278]

Imagine a typical organization that, at the end of every week, runs through some standard processes to report on the success (or otherwise) of the week. The CEO may want to see, for example, the volume of sales from each of their stores, the number of customer complaints and how many were resolved, and the staff turnover and recruiting results. Somewhere in the organization, there is a white-collar worker who is tasked with pulling that report together and then sending it out to all members of the executive team, plus a few other designees.

Pulling the report together will probably involve accessing the sales database and sorting it into some predetermined sequence. This could be by state or by volume of sales. The number of complaints would probably be contained in another database or a different section of the sales database. In any case, it would involve another search and sort process. The staff turnover would likely be in the HR database and the recruitment numbers in yet another.

This whole process is a time consuming, error-prone, and tedious process. It is ideally suited for a software robot (or digital colleague) to execute. The generic term for identifying such processes and automating them is called Robotic Process Automation.

The current thrust of Robotic Process Automation implementations is to identify and remove tedious, error-prone work, thus relieving the current human operator to focus on more creative and cognitively challenging work. It is, however, likely to mean that those affected will be refocused and retrained.

n. The Brain and Growing Older

Whenever I am traveling and someone finds out what I do for a living, very frequently the next question is something like "What can I do to prevent Alzheimer's?" And "Will it help if I do brain-training games?"

I do my best to answer by saying that we don't really know, but there seems to be some things that might avert it, the things that I have listed in this section.

But the Alzheimer's question is really a subset of a larger question: "What is going on in my brain as I grow older?"

I would like to make a number of overall comments before fully jumping into this subject in earnest.

First, in a way, taking a look at the aging brain and what can be done to minimize the negative impacts of aging is a little like doing a summary of the whole book. It includes a little bit of everything.

Second, researching this subject is an enormous task. There's a huge amount of research out there, and it feels pitiful to try and summarize it in a few pages when the subject is really worth many books in and of itself! Of necessity, I will just be scratching the surface.

Third, researching the subject can be a little depressing. Learning about what goes on in the brain as we age – the "normal" decline in various brain processes and the various things that can go wrong – is not the most enjoyable way to spend a couple of days. With that being said, however, I would encourage all of my readers to spend a little more time investigating what is happening in the aging brain and to do what they can about it.

Fourth, much of the research suggests that there are many factors that contribute to the process of slowing down the effect of aging on the brain, for example, exercise, sleep, nutrition, social activity, and meditation – all subjects which are addressed in this section. This further emphasizes the need for an integrated approach to understanding all of these aspects.

Fifth, as in many other aspects of the brain, there are many, many dimensions to understanding the aging process, generally known as life-course factors. These factors, as well as others such as gender:

> *"...enhance or deplete neural resources, thereby influencing the developmental course of brain structure and function, as well as cognition, over time. Life-course factors also influence compensatory processes that are engaged to meet cognitive challenge and to ameliorate the adverse effects of structural and functional decline."* [279]

Sixth, theoretically the concept of "the aging brain" could cover our complete lifespans, starting with birth. The focus in the next few pages, however, is the brain in our later decades rather than our earlier ones. For a really good description of the development of the child's brain, I suggest John Medina's book, *Brain Rules for Baby.* [280]

Now. What does the research say?

Let's pick up again on Buettner's work, [281] in the *Blue Zones for Longevity*; I have covered his work at several different points in the book, but I think it worth-while to see them all in one place:

> ➤ *"Move naturally – use every trip as an opportunity to walk.*
> ➤ *Have a sense of purpose – something to live for beyond work.*
> ➤ *Find a way to 'shed stress.'*
> ➤ *Eat until you are 80% full.*
> ➤ *Orient your diet around plants, vegetables, and fruit.*
> ➤ *Drink alcohol in moderation.*
> ➤ *Belong to a faith-based community that suits you.*
> ➤ *Put family and loved ones first.*
> ➤ *Belong to a social group that suits you."*

If you have been following closely, you will notice that there is a significant overlap between these nine points for longevity and his nine points for happiness, cited earlier. Isn't it fortunate for Dan that there are nine aspects of longevity and nine aspects of happiness? I love it when coincidences happen like that. ☺

The research shows that there is a "normal" degenerative process as the brain ages. And it involves a number of attributes of the brain, attributes very similar to the list of brain attributes that I listed in the section on brain training. Attention, memory, focus, concentration, etc.

Reuter-Lorenz & Park [282] have proposed a theory of how to hang all of the attributes of this degenerative process together and put them into "a conceptual model."
Let's take a look:

The conceptual model has two main parts.

Part 1 is that there are four aspects of the brain that we need to look at:

> ➤ brain structure
> ➤ brain function
> ➤ cognitive function
> ➤ rate of cognitive change

Biological aging impacts both the structure and the functioning of the brain. This, in turn, leads to a level of cognitive functioning and a certain rate of cognitive change.

Part 2 is that there are four brain activities that impact those first four aspects:

> ➢ Life-course factors that impact the biological aging process in a positive way (enrichment)
> ➢ Life-course factors that impact the biological aging process in a negative way (depletion)
> ➢ The brain's natural compensatory activities that it engages in
> ➢ Interventions that we can do to enhance what is going on

2a. Enrichment Factors	2b. Depletion Factors
Intellectual engagement	Stress
Fitness/Exercise	Low Social Economic Status
Multilingualism	Depression
Social Activity	Neuroticism
Education	Head Trauma
Diet	Toxin Exposure
	Vascular Disease

2c. Natural Compensatory Activities	2d. Optional Interventions
Neurogenesis	Social/intellectual engagement
Bilateral recruitment	Life-style Changes
Strengthened connectivity	Cognitive training
Recruitment of new regions	New learning
Enhanced Fronto-parietal recruitment	Diet changes
	Meditation
	Exercise
	Sleep

Bottom line? Yes, there is a natural decline. But there are natural mechanisms in place that slow the decline, and there are some personal actions we can take to assist as well.

o. The Brain and Ethics and Morality

I was finalizing writing this book when I realized that I had omitted to include a section on ethics and the brain. I decided I would include a section with regard to what goes on in our brains when faced with a moral or ethical dilemma, what goes on in our brains when we see someone else faced with such a dilemma, and what goes on in our brains when we see unethical or immoral decisions being made.

Let's dig deeper.

First of all, why is it important?

Funk and Gazzinaga [283] lay it on the line:

> *"Human morality provides the foundation for many of the pillars of society, informing political legislation and guiding legal decisions while also governing everyday social interactions."*

Borg et al [284] provide us with some understanding of what is going on. They identify that immoral and unethical acts recruit some of the same neural networks as disgust, but those acts also use other unique networks:

"… the biological response of disgust is intimately tied to immorality."

This is similar to the process of unfairness.

As we dig deeper, we find that like many of the other topics associated with the brain, the linkage between the brain and ethics/morality is complicated, complex, and not very well understood. The puzzle is well described by the title of Young and Duncan's paper [285]:

"Where in the brain is morality? Everywhere and maybe nowhere."

and they continue:

"On the one hand, morality is made up of complex cognitive processes deployed across many domains and housed all over the brain. On the other hand, no neural substrate or system that uniquely supports moral cognition has been found."

And a couple of years later, the situation still has not improved: [286]

"Neural underpinnings of morality are not yet well understood."

and

"Morality is supported not by a single brain circuitry or structure but by several circuits overlapping with other complex processes."

Salvador and Folger [287] provide us some themes about the bottom-line of the research:

➤ *"Ethical decision-making appears to be distinct from other types of decision-making processes.*
➤ *Ethical decision-making entails more than just conscious reasoning.*
➤ *Emotion plays a critical role in ethical decision-making, at least under certain circumstances.*
➤ *Normative approaches to morality have distinct, underlying neural mechanisms."*

So why would a dislike of unethical and immoral behavior have been an evolutionary advantage or adaptation?

Moll et al [288] summarized some clues:

"… moral behavior is a product of evolutionary pressures that shaped the neurobehavioral processes related to the selective perception of social cues, the experience of moral emotions, and the adaption of behavioral responses to the social milieu."

In other, perhaps more understandable words, we evolved to prefer moral and ethical behavior because it was socially advantageous to do so in terms of survival.

And Gintis et al [289] suggest:

"From an evolutionary viewpoint, we argue that ethical behavior was fitness-enhancing in the years marking the emergence of Homo sapiens because human groups with many altruists fared better than groups of selfish individuals, and the fitness losses sustained by altruists were more than compensated by the superior performance of the groups in which they congregated."

One recent study [290] indicates that this preference for prosocial behavior starts early on in our lives, at least before 12-24 months of age.

"All children demonstrated a neural differentiation in both spectral EEG power density modulations and time-locked ERPs when perceiving prosocial or antisocial agents."

So. Where does that leave us? It appears that we have evolved such that we have a distinct aversion to unethical or immoral behavior, that this aversion recruits similar neural pathways to those that handle disgust, and that this starts early on in life.

Notes and References for "Understand the Brain: Care and Feeding":

[167] Beil, L. (2018, December 8). Parkinson"s Pathways: Researchers begin to explore the gut"s link to this brain disease. Science News, 22–26.

[168] "Vagotomy and subsequent risk of Parkinson's disease" by Elisabeth Svensson PhD, Erzsébet Horváth-Puhó PhD, Reimar W Thomsen PhD, Jens Christian Djurhuus DMSc, Lars Pedersen PhD, Per Borghammer DMSc and Henrik Toft Sørensen DMSc in Annals of Neurology. Published online June 2015

[169] Friedland, R. P., & Chapman, M. R. (2017). The role of microbial amyloid in neurodegeneration. PLOS Pathogens, 13(12), 1–12. http://doi.org/10.1371/journal.ppat.1006654

[170] Neuroendocrinology Letters Volume 29 No. 1 2008 The gut-brain barrier in major depression: Intestinal mucosal dysfunction with an increased translocation of LPS from gram negative enterobacteria (leaky gut) plays a role in the inflammatory pathophysiology of depression

[171] Porges, S. W. (2009). The polyvagal theory: New insights into adaptive reactions of the autonomic nervous system. Cleveland Clinic Journal of Medicine, 76(Suppl_2), 1–8. http://doi.org/10.3949/ccjm.76.s2.17

[172] Jerath, R., Edry, J. W., Barnes, V. A., & Jerath, V. (2006). Physiology of long pranayamic breathing: Neural respiratory elements may provide a mechanism that explains how slow deep breathing shifts the autonomic nervous system. Medical Hypotheses, 67(3), 566–571. http://doi.org/10.1016/j.mehy.2006.02.042

[173] Tang, Y.-Y., Ma, Y., Fan, Y., Feng, H., Wang, J., Feng, S., et al. (2009). Central and autonomic nervous system interaction is altered by short-term meditation. Pnas, 106(22), 1–6.

[174] Harrison, Y., & Horne, J. A. (2000). The Impact of Sleep Deprivation on Decision Making: A Review. Journal of Experimental Psychology: General, 6(3), 236–249.

[175] Finkel, M. (2018, August). Want to fall asleep? Read this story.." National Geographic, 48.

[176] Sprecher, K. E., Koscik, R. L., Carlsson, C. M., Zetterberg, H., Blennow, K., Okonkwo, O. C., et al. (2017). Poor sleep is associated with CSF biomarkers of amyloid pathology in cognitively normal adults. Neurology, 89(5), 445–453. http://doi.org/10.1212/WNL.0000000000004171

[177] Bell, L. (n.d.). The Clean Cycle. Science News.

[178] Simopoulos, A. P. (2011). Evolutionary Aspects of Diet: The Omega-6/Omega-3 Ratio and the Brain. Molecular Neurobiology, 44(2), 203–215. http://doi.org/10.1007/s12035-010-8162-0

[179] Noble, E. E., Hsu, T. M., & Kanoski, S. E. (2017). Gut to Brain Dysbiosis: Mechanisms Linking Western Diet Consumption, the Microbiome, and Cognitive Impairment. Frontiers in Behavioral Neuroscience, 11, 582–10. http://doi.org/10.3389/fnbeh.2017.00009

[180] Freeman, L. R., Haley-Zitlin, V., Rosenberger, D. S., & Granholm, A.-C. (2013). Damaging effects of a high-fat diet to the brain and cognition: A review of proposed mechanisms. Nutritional Neuroscience, 17(6), 241–251. http://doi.org/10.1179/1476830513Y.0000000092

[181] Pistell, P. J., Morrison, C. D., Gupta, S., Knight, A. G., Keller, J. N., Ingram, D. K., & Bruce-Keller, A. J. (2010). Cognitive impairment following high fat diet consumption is associated with brain inflammation. Journal of Neuroimmunology, 219(1-2), 25–32. http://doi.org/10.1016/j.jneuroim.2009.11.010

[182] Pelletier, A., Barul, C., Féart, C., Helmer, C., Bernard, C., Periot, O., et al. (2015). Mediterranean diet and preserved brain structural connectivity in older subjects. Alzheimer's & Dementia, 11(9), 1023–1031. http://doi.org/10.1016/j.jalz.2015.06.1888

[183] Sánchez-Villegas, A., Galbete, C., Martinez-González, M. Á., Martinez, J. A., Razquin, C., Salas-Salvadó, J., et al. (2013). The effect of the Mediterranean diet on plasma brain-derived neurotrophic factor (BDNF) levels: The PREDIMED-NAVARRA randomized trial. Nutritional Neuroscience, 14(5), 195–201. http://doi.org/10.1179/1476830511Y.0000000011

[184] Zamroziewicz, M. K., & Barbey, A. K. (2018). The Mediterranean Diet and Healthy Brain Aging: Innovations From Nutritional Cognitive Neuroscience. In Role of the Mediterranean Diet in the Brain and Neurodegenerative Diseases. London Academic Press.

[185] Molteni, R., Barnard, R. J., Ying, Z., Roberts, C. K., & Gomex-Pinilla, F. (2002). A High-Fat, Refined Sugar Diet Reduces Hippocampal Brain-Derived Neurotrophic Factor, Neuronal Plasticity, and Learning. Neuroscience, 112(4), 803–814.

[186] Colantuoni, C., Schwenker, J., McCarthy, J., Rada, P., Ladenheim, B., Cadet, J.-L., et al. (2001). Excessive sugar intake alters binding to dopamine and mu-opioid receptors in the brain. NeuroReport, 12(16), 3549–3552.

[187] Spangler, R., Wittkowski, K. M., Goddard, N. L., Avena, N. M., Hoebel, B. G., & Leibowitz, S. F. (2004). Opiate-like effects of sugar on gene expression in reward areas of the rat brain. Molecular Brain Research, 124(2), 134–142. http://doi.org/10.1016/j.molbrainres.2004.02.013

[188] Choi, J.-Y., Park, M.-N., Kim, C.-S., Lee, Y.-K., Choi, E. Y., Chun, W. Y., & Shin, D.-M. (2017). Long-term consumption of sugar- sweetened beverage during the growth period promotes social aggression in adult mice with proinflammatory responses in the brain. Scientific Reports, 1–11. http://doi.org/10.1038/srep45693

[189] Tryon, M. S., Stanhope, K. L., Epel, E. S., Mason, A. E., Brown, R., Medici, V., et al. (2015). Excessive Sugar Consumption May Be a Difficult Habit to Break: A View From the Brain and Body. The Journal of Clinical Endocrinology & Metabolism, 100(6), 2239–2247. http://doi.org/10.1210/jc.2014-4353

[190] Riley, E. P., Infante, M. A., & Warren, K. R. (2011). Fetal Alcohol Spectrum Disorders: An Overview. Neuropsychology Review, 21(2), 73–80. http://doi.org/10.1007/s11065-011-9166-x

[191] Squeglia, L. M., & Gray, K. M. (2016). Alcohol and Drug Use and the Developing Brain. Current Psychiatry Reports, 18(5), 2509–18. http://doi.org/10.1007/s11920-016-0689-y

[192] Lisa Weyandt, J. J. S. (2015). Alcohol and Its Effect on Adolescent Brain Development and Executive Functioning: Some Results from Neuroimaging. Journal of Alcoholism & Drug Dependence, 03(05), 1–6. http://doi.org/10.4172/2329-6488.1000220

[193] Squeglia, L. M., Schweinsburg, A. D., Pulido, C., & Tapert, S. F. (2011). Adolescent Binge Drinking Linked to Abnormal Spatial Working Memory Brain Activation: Differential Gender Effects. Alcoholism: Clinical and Experimental Research, 35(10), 1831–1841. http://doi.org/10.1111/j.1530-0277.2011.01527.x

[194] Zheng, H., Kong, L., Chen, L., Zhang, H., & Zheng, W. (2015). Acute Effects of Alcohol on the Human Brain: A Resting-State fMRI Study. BioMed Research International, 2015(2), 1–10. http://doi.org/10.1155/2015/947529

[195] Anya, T., Allan, C. L., Valkanova, V., Zsoldos, E., Filippini, N., Sexton, C., et al. (2017). Moderate alcohol consumption as risk factor for adverse brain outcomes and cognitive decline: longitudinal cohort study. Bmj, 357, 1–20. http://doi.org/10.1136/bmj.j2353

[196] https://tunein.com/podcasts/Ideas/TED-Radio-Hour-p418021/?topicId=126100814

[197] Michel, C., Velasco, C., Fraemohs, P., & Spence, C. (2015). Studying the impact of plating on ratings of the food served in a naturalistic dining context. Appetite, 90(C), 45–50. http://doi.org/10.1016/j.appet.2015.02.030

[198] Higgs, S., & Thomas, J. (2016). ScienceDirect Social influences on eating. Current Opinion in Behavioral Sciences, 9, 1–6. http://doi.org/10.1016/j.cobeha.2015.10.005

[199] Hillman, C. H., Erickson, K. I., & Kramer, A. F. (2008). Be smart, exercise your heart: exercise effects on brain and cognition. Nature Perspectives, 9, 1–8.

[200] Ferris, L. T., Willams, J. S., & Shen, C. L. (2007). The Effect of Acute Exercise on Serum Brain-Derived Neurotrophic Factor Levels and Cognitive Function. Medicine & Science in Sports & Exercise, 39(4), 728–734. http://doi.org/10.1249/mss.0b013e31802f04c7

[201] Erickson, K. I., Hillman, C. H., & Kramer, A. F. (2015). ScienceDirect Physical activity, brain, and cognition. Current Opinion in Behavioral Sciences, 4, 27–32. http://doi.org/10.1016/j.cobeha.2015.01.005

[202] Bartel, S. (2016). Exercise-induced Improvements in Cognitive Functioning and Brain Structure in Older Adults. University of Saskatchewan Undergraduate Research Journal, 2(2), 1–10.

[203] Kramer, A. F., & Erickson, K. I. (2007). Capitalizing on cortical plasticity: influence of physical activity on cognition and brain function. Trends in Cognitive Sciences, 11(8), 342–348. http://doi.org/10.1016/j.tics.2007.06.009

[204] Colcombe, S. J., Erickson, K. I., Scalf, P. E., Kim, J. S., Prakash, R., McAuley, E., et al. (2006). Aerobic Exercise Training Increases Brain Volume in Aging Humans. Journal of Gerontology MEDICAL SCIENCES, 61A(11), 1166–1170.

[205] Molteni, R., Wu, A., Vaynman, S., Ying, Z., Barnard, R. J., & Gomez-Pinilla, F. (2004). Exercise Reverses the Harmful Effects of Consumption of a High-Fat Diet on Synaptic and Behavioral Plasticity Associated to the Action of Brain-Derived Neurotrophic Factor. Neuroscience, (123), 429–440. http://doi.org/10.1016/S0306-4522(03)00742-5

[206] Cotman, C. W., Berchtold, N. C., & Christie, L.-A. (2007). Exercise builds brain health: key roles of growth factor cascades and inflammation. Trends in Neurosciences, 30(9), 464–472. http://doi.org/10.1016/j.tins.2007.06.011

[207] Dufour, C. A., Marquine, M. J., Fazeli, P. L., Henry, B. L., Ellis, R. J., Grant, I., et al. (2013). Physical exercise is associated with less neurocognitive impairment among HIV-infected adults. Journal of NeuroVirology, 19(5), 410–417. http://doi.org/10.1007/s13365-013-0184-8

[208] MacIntosh, B. J., Crane, D. E., Sage, M. D., Rajab, A. S., Donahue, M. J., McIlroy, W. E., & Middleton, L. E. (2014). Impact of a Single Bout of Aerobic Exercise on Regional Brain Perfusion and Activation Responses in Healthy Young Adults. Plos One, 9(1), e85163–7. http://doi.org/10.1371/journal.pone.0085163

[209] Marston, K. J., Newton, M. J., Brown, B. M., Rainey-Smith, S. R., Bird, S., Martins, R. N., & Peiffer, J. J. (2017). Intense resistance exercise increases peripheral brain-derived neurotrophic factor. Journal of Science and Medicine in Sport, 1–5. http://doi.org/10.1016/j.jsams.2017.03.015

[210] Buettner, D. (2012). The Blue Zones: 9 Lessons for Living Longer From the People Who've Lived the Longest. National Geographic.

[211] Amen, D. (2009). The Brain in Love: 12 Lessons to Enhance Your Love Life. Harmony.

[212] Sukel, K. (2013). This Is Your Brain on Sex : The Science Behind the Search for Love. SIMON & SCHUSTER.

[213] Fisher, H. E., Aron, A., & Brown, L. L. (2006). Romantic love: a mammalian brain system for mate choice. Philosophical Transactions of the Royal Society B: Biological Sciences, 361(1476), 2173–2186. http://doi.org/10.1098/rstb.2006.1938

[214] Tarlacı, S. (2012). The Brain in Love: Has Neuroscience Stolen the Secret of Love? NeuroQuantology, 10(4), 1–13. http://doi.org/10.14704/nq.2012.10.4.581

[215] Xu, X., Aron, A., Brown, L., Cao, G., Feng, T., & Weng, X. (2010). Reward and motivation systems: A brain mapping study of early-stage intense romantic love in Chinese participants. Human Brain Mapping, 32(2), 249–257. http://doi.org/10.1002/hbm.21017

[216] Tarlacı, S. (2012). The Brain in Love: Has Neuroscience Stolen the Secret of Love? NeuroQuantology, 10(4), 1–13. http://doi.org/10.14704/nq.2012.10.4.581

[217] Seshadri, K. G. (n.d.). The neuroendocrinology of love. Indian Journal of Endocrinolgy Metabolism, 20(4), 558–563.

[218] Levin, R. J. (2016). Female Orgasm. In N. Naples, R. C. Hoogland, M. Wickramasinghe, & W. C. A. Wong (Eds.), Encyclopedia of Gender and Sexuality Studies (1st ed.).

[219] Wheatley, J. R., & Puts, D. A. (2014). Evolutionary Science of Female Orgasm. In The Evolution of Sexuality (pp. 123–148). Cham: Springer International Publishing. http://doi.org/10.1007/978-3-319-09384-0_7

[220] Anand, V., Jones, J., & Gill, P. S. (2013). The Relationship Between Spirituality, Health and Life Satisfaction of Undergraduate Students in the UK: An Online Questionnaire Study. Journal of Religion and Health, 54(1), 160–172. http://doi.org/10.1007/s10943-013-9792-0

[221] Levin, J. (2016). "For They Knew Not What It Was": Rethinking the Tacit Narrative History of Religion and Health Research. Journal of Religion and Health, 1–19. http://doi.org/10.1007/s10943-016-0325-5 n

[222] Buettner, D. (2012). The Blue Zones: 9 Lessons for Living Longer From the People Who've Lived the Longest. National Geographic.

[223] Buettner, D. (2017). The Blue Zones of Happiness: Lessons From the World's Happiest People. National Geographic.

[224] Lassiter, J. M., Saleh, L., Grov, C., Starks, T., Ventuneac, A., & Parsons, J. T. (2017). Spirituality and Multiple Dimensions of Religion Are Associated With Mental Health in Gay and Bisexual Men: Results From the One Thousand Strong Cohort. Psychology of Religion and Spirituality, 1–9. http://doi.org/10.1037/rel0000146

[225] Lassiter, J. M., Saleh, L., Grov, C., Starks, T., Ventuneac, A., & Parsons, J. T. (2017). Spirituality and Multiple Dimensions of Religion Are Associated With Mental Health in Gay and Bisexual Men: Results From the One Thousand Strong Cohort. Psychology of Religion and Spirituality, 1–9. http://doi.org/10.1037/rel0000146

[226] Roth, D. L., Usher, T., Clark, E. M., & Holt, C. L. (2016). Religious Involvement and Health Over Time: Predictive Effects in a National Sample of African Americans. Journal for the Scientific Study of Religion, 55(2), 417–424. http://doi.org/10.1111/jssr.12269

[227] Anand, V., Jones, J., & Gill, P. S. (2013). The Relationship Between Spirituality, Health and Life Satisfaction of Undergraduate Students in the UK: An Online Questionnaire Study. Journal of Religion and Health, 54(1), 160–172. http://doi.org/10.1007/s10943-013-9792-0

[228] Newberg, A. B. (2014). The neuroscientific study of spiritual practices. Frontiers in Psychiatry, 5, 1–6. http://doi.org/10.3389/fpsyg.2014.00215/abstract

[229] Miller, L., Bansal, R., Wickramaratne, P., Hao, X., Tenke, C. E., Weissman, M. M., & Peterson, B. S. (2014). Neuroanatomical Correlates of Religiosity and Spirituality. JAMA Psychiatry, 71(2), 128–8. http://doi.org/10.1001/jamapsychiatry.2013.3067

[230] Urgesi, C., Aglioti, S. M., Skrap, M., & Fabbro, F. (2010). The Spiritual Brain: Selective Cortical Lesions Modulate Human Self-Transcendence. Neuron, 65(3), 309–319. http://doi.org/10.1016/j.neuron.2010.01.026

[231] Holbrook, C., Hahn-Holbrook, J., & Holt-Lunstad, J. (2015). Self-reported spirituality correlates with endogenous oxytocin. Psychology of Religion and Spirituality, 7(1), 46–50. http://doi.org/10.1037/a0038255

[232] van Elk, M., & Aleman, A. (2017). Brain mechanisms in religion and spirituality: An integrative predictive processing framework. Neuroscience & Biobehavioral Reviews, 73, 359–378. http://doi.org/10.1016/j.neubiorev.2016.12.031

[233] Newberg, A. B. (2015). The Neurotheology Link: An Intersection Between Spirituality and Health. Alternative and Complementary Therapies, 21(1), 13–17. http://doi.org/10.1089/act.2015.21102

[234] Sayadmansour, A. (2014). Neurotheology: The relationship between brain and religion. Iranian Journal of Neurology, 13(1), 52–55.

[235] Buettner, D. (2017). The Blue Zones of Happiness: Lessons From the World's Happiest People. National Geographic.

[236] Frederickson, B. L. (n.d.). Positivity: Top-Notch Research Reveals the Upward Spiral That Will Change Your Life. Harmony.

[237] Dweck, C. S. (2007). Mindset: The New Psychology of Success. Ballantine Books.

[238] Chen, L., Bae, S. R., Battista, C., Qin, S., Chen, T., Evans, T. M., & Menon, V. (2017). Positive Attitude Toward Math Supports Early Academic Success: Behavioral Evidence and Neurocognitive Mechanisms. Psychological Science, 29(3), 390–402. http://doi.org/10.1177/0956797617735528

[239] Grant, A. M., & Schwartz, B. (2011). Too Much of a Good Thing. Perspectives on Psychological Science, 6(1), 61–76. http://doi.org/10.1177/1745691610393523

[240] Sin, N. L., Graham-Engeland, J. E., & Almeida, D. M. (2015). Daily positive events and inflammation: Findings from the National Study of Daily Experiences. Brain, Behavior, and Immunity, 43, 130–138. http://doi.org/10.1016/j.bbi.2014.07.015

[241] https://developingchild.harvard.edu/science/key-concepts/toxic-stress/

[242] Noble, K. G., Houston, S. M., Brito, N. H., Bartsch, H., Kan, E., Kuperman, J. M., et al. (2015). Family income, parental education and brain structure in children and adolescents. Nature Neuroscience, 18(5), 773–778. http://doi.org/10.1038/nn.3983

[243] Hanson, J. L., Hair, N., Shen, D. G., Shi, F., Gilmore, J. H., Wolfe, B. L., & Pollak, S. D. (2013). Family Poverty Affects the Rate of Human Infant Brain Growth. Plos One, 8(12), e80954–9. http://doi.org/10.1371/journal.pone.0080954

244 Buettner, D. (2012). The Blue Zones: 9 Lessons for Living Longer From the People Who've Lived the Longest. National Geographic.

245 Kabat-Zinn, J. (2013). Full Catastrophe Living (Revised Edition): Using the Wisdom of Your Body and Mind to Face Stress, Pain, and Illness. Bantam. (p 21)

246 Gotink, R. A. (2016, October 27). Mindfulness: Why the Brain Matters to the Heart. (H. A. P. Pols, Ed.). Erasmus Universiteit Rotterdam.

247 Gotink, R. A., Meijboom, R., Vernooij, M. W., Smits, M., & Hunink, M. G. M. (2016). 8-week Mindfulness Based Stress Reduction induces brain changes similar to traditional long-term meditation practice – A systematic review. Brain and Cognition, 108, 32–41. http://doi.org/10.1016/j.bandc.2016.07.001

248 Cotier, F. A., Zhang, R., & Lee, T. M. C. (2017). A longitudinal study of the effect of short-term meditation training on functional network organization of the aging brain. Scientific Reports, 1–11. http://doi.org/10.1038/s41598-017-00678-8

249 Lazar, S. W., Bush, G., Gollub, R. L., Fricchione, G. L., Khalsa, G., & Benson, H. (2000). Functional brain mapping of the relaxation response and meditation. Neuroreport Autonomic Nervous System, 11(7), 1581–1585.

250 Kang, D.-H., Jo, H. J., Jung, W. H., Kim, S. H., Jung, Y.-H., Choi, C.-H., et al. (2013). The effect of meditation on brain structure: cortical thickness mapping and diffusion tensor imaging. Social Cognitive and Affective Neuroscience, 8(1), 27–33. http://doi.org/10.1093/scan/nss056

251 Vestergaard-Poulsen, P., van Beek, M., Skewes, J., Bjarkam, C. R., Stubberup, M., Bertelsen, J., & Roepstorff, A. (2009). Long-term meditation is associated with increased gray matter density in the brain stem. NeuroReport, 20(2), 170–174. http://doi.org/10.1097/WNR.0b013e328320012a

252 Habibi, A., & Damasio, A. (2014). Music, feelings, and the human brain. Psychomusicology: Music, Mind, and Brain, 24(1), 92–102. http://doi.org/10.1037/pmu0000033

253 Habib, M., & Besson, M. (2009). What do Music Training and Musical Experience Teach Us About Brain Plasticity? Music Perception: an Interdisciplinary Journal, 26(3), 279–285. http://doi.org/10.1525/mp.2009.26.3.279

254 Gordon, R. L., Fehd, H. M., & McCandliss, B. D. (2015). Does Music Training Enhance Literacy Skills? A Meta-Analysis. Frontiers in Psychology, 6(543), 3958–16. http://doi.org/10.3389/fpsyg.2015.01777

255 Hille, A., & Schupp, J. (2015). How learning a musical instrument affects the development of skills. Economics of Education Review, 44, 56–82. http://doi.org/10.1016/j.econedurev.2014.10.007

256 Hallam, S. (2015). The power of music: a research synthesis of the impact of actively making music on the intellectual, social and personal development of children and young people (pp. 1–174). University College, London.

257 Bugos, J. A., Kochar, S., & Maxfield, N. (2015). Intense piano training on self-efficacy and physiological stress in aging. Psychology of Music, 44(4), 611–624. http://doi.org/10.1177/0305735615577250

258 Benz, S., Sellaro, R., Hommel, B., & Colzato, L. S. (2016). Music Makes the World Go Round: The Impact of Musical Training on Non-musical Cognitive Functions—A Review. Frontiers in Psychology, 6(926), 162–5. http://doi.org/10.3389/fpsyg.2015.02023

259 Perkins, R., & Williamon, A. (2013). Learning to make music in older adulthood: A mixed-methods exploration of impacts on wellbeing. Psychology of Music, 42(4), 550–567. http://doi.org/10.1177/0305735613483668

260 Hallam, S. (2015). The power of music: a research synthesis of the impact of actively making music on the intellectual, social and personal development of children and young people (pp. 1–174). University College, London.

261 Zentner, M., Grandjean, D., & Scherer, K. (2008). Emotions evoked by the sound of music: Characterization, classification, and measurement. Emotion, 8, 494-521

262 Description taken from http://musicpsychology.co.uk/musical-emotions-unique-and-complex/

263 Balteş, F. R., & Miu, A. C. (2014). Emotions during live music performance: Links with individual differences in empathy, visual imagery, and mood. Psychomusicology: Music, Mind, and Brain, 24(1), 58–65. http://doi.org/10.1037/pmu0000030

[264] Koelsch, S. (2014). Brain correlates of music-evoked emotions. Nature Reviews Neuroscience, 15(3), 170–180. http://doi.org/10.1038/nrn3666

[265] Salimpoor, V. N., Zald, D. H., Zatorre, R. J., Dagher, A., & McIntosh, A. R. (2015). Predictions and the brain: how musical sounds become rewarding. Trends in Cognitive Sciences, 19(2), 86–91. http://doi.org/10.1016/j.tics.2014.12.001

[266] https://www.focusatwill.com/

[267] Simons, D. J., Boot, W. R., Charness, N., Gathercole, S. E., Chabris, C. F., Hambrick, D. Z., & Stine-Morrow, E. A. L. (2016). Do "Brain-Training" Programs Work? Psychological Science in the Public Interest, 17(3), 103–186. http://doi.org/10.1177/1529100616661983

[268] Simons, D. J., Boot, W. R., Charness, N., Gathercole, S. E., Chabris, C. F., Hambrick, D. Z., & Stine-Morrow, E. A. L. (2016). Do "Brain-Training" Programs Work? Psychological Science in the Public Interest, 17(3), 103–186. http://doi.org/10.1177/1529100616661983

[269] AAlbers, G., McNally, R. J., Heeren, A., de Wit, S., & Fried, E. I. (2018). Social media and depression symptoms: A network perspective. Journal of Experimental Psychology: General, 1–9. http://doi.org/10.1037/xge0000528

[270] Carr, N. (2011). The Shallows: What the Internet Is Doing to Our Brains. W. W. Norton & Company.

[271] Rasiah, R. R. V. (2014). Transformative Higher Education Teaching and Learning: Using Social Media in a Team-based Learning Environment. Procedia - Social and Behavioral Sciences, 123, 369–379. http://doi.org/10.1016/j.sbspro.2014.01.1435

[272] Leonardi, P. M. (2014). Social Media, Knowledge Sharing, and Innovation: Toward a Theory of Communication Visibility. Information Systems Research, 25(4), 796–816. http://doi.org/10.1287/isre.2014.0536

[273] Allen, K. A., Ryan, T., Gray, D. L., McInerney, D. M., & Waters, L. (2014). Social Media Use and Social Connectedness in Adolescents: The Positives and the Potential Pitfalls. The Australian Educational and Developmental Psychologist, 31(01), 18–31. http://doi.org/10.1017/edp.2014.2

[274] Costello, C. R., McNeil, D. E., & Binder, R. L. (2016). Adolescents and Social Media: Privacy, Brain Development, and the Law. J Am Acad Psychiatry Law, 44(3), 313–321.

[275] Sherman, L. E., Payton, A. A., Hernandez, L. M., Greenfield, P. M., & Dapretto, M. (2016). The Power of the Like in Adolescence. Psychological Science, 27(7), 1027–1035. http://doi.org/10.1177/0956797616645673

[276] Barr, N., Pennycook, G., Stolz, J. A., & Fugelsang, J. A. (2015). The brain in your pocket: Evidence that Smartphones are used to supplant thinking. Computers in Human Behavior, 48(C), 473–480. http://doi.org/10.1016/j.chb.2015.02.029

[277] Ward, A. F., Duke, K., Gneezy, A., & Bos, M. W. (2017). Brain Drain: The Mere Presence of One's Own Smartphone Reduces Available Cognitive Capacity. Journal of the Association for Consumer Research, 2(2), 140–154. http://doi.org/10.1086/691462

[278] van der Aalst, W. M. P., Bichler, M., & Heinzl, A. (2018). Robotic Process Automation. Business & Information Systems Engineering, 60(4), 269–272. http://doi.org/10.1007/s12599-018-0542-4

[279] Reuter-Lorenz, P. A., & Park, D. C. (2014). How Does it STAC Up? Revisiting the Scaffolding Theory of Aging and Cognition. Neuropsychology Review, 24(3), 355–370. http://doi.org/10.1007/s11065-014-9270-9

[280] Medina, J. (2014). Brain Rules for Baby: How to Raise a Smart and Happy Child from Zero to Five (2nd ed.). Pear Press.

[281] Buettner, D. (2012). The Blue Zones: 9 Lessons for Living Longer From the People Who've Lived the Longest. National Geographic.

[282] Reuter-Lorenz, P. A., & Park, D. C. (2014). How Does it STAC Up? Revisiting the Scaffolding Theory of Aging and Cognition. Neuropsychology Review, 24(3), 355–370. http://doi.org/10.1007/s11065-014-9270-9

[283] Funk, C. M., & Gazzaniga, M. S. (2009). The functional brain architecture of human morality. Current Opinion in Neurobiology, 19(6), 678–681. http://doi.org/10.1016/j.conb.2009.09.011

[284] Borg, J. S., Lieberman, D., & Kiehl, K. A. (2008). Infection, Incest, and Iniquity: Investigating the Neural Correlates of Disgust and Morality. Journal of Cognitive Neuroscience, 20(9), 1529–1546.

[285] Young, L., & Dungan, J. (2012). Where in the brain is morality? Everywhere and maybe nowhere. Social Neuroscience, 7(1), 1–10. http://doi.org/10.1080/17470919.2011.569146

[286] Pascual, L., Rodrigues, P., & Gallardo-Pujol, D. (2013). How does morality work in the brain? A functional and structural perspective of moral behavior. Frontiers in Integrative Neuroscience, 7, 1–8. http://doi.org/10.3389/fnint.2013.00065/abstract

[287] Salvador, R., & Folger, R. G. (2009). Business Ethics and the Brain. Business Ethics Quarterly, 19(1), 1–30.

[288] Moll, J., de Oliveira-Souza, R., & Eslinger, P. J. (2003). Morals and the human brain: a working model. NeuroReport, 14(3), 299–305.

[289] Gintis, H., Henrich, J., Bowles, S., Boyd, R., & Fehr, E. (2008). Strong Reciprocity and the Roots of Human Morality. Social Justice Research, 21(2), 241–253. http://doi.org/10.1007/s11211-008-0067-y

[290] Cowell, J. M., & Decety, J. (2015). Precursors to morality in development as a complex interplay between neural, socioenvironmental, and behavioral facets. Proceedings of the National Academy of Sciences, 112(41), 12657–12662. http://doi.org/10.1073/pnas.1508832112

Section C.
Understanding Your Self

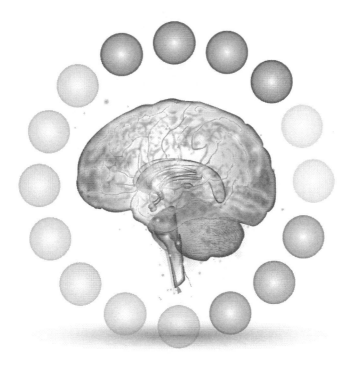

This is what is in Section C.

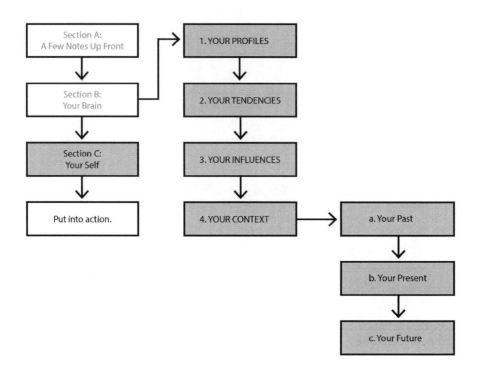

You – Some General Comments

As I have discussed a couple of times during the earlier part of the book, all of the information about the structure of the brain, the huge numbers involved, the brain fundamentals, and the 5 P's are all *general* descriptions about what could be going on in your brain at any given time. It really is quite complex as you have seen. And, I am about to make it more complex. On top of all this comes…guess what? You! The self that is you. The specific things that have happened to you, are happening to you, and could happen to you make for a unique layering on top of all the general brain stuff.

That is what this section is all about. Your unique self. Now, before we get all excited and believe that we finally have the answer to understanding ourselves, there are a couple of "heads-up" warnings I need to give. You, your unique self, is full of complexity, and identifying and describing that complexity will not be a simple task. Psychologists, therapists, philosophers, and many others have been addressing this for centuries, and I am not claiming that I have solved the problem. I am also not claiming that the approach I am outlining below is a scientifically proven model.

In over 35 years of coaching and counseling people and helping them do some self-examination, I have developed a series of topics and models that seem to assist them in identifying some factors that seem to have an impact for them as they move forward. It is different for everyone; some people resonate with some of the thoughts and models, while, for others, the very same thoughts and models leave them cold. There is no overall "blueprint" which, when examined, will lead you to the answers. It's all in what works for you as an individual.

The purpose of this section is to help you take a look at and think about those areas that might be impacting YOU in your day-to-day reactions and interactions at home and work. Where useful, I have referred back to what we have already covered about the brain and its functioning.

Dr. Evian Gordon once stated, "The difference between an expert and a novice is a model." In this section, I am going to give you a number of models so that you become an expert on yourself. I should also add that this field of assessments is littered with many two by two matrices and many of the models that I give will be in this two x two format.

BUT first, a word of CAUTION: this section is not therapy nor is it a replacement for therapy. It is simply intended to point out in, hopefully, a logical manner, some areas that have proven valuable for other people to look at. For some people, it helps to have a coach along the journey of discovery.

The next page outlines the list of topics that I suggest you use as a way of looking at your SELF. You might look at them as layers of your "personal onion." Although I will, of necessity, outline them and discuss them separately, they all interact.

As you go through each of the sections, keep looking at themes or patterns that seem to repeat themselves.

I have broken the complex issue of "YOU" into the topics on the next page.

1. Your Profiles
   a. Your Personal Threat Profile
   b. Your Personal Threat Context
   c. Your Brain Profile
   d. Your Chronotype
   e. Your Conversational Focus
      i. The Eight Topic Areas of Teams
      ii. Advocacy/Inquiry Matrix
      iii. TAPS Model
   f. Other Personality/Behavioral Profiles
      i. Your Five Factor Inventory
      ii. Your Zimbardo Time Perspective Inventory
      iii. Social Style
      iv. Belbin Team Inventory
   g. Your Leadership Style
      i. LWS
      ii. Zenger-Folkman
      iii. Leadership Circle
2. Your Tendencies
   a. Biases and Habits
   b. Patterns of Behavior
   c. Triggers
   d. World View and Personal Paradigms
3. Your Influencers
   a. Cialdini Six
   b. Others More Specific to You
4. Your Context
   a. Your Past
      i. Genetics
      ii. Your Personal Experiences
   b. Your Future
      i. Purpose, Vision, Passions, and Dreams
      ii. Values
      iii. Environment
   c. Your Present
      i. Strengths and Weaknesses
      ii. The Players on Your Team
      iii. Your Current Outlook

Section C Part 1: Your Profiles

Putting Profiles in Context

Profiles are simply a way of taking a review of yourself using a number of factors or dimensions. This section will specifically focus on what I called earlier, the layers of your "personal onion."

When looking at profiles, most frequently there are two ways of assessing your profile: the "Quick and Dirty Method" and the "Detailed Assessment Method."

With the Quick and Dirty Method, once you understand the dimensions of the profile, then you take an educated guess as to where you stand. The main advantage of this approach is that you can get a very quick assessment of a) understanding yourself and b) understanding how you might behave and c) understanding how you might come across to others and d) taking a guess about understanding what drives other people. This can all be done in a short span of time, which, in our current environment, has to be considered as an additional advantage. The disadvantage, clearly, is that it is just a first pass, and you can easily get it wrong or not understand some of the subtleties and nuances. Finally, in contrast to the Detailed Assessment Method, it is the cheapest in terms of direct time and cost.

With the Detailed Assessment Method, typically you will answer a number of questions using a questionnaire called an assessment. With some profile assessments, there are as few as ten questions, but with others there may be as many as two hundred and fifty. Then, using your answers to the questions, the assessment results describe some aspects of your personality or traits.

In each of the profiles that I describe, I have suggested ways in which you can take either approach – the Quick and Dirty Method and/or the Detailed Assessment Method. In either case, the profiles range from the very simple do-it-yourself through to the highly complex that require a coach for interpretation. So, for each profile, I have recommended whether the approach is one that is do-it-yourself or whether it is better to have a coach.

There are literally thousands of personality, character, or behavioral assessments available in the marketplace.* You may already have taken one or more assessments, in which case use the information from the ones that you have.

As you look at any of the assessments, keep the following things in mind as you read your results and treat the data that they contain with "a large pinch of salt":

> ➤ All, even the very best of them, are attempting to take all of the complexities of our characters and behaviors and boil them down to a certain number of dimensions or "labels." While that might be useful for a quick and dirty look at what is going on, it only gives a first glimpse. They are using averages across a wide range of character types; while the average might be useful in general, it may not be specific enough to apply to you.

---

* In about 2012, I was asked to investigate the market for individual assessments and identified over 2500 at that time!

203

➢ Most of the assessments are based on your own feedback (or self-report, as it is known). At best, we are not very good at self-assessment. At worst, we make things up or report what we wished we were like. If you want to get a little more accuracy, then choose an assessment which includes feedback from other people. But remember, they too are not very good at assessing characters and observing behaviors unless they have been trained to do so. They may be slightly better than you at picking up your peculiarities but not much better.

➢ If you do choose one that has the opportunity to get feedback from other people, please avoid the temptation to go straight to the part where they give "free" form comments. It will cloud your thinking about what else is contained in the report overall. Typically, people thumb straight to the part where the unstructured comments are given, read them through, then try and work out who said what about you. ☺ This is not very helpful and can prime your brain with these opinions and crowd out other useful information that the report might contain.

➢ There are a lot of assessments available that are little better than astrological readings. They might be fun, but do they actually tell you much about yourself other than the fact that all of a sudden, we say, "Oh yes…that's just like me"?

➢ Use the data in the assessment as a starting point for investigating further. You can do this either on your own, with close members of your family, or with people who you work with. If it is important at this time of your life to get some better insight into yourself, consider using a coach.

I have selected seven profiles for you to take a first cut at understanding yourself. There are, quite literally, thousands out there. I have simply selected those that I have found to be most useful. Having made this selection, I must, at this point, offer a minor justification about my selection. This justification is specifically addressed to the hundreds of thousands of vendors, consultants, and researchers who are practitioners in this area. If you are not one of those people, you can skip the next paragraph. ☺

The choice of profile assessments is a personal choice of what has worked for my clients in the past. I understand that there are many, many more out there, and I am sure that they will have worked for you and your clients. Keep using them. Some of you will read this section and be aghast. What do you mean you haven't included the Myers-Briggs assessment? Why, it's the widest used assessment in the world? For me, I have found it not to be that useful to my clients, and there is much debate on its accuracy and retest validity.* I choose not to use it.

---

* Rita Carter cites a review of eleven studies of test-retest inconsistencies with MBTI; depending on the study, as low as 21% of people had the same type on the test when retested. The maximum showing the same type was 61%. This is appallingly low for this type of assessment.

Profile #1: Your Personal Threat Profile

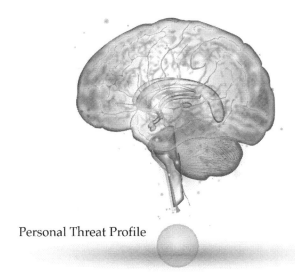

Personal Threat Profile

The various facets of your Personal Threat Profile were explained in Section B Part 2c, "the Five Driving Forces." These are the specific facets that are likely to trigger you and cause you stress. If you want to "dig deeper," then review each of the facets and give yourself a ranking on a scale of 1 to 10 for each facet. Then identify those to which you have responded with the highest scores and those to which you have responded with the lowest scores. These will tend to be the main drivers of your Personal Threat Profile.

If you were to sort your answers by their individual ranking, you might find something as follows for the facets that are most important to you.

The degree to which you need to associate with people you trust?	10
Your need for people to be authentic with you?	10
The degree to which you need recognition from others that are important to you?	10
The degree to which you need tradition in your life?	9.5
The degree to which you need harmony and stability in work situations?	9.5

This example is a real life, but anonymous, example of a senior female executive. As you will see from her top two rankings, it was important to her to be around people she trusted and who were authentic with her. The next three indicate that she wanted to receive recognition about her achievements and actions from people that were important to her. And she wanted tradition and harmony in her life.

Examining this list, she realized that she didn't trust her boss, partly because she didn't feel like he was authentic with her. In addition, what made it worse was that when she did achieve something significant, like producing 30% more revenue than budget, he didn't even mention it! These things triggered her every time she thought of him or thought of work.

Furthermore, she realized that most of the people in the senior team in her department seemed to be like him. And that the work environment in that department was unlikely ever to give her the sense of tradition, harmony, and stability that she required.

She applied and received a transfer and now reports a significantly less stressful and much more meaningful work life.

At the other end of the scale, these were her lowest rankings:

The degree to which you like positive surprises in work situations?	3
Your ability to go with the flow in work situations?	3
Your ability to go with the flow in social or private situations?	3

As you can see, these rankings support those at the top of the scale. She did not like surprises at work, even positive ones, and when things do change at work or at home, she felt ill-equipped just to go with the flow.

In my initial conversation with her, I pointed out the fact that even her lowest scores were still 3. Her reply was that she worried about everything!

Finding a new role changed many aspects of her life. She found that in an environment where there was more tradition and less change, she could relax – and even became more adept at handling those changes that did, inevitably, come along.

Profile #2: Your Personal Threat Context

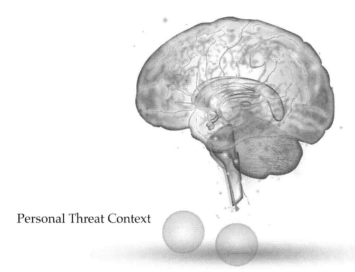

Personal Threat Context

Your Personal Threat Profile described above gives you your susceptibility to being triggered by certain types of situations, events, or actions. Your Personal Threat Context gives you your sensitivity to being triggered. This was described in detail in Section B Part 2d. If you wish to dig deeper, then review each of the areas and give yourself a ranking for that area. You might also go online. There are many stress profiles available.

The important thing is to understand the stresses that are being caused by other aspects of your life.

Profile #3: Your Brain Profile

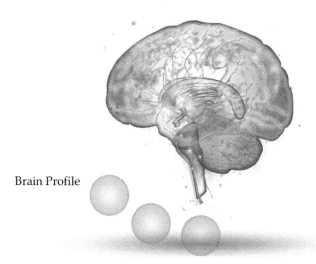

Brain Profile

There are a number of brain profiling assessments available on the market. At the time of writing, the most comprehensive, objective direct measurement of these brain profiles that I can find is the Total Brain assessment.[291] The last time I reviewed it, it measured a number of capacities of the brain, some of which are by direct measurement and some of which are by self-report.

Knowing these capacity scores will provide you with another viewpoint on how you might react when receiving social and emotion cues, i.e., those things that are the origination of emotional threats and rewards.

In addition, this assessment provides guidance on which brain apps can then be used to train and enhance those capacities of your brain that might be compromised. Finally, after a period of training, you can reassess your brain and compare the results with your original assessment.

This model does not lend itself to a Quick and Dirty approach.

The detailed assessment method is achieved by taking the online brain profile assessment then doing some training exercises and retaking the assessment to track your improvements. [292]

Can you do-it-yourself? You can. The results from the website assessment will guide you through your learning and will guide you to exercises that can help train your brain in the areas that may have arisen as compromised. It does help, however, to have a coach who has been trained in this assessment to guide you through, in addition to what is available on the website.

Profile #4: Your Chronotype

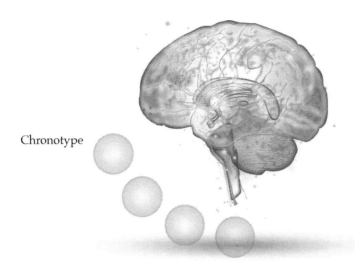

Chronotype

The fifth brain dynamic that I discussed earlier in this book dealt with brain rhythms. I outlined the fact that we are driven by a number of rhythms or cycles that impact our energy. I discussed the owl-lark spectrum, circadian rhythms, and ultradian rhythms. Your chronotype is simply your preference in terms of what time of day you are at your peak.

Daniel Pink [293] spends much of his book, *When*, on the interaction between the owl-lark and circadian rhythms and provides many examples of how this impacts the timing of when we should do different types of tasks.

You can use a Quick and Dirty Method by simply reviewing when you do your best work. Morning? Evening? Some other time in the middle? Then align the tasks that you have to do around that discovery.

You can carry out a more detailed approach by searching for the "Munich Chronotype Questionnaire" on the Internet – there are many self-assessment versions available for free.

Do-it-yourself? Absolutely. Once you discover your type, you can make your adjustments to suit – that is, if you wish to change. ☺

Profile #5: Your Conversational Focus

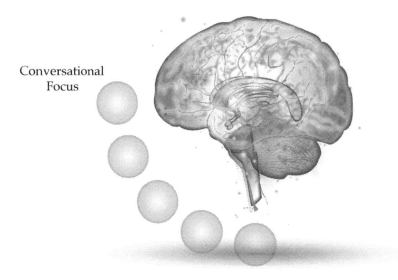

Conversational
Focus

There are three models associated with your conversational focus:

1. Grassi 8 Factor Model

Many years ago, I worked with a gentleman called John Grassi.* His fascination was with the conversations that teams had amongst themselves. He found that when teams had discussions, sometimes they went away feeling satisfied with the discussion and at other times, dissatisfied. When the teams were satisfied, he identified that they had covered eight topic areas. He discovered that teams, and individuals in the teams, have a tendency to prefer one of these eight. He drew them up in tabular format so, in honor of his work, I repeat the same format on the next page.

As you watch yourself and other individuals, you can easily pick out tendencies to focus on one or more of these areas, often to the exclusion of others.

Quick and Dirty Method? Just review where you or your team spend the most time … if you want to go into more detail, record the amount of time spent in each of the areas.

I am not aware of any assessments available to carry out a more detailed assessment approach. Please let me know if you find one.

Can you do-it-yourself? No coach is necessary for the discovery part of this process. A coach may be useful, however, in order to determine what to do with the results and how to change if a change is necessary.

---

* I have lost touch with Grassi. If anyone knows of his further research and work, please let me know.

Opportunities	Constraints/Restraints
Positive, future orientation – naturally identifies many opportunities and alternatives.	Identifies the <u>constraints</u> to be faced (those barriers which are outside of the control of the enterprise, group or individual) or <u>restraints</u> that need to be addressed or accounted for (those barriers which are imposed by the enterprise, group, or individual).
Similarities	**Dissimilarities**
Identifies what will be similar to things that currently exist or have happened in the past.	Identifies the differences between what will exist in the future and what currently exists or has happened in the past.
Look	**Feel**
How will others see us? What will this look like, or need to look like, to the external world?	What do we want it to feel like as we are living in this future world?
Continuities	**Discontinuities**
As a result of all of the above, what will remain the same, and what needs to continue to be done?	As a result of all of the above, what needs to be started or stopped?

2. Advocacy/Inquiry Matrix

This model is very simple. It suggests that you examine the amount of time that you spend in expounding or defending a viewpoint, position, or action (advocacy) or asking questions about another person's viewpoint, position, or action (inquiry). It can be represented by the following four quadrants:

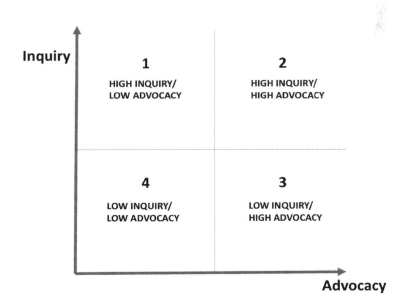

If you are seen in Quadrant 1, as High Inquiry/Low Advocacy, people might see you as very questioning and very interested, but they might not get to know where you stand. At least not until they ask. Then you are likely to give a little away, and go back to asking questions.

On the other hand, if you are in Quadrant 3, Low Inquiry/High Advocacy, you will likely be seen as opinionated and uncaring. If/when you do ask questions, it is possible that you will not listen to or will challenge the answers that you receive.

Being able to hang out in Quadrant 2, either naturally or by choice, is an optimum place to be. You can elect when to ask questions and listen and when to offer up your own opinion.

Quadrant 4? You might be learning a lot from listening to other people, but they will not know where you stand and not have the benefit of your opinion.

The brain-based issue here is that of being "told what to do." As we have seen in the 5 P's, the brain wants autonomy and a sense of choice. Advocacy, unless requested, can feel a lot like being told what to do. Especially when the telling comes from people who are in Quadrant 3.

Quick and Dirty Method? Just review where you or your team spends the most time…if you want to go into more detail, record the amount of time spent in each of the four quadrants.

An improvement on this? Have other people tell you where they think you spend your time.

I am not aware of any assessments available to carry out a more detailed assessment approach. Please let me know if you find one.

Can you do-it-yourself? No coach is necessary for the discovery part of this process. A coach may be useful, however, in order to determine what to do with the results and how to change if a change is necessary.

3. TAPS Model

In some ways, this is an extension of the Inquiry/Advocacy Matrix Model. In his book, Rock [294] suggests that the small components of conversations tend to have two dimensions to them. The first is whether the conversation is about the problem or the solution. The second is whether you are asking or telling (the inquiry/advocacy dimension). He draws a slightly different model, as shown on the next page. The acronym TAPS is derived from the initial letter of each of the extremes of the two dimensions.

Quick and Dirty Method? Just review where you or your team spend the most time…if you want to go into more detail, record the amount of time spent in each of the four quadrants. And you might take a look at where you spend your time in different situations. What about when you are under stress?

An improvement on this? Have other people tell you where they think you spend your time.

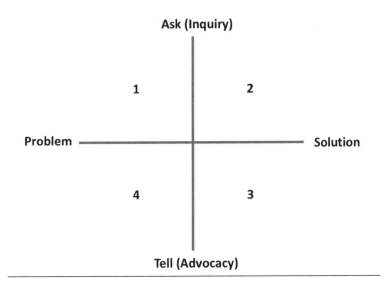

For many people, the way that the process operates typically goes something like this:

We start off by asking what the problem is about, i.e., Quadrant 1. We might hang out in this quadrant for some time in order to fully understand the details of the problem. How long you hang out here and how comfortable you feel hanging out there will depend upon many other aspects of your character.

Many of us will then jump straight to Quadrant 3 and start advocating a solution without any further inquiry. The brain likes to have things neat, sewn up, and predictable. We are trained (and the brain loves) to be problem solvers. So, we start to tell people what to do. By now, with your knowledge of the brain, you can imagine what this does to certain types of Threat Profile. It feels like being told what to do because that is what it is! And the advice that you give at this point has a high chance of being rejected!

The more enlightened of us will go from Quadrant 1 and drop down to Quadrant 4. This ensures our understanding of the problem. This can often help the problem owner because we will rephrase, reframe, and often add structure to what was an unstructured problem statement. This can help in and of itself. This simple act will often result in the problem owner saying things like "Oh, I never looked at it that way."

Then, unfortunately, the unwary will then jump across to Quadrant 3 with the problems that I outlined above.

The real richness in the subsequent discussion comes from Quadrant 2. Having the other person, i.e., the problem owner, do the thinking about the solution. And hang out there for some time.

I am not aware of any assessments available to carry out a more detailed assessment approach. Please let me know if you find one.

Do-it-yourself? Yes. No coach is necessary for the discovery part of this process. A coach may be useful, however, in order to determine what to do with the results and how to change if a change is necessary.

Profile #6: Your Behavioral Profile

Behavioral Profile

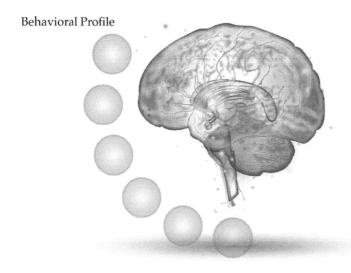

There are several assessments available that determine one's behavioral profile. Here, I have selected four of these assessments to address in detail and have provided a few diagrams and tables to assist in your understanding of them.

While some of these approaches are relatively complex, others are very simple; therefore, it is up to you to determine whether you need a coach to guide you through a specific approach.

Behavioral Profile #1: Your Five Factor Inventory

This approach uses five dimensions, as you will see below. Combined, they make up the acronym O.C.E.A.N. which I find useful for remembering them all. In recent years, the Five Factor Model or Inventory [295] has become the de facto standard or approach for assessing human behavioral traits. Research indicates that these traits are observable at an early stage of child development and appear to be consistent over long periods of time as we mature.

These five factors are:

O. Openness to experience describes a person's degree of intellectual curiosity, creativity, and preference for novelty and variety. Some disagreement remains about how to interpret this factor.

C. Conscientiousness is a tendency to show self-discipline, act dutifully, and aim for achievement. Conscientiousness also refers to planning, organization, and dependability.

E. Extroversion describes energy, positive emotions, assertiveness, sociability, talkativeness, and the tendency to seek stimulation in the company of others.

A. Agreeableness is the tendency to be compassionate and cooperative towards others rather than suspicious and antagonistic.

N. Neuroticism describes vulnerability to unpleasant emotions like anger, anxiety, depression, or vulnerability. Neuroticism also refers to an individual's level of emotional stability and impulse control and is sometimes referred to as emotional stability.

For each of these five factors, there is a spectrum of characteristics. The table below shows some of the major characteristics at either end of the spectrum. [296] Not all of these characteristics would be shown by everyone.

There is also some evidence [297] that people with these five different traits consistently use different words in everyday life.

Open-Minded: creative, questioning, artistically interested, emotionally open, adventurous, liberal, romantic, playful	**OPENNESS**	**Conservative**: uncreative, unquestioning, dogmatic, habit-driven, routine-bound, conventional, unromantic, cautious
Conscientious: organized, efficient, methodical, dutiful, tenacious, dependable, hard-working, responsible	**CONSCIENTIOUSNESS**	**Careless**: disorganized, sloppy, inefficient, reckless, immature, extravagant, rebellious, exhibitionist
Extrovert: talkative, bold (socially), energetic, gregarious, assertive, thrill-seeking, cheerful, enthusiastic	**EXTROVERSION**	**Introvert**: shy, quiet, bashful, withdrawn, reserved, polite, timid, reclusive
Agreeable: warm, kind, cooperative, trusting, friendly, open, forgiving, team-worker	**AGREEABLENESS**	**Disagreeable**: unsympathetic, rude, stubborn, critical, quarrelsome, distant, distrustful, obstructive
Stable: even-tempered, satisfied, content, relaxed, optimistic, self-accepting, tolerant, laid-back, self-sufficient	**NEUROTICISM**	**Uptight**: moody, jealous, envious, touchy, anxious, angry, depressed, self-obsessed

One Quick and Dirty way of doing this is simply to circle the characteristics that are most like you most of the time. For example, under "Agreeableness," you might find that for most of the time, you are warm, cooperative, and trusting. Occasionally, you are distant and quarrelsome. You could take it a step further and rank yourself on a scale of 1 to 10 for each dimension.

If you want to explore this model in more detail, there are many assessments based upon it readily available on the Internet, although there might be a small charge.

Can you do-it-yourself? Probably not. This is a relatively complex, five-dimensional approach. If you look at the different combinations between all of the five dimensions and the way that these different combinations might interact, then it would be useful to have a coach.

Behavioral Profile #2: Your Zimbardo Time Perspective Inventory

Zimbardo and Sword's approach [298] is relatively simple but extremely useful. The premise is that we all spend our time either focusing on the past, the present, or the future. In each of these three areas, we tend to dwell on either the positive or the negative. In diagrammatic form, it looks thus:

	Positive Outlook	**Negative Outlook**
Past	Focus on the good things that have happened	Focus on all the things that went wrong in the past
Present	Live in the moment, seeking pleasure, novelty, and sensation and avoiding pain	Feel that planning for future decisions is not necessary because predetermined fate plays the guiding role in one's life
Future	Plan for the future and trust that things will work out	Feel that the future is predetermined and apocalyptic, or they simply have no future orientation

Adapted from their words:

> *"When one of these time perspectives is weighed too heavily, we can lose out on what's really happening now and/or lose sight of what could happen in the future. This can cause us to be unsteady, unbalanced, or temporarily biased.*
>
> *Being out of balance in this way also shades the way we think and negatively impacts our daily decision-making. For instance, if you are stuck in a past negative experience, you might think that from now on everything that happens to you will be negative. Why even bother to plan for the future? Or if your focus is simply on the positive aspects of today, with little or no regard for the future, then you might engage in risky behaviors that unintentionally endanger you or others because you are living in the moment and not thinking about the consequences of today's actions."*

Quick and Dirty Method? Just review where you tend to spend your thoughts and spoken words. Is this position useful to you as you move forward? How do others see this?

If you want to take it a step further, you could allocate a percentage to each of the six components.

A quick search on the web for "time perspective theory assessments" will generate an easy way to take a fuller and more detailed assessment yourself. [299]

Do-it-yourself? Probably. This is a relatively easy approach to get your arms around. It doesn't require a coach for understanding...it may require a coach to help you think what you might want to do about your findings.

Behavioral Profile #3: Social Style

Once again, we have a two x two matrix. I did warn you that there are a number of them. ☺ And, once again, one of the dimensions is our good old friend, the "Ask" (inquiry) or "Tell" (advocacy) dimension.

Here's how to perform a Quick and Dirty version of the Social Styles Model. First, take a look at the horizontal axis and position yourself somewhere along that line. If you tend to take a "Tell" position, then you will be to the right of the middle. If you tend to stand back and take an "Ask" orientation, then you will be to the left of the middle. Now take a look at the vertical axis. Do people have a tough time getting to know you? In which case, you will be above the midpoint. If, on the other hand, you wear your heart on your sleeve and people tend to get to know you easily, then you will be below the midpoint. This exercise places you in one of the four quadrants.

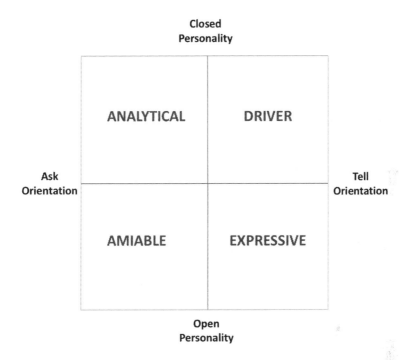

An improvement on this Quick and Dirty approach? Have other people tell you where they think you spend your time.

There are many more detailed variants of this assessment online, some legitimate (i.e., done with the approval of the current holders of the IP) and some not so. You will probably have to pay a nominal fee. At the time of writing, I believe the legitimate version of this assessment is offered by Tracom. [300]

This assessment is well described in the book *Social Style/Management Style*. [301]

Each of us has some degree of each of the four styles. And the style we exhibit may change depending on our stress level. Even the most tolerant of "Amiable" characters can become a demon when pushed too far or otherwise stressed. The most energetic of "Drivers" can just opt out and become passive if pushed or stressed too much.

No coach is necessary for the discovery part of this process, and even if you choose the more detailed assessment method, you can do-it-yourself. A coach may be useful, however, in order to determine what to do with the results and how to change if a change is necessary.

From the Personal Threat Profile point of view, we can now start to take a look at the motives and fears of each of the four types. They are as shown in the table below.

Type	Motivators	Fears (and relationship to the P's)
Driver	Prediction-oriented Control, results, efficiency, competition	Prediction-oriented Failure, non-commitment to results from others
Analytical	Prediction-oriented Logic, organization, being right, thoughtful	Prediction-oriented Being pushed into things; being forced to act too quickly, being wrong
Amiable	Participation-oriented It's about the relationship: Being liked, approval, cooperative, team player, needs psychological safety	Participation-oriented Being rejected; being disapproved of
Expressive	Participation-oriented Exhilaration and stimulation, enthusiasm, unstructured, spontaneity, pleasure	Participation-oriented Not being good enough, not being recognized, boredom, loss of a dream

Behavioral Profile #4: Belbin Team Profile [302]

The research of Dr. Meredith Belbin in the 1970s lead to the development of Belbin Team Roles, nine clusters of behavior that individuals adopt when participating in a team. An assessment is available for these roles by searching the Internet or going to the Belbin site.

The nine behavioral clusters are listed in the table below.

Role	Description
Resource Investigator	Uses his/her inquisitive nature to find ideas to bring back to the team.
Team Worker	Helps the team to gel, using their versatility to identify the work required and complete it on behalf of the team.
Coordinator	Needed to focus on the team's objectives, draw out team members, and delegate work appropriately.
Plant	Tends to be highly creative and good at solving problems in unconventional ways.
Monitor Evaluator	Provides a logical eye, making impartial judgements where required and weighs up the team's options in a dispassionate way.
Specialist	Brings in-depth knowledge of a key area to the team.
Shaper	Provides the necessary drive to ensure that the team keeps moving and does not lose focus or momentum.

Implementer	Needed to plan a workable strategy and carry it out as efficiently as possible.
Completer-Finisher	Most effectively used at the end of tasks to polish and scrutinize the work for errors, subjecting it to the highest standards of quality control.

I have included an expanded description of these roles in Appendix C.

We each tend to focus on, and be good at, one or a few of these roles.

Profile #7: Your Leadership Style

Leadership Profile

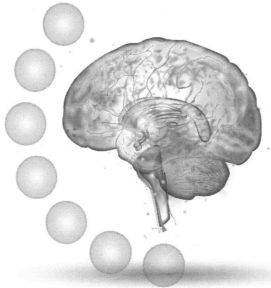

There are a number of assessments that are specifically focused on leadership styles rather than general behavioral/character/personality characteristics. There are hundreds of leadership assessments out there, but I have selected three to focus on in more detail so that you can get a sense of the type of areas that are addressed within these assessments.

In each of these cases, I do not recommend a Quick and Dirty approach, and in each case, I strongly advised you to engage the help of a coach. As a first pass, however, you could simply review each of the components of the model and rate yourself.

Another word of caution. There is little or no agreement in the field of leadership development as to the "optimum" leadership model upon which to base the "optimum" leadership development assessment. You will find some similarities between these three approaches – and some significant differences.

Leadership Style #1: Leadership Work Styles (LWS)

This model is based upon early work done by Timothy Leary in the sixties. It has gone through several evolutions since then.

It uses a multi-rater [†] approach and a long, detailed question set to identify your position, relative to others like you, on twelve dimensions. These dimensions are on the following page.

[†] Input from other people

	Measures the degree to which you see
Achievement	- yourself as needing to achieve results.
Self-Actualization	- the need to grow yourself.
Humanistic-Encouraging	- yourself wanting to be of assistance to others.
Affiliative	- yourself as being sensitive to the needs and processes of your work team.
Approval	- yourself as needing approval from others.
Conventional	- yourself as following the rules or the way things have always been done.
Dependent	- yourself as being reliant upon others for direction.
Avoidance	- yourself representing the voice of caution.
Oppositional	- yourself as being a critical thinker.
Power	- yourself as able to be decisive and take charge.
Competitive	- yourself as being in competition with and wanting to beat others.
Perfectionistic	- the need for perfection in what you do and in what others do.

The first four of these are offered as constructive styles, the second four are destructive, people-oriented styles, and the final four are destructive, task-oriented styles.

When you take the assessment, you are "ranked" on a percentage from the center of a circumplex, comparing your score with other people like you. This results in what looks like a refined version of a Rorschach "blob," giving a visual picture of your tendencies.

This is one of the few assessments that actually has a "target" profile. This target profile is based upon research which correlates certain styles with excellent leadership.

The assessment is available through: Human Synergistics. [303]

As you review these different characteristics, you will find many overlaps with the facets of the 5 P's Model.

Leadership Style #2: Extraordinary Leader

The work done by Zenger & Folkman [304] is some of the better research and writing in the leadership field. I recommend their book to all leaders or aspiring leaders. Some of the reasons I like this assessment is that it is well explained and written up, easy to remember, research based, and visually presented.

They identify 5 main pillars which expand into the following 16 components of Extraordinary Leadership.

Character	Character
Personal Capability	Technical & professional expertise
	Solving problems and analyzing issues
	Innovation
	Practicing self-development
Focus on Results	Focus on results
	Establish stretch goals
	Take responsibility for outcomes/initiatives
Interpersonal Skills	Communicating powerfully and prolifically
	Inspiring and motivating others to high performance
	Building relationships
	Developing others
	Collaboration and teamwork
Leading Organizational Change	Developing strategic perspectives
	Championing change
	Connecting internal groups with the outside world

Their work also identifies a couple of other key points:

The first key point is that you don't have to be good at everything. But here's some interesting data. Their research shows that leaders that had no perceived strengths were rated in the 34th percentile of leadership capability, i.e., in the bottom third. If a leader had a strength in just one area, then his/her evaluation went to the 64th percentile. The second strength took it to the 72nd percentile. Three strengths went to 81st, four was 89th, and five was 91st. Out of 16 strengths, you didn't need to be good at all of them to be seen as a great leader.

The second key point, however, is that if you have some fatal flaws, i.e., areas in which not only do you not have a strength, but you actually have a weakness, then that will be your downfall. That is what people will judge you by and remember you by. Not your strengths.

The lesson here is that if you are not good at everything, don't worry. But, if you have fatal flaws, then you need to work on them.

So, what's a fatal flaw? Well, if you reviewed all of your attributes, you rank them from your weakest attributes to your strongest attributes. Fatal flaws tend to come from two areas. The bottom ranked attributes that you are weak at. That's obvious. But fatal flaws can also come from your major strengths – where you use them all the time, inappropriately or as the only tool you have.

You can access this assessment on Zenger & Folkman's website. [305] But you will have to pay for it. And you will need a coach.

Leadership Style #3: Leadership Circle

The Leadership Circle has many similarities to LWS but, in many ways, is more complex. This is good news and bad news. OD and HR folks tend to like it because it is all-encompassing. That's OK for them as they have had days if not longer to study the principles. For many managers and leaders who cannot devote that amount of time, I see it as too complicated. It has, however, gained significant ground over recent years as a leadership development tool in the marketplace, hence, its inclusion here.

Like LWS it is based upon a circumplex with similar axes but the use of different words. The vertical axis is labeled "Creative" at the top and "Reactive" at the bottom. The horizontal axis is labeled "Relationship" on the left and "Task" on the right, the mirror image of LWS. This results in four quadrants.

There are five creative competencies and three reactive styles, each of which is broken into subcomponents as shown below.

When you take the assessment, you are "ranked" on a percentage from the center of the circumplex, again like LWS. This results in what looks like a refined version of a Rorschach "blob," giving a visual picture of your tendencies.

Creative Competencies	Relating	Caring, Connection, Fosters Team Play, Collaborator, Mentoring & Developing, Interpersonal Intelligence
	Self-Awareness	Selfless Leader, Balance, Composure, Personal Learner
	Authenticity	Integrity, Courageous, Authenticity
	Systems Awareness	Community, Concern, Sustainable Productivity, System Thinker
	Achieving	Strategic Focus, Purposeful, Visionary, Achieves Results, Decisiveness

Reactive Styles	Complying	Conservative, Pleasing, Belonging, Passive
	Protecting	Distance, Critical, Arrogance
	Controlling	Autocratic, Ambition, Driven, Perfect

And lest you think that the "Reactive Styles" are all about negative aspects, they identify some "Gifts" in these styles as follows on the next page:

223

Reactive Styles	Complying	Loved, Meeting Expectations, Accepted, Loyalty to Purpose, Fidelity to Values, Service to Others, Sensitivity to Needs, Builder of Community & Organizations, Self-mastery, Non-attached Vision Focus, Seeds of Social and Emotional Intelligence
	Protecting	Superior, Right, Self-sufficient, Wisdom Through Detachment, Care and Reflection, Discernment Through Curiosity and Wisdom, Challenging Limited Thinking, Strength of Character (no need for credit), Mentoring Others into Their Bigness Seeds of Caring, Awareness, Purposeful Courage
	Controlling	Excel, Achieve, Dominate, Control, Win, Continuous Improvement, Acceptance of Self and Others "As Is," Desire for Outstanding Results, Energy & Drive, Service Through Persistence and Influence, Integrity to Do What is Needed Even if Controversial, Seeds of Visionary Leadership

There is a write-up [306] available – but be warned; it is written as a white paper by the CEO of the company and hence, might have some less than critical thinking.

[291] https://www.totalbrain.com/

[292] https://www.totalbrain.com/

[293] Pink, D. (2018). When: The Scientific Secrets of Perfect Timing. Riverhead Books.

[294] Rock, D. (2007). Quiet Leadership: Six Steps to Transforming Performance at Work. HarperBusiness.

[295] This inventory was originally published in 1978 by Costa and McCrae and had gone through several evolutions since then. The latest version is known as NEO-PI3.

[296] Carter, R. (2008). Multiplicity: The New Science of Personality, Identity, and the Self (1st ed.). Little, Brown and Company.

[297] Psychology Today, July/August 2015, p 9

[298] Zimbardo, P. G., & Sword, R. (2017). Unbridled and Extreme Present Hedonism. In B. Lee (Ed.), The Dangerous Case of Donald Trump.

[299] Here's one example ... http://www.thetimeparadox.com/zimbardo-time-perspective-inventory/

[300] www.tracomcorp.com

[301] Bolton, R., & Bolton, D. G. (1984). Social Style / Management Style: Developing Productive Work Relationships. AMACOM.

[302] These descriptions (and those in Appendix E) were downloaded from https://www.belbin.com/about/belbin-team-roles/

[303] https://www.humansynergistics.com/

[304] Zenger, J., & Folkman, J. (2009). The Extraordinary Leader: Turning Good Managers into Great Leaders (2nd ed.). McGraw-Hill Education.

[305] http://zengerfolkman.com/the-extraordinary-leader/

[306] Anderson, R. J., Jr. (2006). The Leadership Circle Profile: breakthrough leadership assessment technology. Industrial and Commercial Training, 38(4), 175–184. http://doi.org/10.1108/00197850610671946

Section C Part 2: Your Tendencies

Section C Part 2a. Biases and Habits

Biases, Habits, Etc.

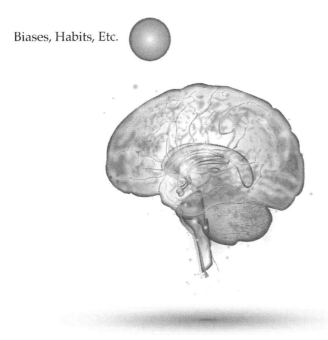

Biases

We first took a look at biases in Brain Dynamic #1. We learned about the number of biases that we are subject to at the social, cognitive, and neuronal level. If you didn't do so at the time, now would be a good time to refer to Appendix A on bias and examine your own biases in each of the three areas. To what degree are you affected by the social biases that I identify there? How about the cognitive biases? What about neurodiversity biases? And, are you sufficiently aware of your own biases and the impact that they have on you on a day-to-day basis?

It might be interesting to take a couple of other slices at this bias pie, rather than just relying on your own self-report. Here are a couple of simple actions you could take:

> **Implicit Association Tests**. [307] Log onto this website run by Harvard researchers, and test out some of your own biases. You might be surprised at the results. I know I was.
> **Ask**. Ask your friends, family, co-workers, etc. what they have noticed. You might be surprised at the results. I know I was.

As we have learned, there are hundreds of biases; here, I want to pull out just a few of the more "obvious" and well-known biases and see their impact.

One starting point would be Dvorsky's "The 12 Cognitive Biases that Prevent You from Being Rational" [308] as a basis for this section. The title caught my attention as it ties Brain Dynamics 1 and 2 together (i.e., we are biased, and we behave irrationally). I suggest that you read each, put a check mark against those that you recognize in yourself (or rank it on a scale of 1 to 10), and then think about the impact that it might have on you and on others. Some of them are obvious – and some less so. Have fun learning about yourself.

Bias and Description
1. Confirmation Bias: This bias is mostly a nonconscious act whereby we seek out and reference only those perspectives that fuel our pre-existing views, while at the same time ignoring or dismissing opinions – no matter how valid – that threaten those views.
2. In-group Bias: A manifestation of our innate tendencies to favor people who are just like us. In-group bias causes us to overestimate the abilities and values of our immediate group at the expense of people we don't really know.
3. Gambler's Fallacy: We tend to put a tremendous amount of weight on previous events, believing that they'll somehow influence future outcomes. It's also the sense that we have that our luck has to eventually change and that good fortune is on the way.
4. Post-Purchase Rationalization: Remember that time you bought something totally unnecessary, faulty, or overly expensive, and then you rationalized the purchase to such an extent that you convinced yourself it was a great idea all along? Research suggests that it stems from the principle of commitment and our desire to stay consistent.
5. Neglecting Probability: Virtually all of us know and acknowledge the fact that the probability of dying in an auto accident is significantly greater than getting killed in a plane crash — but our brains won't allow this logic.
6. Observational Selection Bias: This is that effect of suddenly noticing things we didn't notice before – but we wrongly assume that the frequency has increased. A perfect example is what happens after we buy a new car, and we inexplicably start to see the same car virtually everywhere.
7. Status-Quo Bias: As we have seen, we tend to be apprehensive of change, which often leads us to make choices that guarantee that things remain the same or change as little as possible. Needless to say, this has ramifications in everything from politics to economics.
8. Negativity Bias: People tend to pay more attention to bad news. Social scientists theorize that it's on account of our selective attention and that, given the choice, we perceive negative news as being more important or profound.
9. Bandwagon Effect: Though we're not conscious of it, many of us love to go with the flow. When the masses start to pick a winner or a favorite, that's when our individualized brains start to shut down and enter into a kind of hive-mind mentality.
10. Projection Bias: As individuals trapped inside our own minds 24/7, it's often difficult for us to project outside the bounds of our own consciousness and preferences. We tend to assume that most people think just like us.
11. The Current Moment Bias: Most of us have a really hard time imagining ourselves in the future and altering our behaviors and expectations accordingly. Most of us would rather experience pleasure in the current moment while leaving the pain for later.
12. Anchoring Effect: Also known as the relativity trap, this is the tendency we have to compare and contrast only a limited set of items. It's called the anchoring effect because we tend to fixate on a value or number that in turn gets compared to everything else.

Let me throw a couple more in for good measure. One that seems to be getting a lot of attention during the time I am writing this book is the Dunning-Kruger effect. It is a simple one. It is the tendency for unskilled individuals to overestimate their own ability and for experts to underestimate their ability.

How about one known as "the law of the instrument" – it's a fancy name for something that you have come across many times. It refers to an overreliance on a familiar tool or method, ignoring or undervaluing alternative approaches. "If all you have is a hammer, everything looks like a nail."

Finally, I must point out that there is some controversy as to whether some of these biases count as irrational or whether they result in useful attitudes or behavior. For example, when getting to know others, people tend to ask leading questions which seem biased towards confirming their assumptions about the person. This kind of confirmation bias has been argued to be an example of social skill, i.e., a way to establish a connection with the other person.

Hopefully this quick review has influenced you to take a deeper look at biases – especially your own; in the meantime, have you reached any conclusions about how your biases influence you at home and work?

Habits

To the brain, habits have a similar benefit to biases. It means the brain doesn't have to consciously think about everything all of the time. A habit is a set of responses laid down in the past, which are often caused by triggers. Remember that the brain is constantly looking for a way to be efficient with information. Habits create that efficiency even in cases where it may not always be the best choice.

Let's take a quick look at their impact on our lives.

Wikipedia describes a habit as:

"a routine of behavior that is repeated regularly and tends to occur unconsciously."

It is fascinating to note that habits were a subject of interest even a hundred years ago. The American Journal of Psychology (1903) defined a habit in this way:

"A habit, from the standpoint of psychology, is a more or less fixed way of thinking, willing, or feeling acquired through previous repetition of a mental experience. Habitual behavior often goes unnoticed in persons exhibiting it because a person does not need to engage in self-analysis when undertaking routine tasks. Habits are sometimes compulsory."

A social or emotional habit, for example, might be as follows: You are a manager, and one of the people that works for you comes to you with a tough problem asking for your help in resolving it. You might respond in a number of ways. On the one hand, you might spend some time coaching the person and help them think through different possible solutions. On the other hand, you might simply give them a directive as to how to solve it. Research indicates that without explicit training, we, as managers, tend to default one way or other, with most managers defaulting to the directive approach. This might be the best response in some situations, but it tends not to help the learning and growth of the person asking the question.

Another example of a habit might be your responses in a meeting. It might be that you are always open to new ideas when the team that works for you presents, and you collaborate well to implement those ideas. When similar ideas, however, are presented by your peers then you are not so open and, in some cases, will subtly sabotage the new approach.

The fact of having habits is neither good nor bad. They are efficient, and we don't have to spend conscious brain energy thinking about them. We tend to make judgments about habits – our own and other peoples' – as "good" habits or "bad" habits. Overall, unless we make special efforts, they are frequently out of our awareness, are unintentional, and are often uncontrollable.

Here, I want to mainly focus on social and emotional habits. What I mean by this is that I am more interested in the manner in which you use habits to respond to social and work situations rather than if you smoke, drink, or floss your teeth after meals. ☺

The reasons that you will want to identify habits is the same as for biases, i.e.,

> ➢ to make sure that you are consciously aware of them
> ➢ to make a decision as to whether they are still useful to you at this stage of your life

One approach to identifying habits is some self-reflection. For some people, this is simply a matter of taking some time to look inward and is an easy activity; if you can reflect and identify your own habits, that is excellent.

Another step might be to pay attention the next time you notice yourself getting an emotion at work or home, e.g., angry, tense, stressed, on the one hand, or feeling light, happy, and content on the other. Ask yourself questions like, what am I thinking? What expectations do I have? When have I noticed this before? Who is around? What just happened? What did I interpret from that? If you like to keep a journal, then jot some notes down; if not, then just notice.

Then ask yourself the following questions: What is the impact of my habit? What is the impact to myself? What is the impact when I am working with another person? What is the impact to the group of people with whom I work?

In a little more detail, Charles Duhigg, [309] an eminent researcher on habits, suggests that there are three parts to a habit, namely a trigger, a routine, and a reward. As you look at your own habits, you could look at what triggers you, what the routine is, and what the reward is.

Let's look at a personal example, brushing your teeth. What is the trigger? For most of us, it is the act of waking up. We do it automatically either just when we have woken or after breakfast or both. The routine? We tend to do it at the same time, in the same place, in the same posture, and, for most people, in the same sequence every day. This may be the reason why I have had so much difficulty in adopting the use of an electric toothbrush. ☺ It requires me to do something different. It is not the same habit. Now, how about the reward? Two-fold. Socially acceptable breath (short-term) and healthier teeth (long-term).

A good start in the investigation of our own habits is to name as many of them as you can (good and bad) and outline the impact they have on you and on others. If you get stuck, ask people who know you well. For each habit you identify, you could then look at the triggers, the routine, and the reward.

Another take on the activity of assessing our habits is to take a look at what you do under stress. For example, as a manager at work, what happens when you start to get stressed out, for whatever reason. In the work that I do with groups, I find a number of typical habit responses. They cover things like:

> ➢ I tend to start to micromanage.
> ➢ I tend not to listen as carefully.
> ➢ I get very directive.
> ➢ I get combative.
> ➢ I tend to prevaricate.
> ➢ I just do it myself and don't delegate.

We all tend to have habits that get engaged when we are under pressure or stressed. We will sometimes even look back in regret at how we behaved in certain situations (although some of these behaviors are certainly not habitual ☺). If you recall when we talked about one of the brain's biggest and most constant struggles (Brain Principles 3 and 4), it is likely that when we are under pressure or stressed, the PFC is taken off-line or is less able to perform its function of "braking" our limbic response. That's the time when your habits are likely to come roaring out.

Another dimension is to look at the time of day or the time of the week. For example, when you get home from work in the evening, are there things that you do without even thinking about them? There are the obvious and necessary ones like putting your keys in the draw or hanging your outdoor wear in the closet, etc. What about the ones that are less necessary like pouring that glass of wine or beer, eating that cookie, or downing that half bowl of ice-cream? ☺

Finally, you could look for any tie-in that you can make between any habits that you might have and your Personal Threat Profile.

All of this self-examination is simply to get you in the position of becoming "the expert on yourself." [310]

Section C Part 2b. Patterns

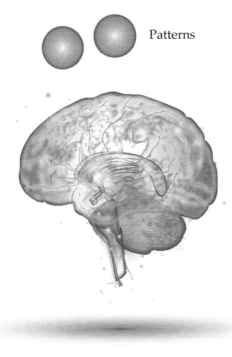

Patterns

We all tend to develop patterns during our lives. These can be long-term, medium, or short-term patterns. Unfortunately for us, we are often the last person to actually notice the pattern. Our family, friends, and work colleagues will often notice them before we do. "Oh, he's always sick after he comes back from vacation."

Once again, there are the same two main reasons that you will want to identify patterns:

> ➢ to make sure that you are consciously aware of them and
> ➢ to make a decision as to whether they are still useful to you at this stage of your life

One way to identify these patterns is to ask other people and listen to their answers, regardless of how hard they are to hear or how unlikely you think these answers are. This exercise has some significant value in it as it is often very difficult to see and recognize our own patterns; however, their answers will also tend to reflect their biases and patterns too, so use this feedback simply as some more data, but don't allow yourself to let it become definitive. Use your own analysis as well.

In thinking about your own patterns, think of the following as examples:

> ➢ Ultra-short-term: Whenever someone in authority is in a meeting, I tend to keep quiet about my views.
> ➢ Short-term: I always spend Monday mornings hanging out with my co-workers sharing our opinions of the sports events over the weekend.
> ➢ Medium-term: I find I get bored with projects if they go on too long.
> ➢ Long-term: I find that I move jobs every two years or so, and the new job is never as good as I hoped for.

So how do we identify these longer-term patterns?

One way, again, is to ask other people – but with the same warnings that I offered above.

Another way is to perform your own analysis. This will mean looking at some life cycle analysis for yourself. The general principles for performing this analysis are the same regardless of whether you are looking at long-term, medium, or short-term patterns. The principles involve the use of a diagram as shown below.

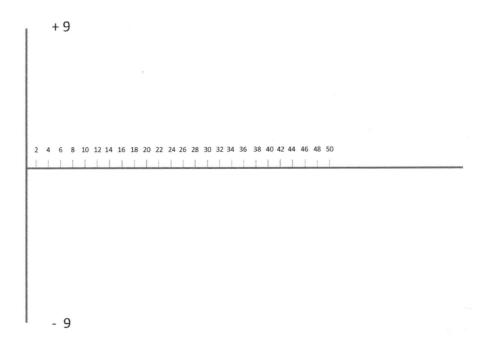

On the horizontal axis, draw a line that represents the time span that you wish to examine. The ones shown represent a span of 48 years which is how old Fred* was when he drew this. The vertical axis will consist of a rating from -9 to +9 and will measure overall happiness. At each relevant point, you attach a description of the event that occurred. Where you remember events, situations, or activities as positive, you will record them above the line. Where you remember them as negative, they will go below the line.

I have included an (incomplete) example on the next page (turn sideways to view).

In this case, we can easily see that Fred's low points have been loss of relationships and that many of his high points have been job and academically oriented.

Take a few moments to reflect on your patterns and the impact that they have on you at work and home. What about the impact on others? Once you have identified your patterns, assess them as to whether they have been useful to you in your life, are currently useful to you in your life, and are likely to be useful to you in your life.

---

* Real person but name changed.

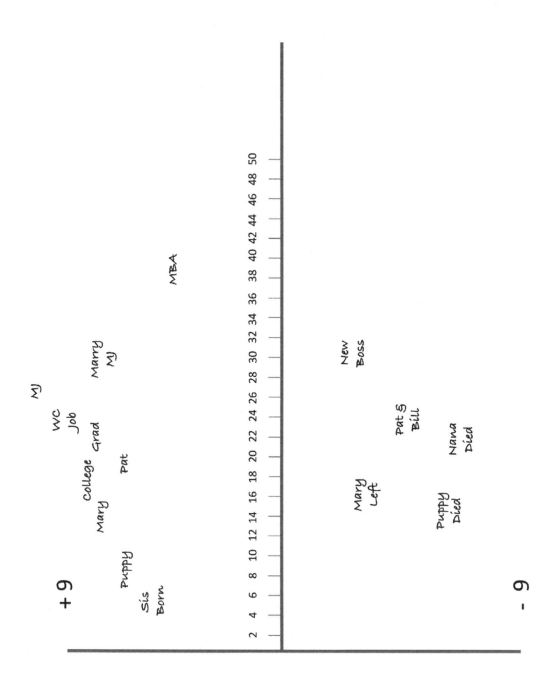

Section C Part 2c. Triggers

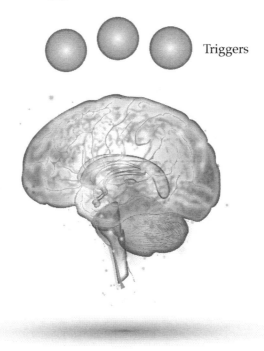

Triggers

In some ways, triggers could be dealt with as part of biases or habits. Triggers are often the kickoff point for those. This section is specifically intended to encourage you to take a look at the things, statements, or events that tend to trigger you. A trigger can cause a positive or negative impact on you, on how you react immediately, and how you react going forward, both in the short-term and in the long-term. Most triggers are directly related to your Personal Threat Profile so if you haven't reviewed that, now would be a good time to do so.

Let's take a look at some behavioral or emotional triggers that occur in the work place.

For the first example, let's assume you are in a meeting and the discussion is going well. The discussion is all about what has happened in a given situation, and everyone in the meeting is adding in their viewpoint. Eventually the discussion turns to what can be done. Although you are new to the group, you have been thinking about this issue for a long time. In fact, you consider yourself something of an expert on the subject. So, you put forward an approach that you have seen in the past. Your suggestion is met by a couple of smiles around the table. One person responds by saying, "We tried that before, and it didn't work then so there's no reason why it would work now." You withdraw from the discussion and spend the rest of the meeting thinking about other things – what you are going to do next week and maybe how wrong you were to join this company in the first place!

The trigger here could be simply that someone pushed back on your idea; it could also be that it was said in a dismissive manner. You might take a look at whether this type of response causes you to get triggered regularly. In this case, the trigger caused a negative response in you. It probably touched off something in your Personal Threat Profile.

For the second example, you are reading an email. It is from someone you get many emails from, most of which are highly critical of one of the people who reports to you. You hardly take the time to read it before you explode. It is the last straw, and you go marching into your boss.

The trigger here could be the criticism of someone that works for you. Or it could be the fact that you have another email from this person that has already taken up so much of your time that any email with any content would cause you to explode.

For our third example, you are driving home and hear a song that you haven't heard for years and all of a sudden you feel overwhelmed with emotion. Maybe you know why or maybe you don't.

Is the trigger the song, the singer, or the reminiscence of the important time in your life when that song was played on the radio?

We all have those things that trigger us off.

So, how do we identify these triggers? Once again, two approaches. Ask other people or perform your own analysis. In this instance, it might be a good idea to do both and compare what you learn from each one.

Once you have identified those areas that trigger you, take a look at what might be going on "behind the scenes" with these triggers. Keep in mind that triggers are personal and are often associated with significant emotional events from your history.

A trigger can cause a positive or negative impact on you, on how you react immediately, and on how you react going forward both in the short-term and in the long-term.

Identify as many of your triggers as you can (positive or negative) and outline the impact they have on you and on others.

As I mentioned earlier, in most cases, the triggers will be the things that you are sensitized to as a result of your Personal Threat Profile. In other cases, they may be triggers for other reasons.

Section C Part 2d. World View and Personal Paradigms

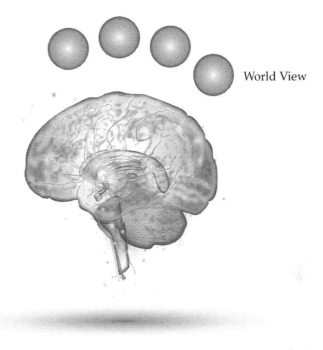

World View

Each of us brings with us a history of events, experiences, stories, mythologies, etc. through which we view the world.

This "world view" has been built up over the whole period of our lives. It provides us with the foundation upon which we operate on a day-to-day basis. It provides us with a huge, deeply rooted set of thoughts, laws, knowledge, principles, and rules upon which we layer any given situation and make judgments and decisions. Each aspect of this world view works in concert with, integrates with, and is probably foundational to our biases.

This world view saves us time – if we had to think everything through for every piece of data or event that took place in our lives, our nervous and mental systems would be on overload. This world view provides us with a shortcut for many of our daily processes.

This world view also, however, tends to "restrict'" our responses to everyday situations. Everything that happens – whether it be an event, a new piece of data or a simple conversation – is viewed through our world view. If the situation doesn't align with our world view, we will frequently react strongly to the situation with which we are faced.

I'll give you four examples of how this world view works:

For a first example, you are thinking about going into town to see a movie, and a set of thoughts start to run through your mind…ah, but it's Friday night, and traffic will be a lot worse on the way in so I'll have to leave earlier than I would otherwise…and I know that my spouse always tends to run late, and that frustrates me because I was brought up with the rule that if you're not five minutes early then you are late. You can probably add more to this fictional story.

For a second example, one lunch time, a close friend of mine, let's call her C., was meeting her friend for lunch, and they decided to go to a nearby salad bar. They walked in and were happy to see that the restaurant was fairly empty – and that there was no line for the salad bar. They took their seats, had a chat for a few moments, and then went over to get their food. As they got close to the food bar, C. turned to walk around the bar and badly bumped into her friend. Her friend was somewhat irate and admonished her for "going around the salad bar the wrong way." C. replied by apologizing (again) and saying that she didn't know that there was a rule about the direction that one walked around salad bars, but her friend was adamant, finally saying, "But everyone knows that you walk around a salad bar counterclockwise!" Who knows where her friend's world view came from, but it was deeply seated.

For a third example, another story from another close friend – let's also call her C. She and her long-term boyfriend had a great relationship. They made decisions jointly, enjoyed many of the same pursuits, and were talking about getting engaged. Circumstances came about that made them have to make a few trips together over a short period of time. I met with her after those journeys – and she was excited about a "discovery" that they had made. Part way through the third trip, she noticed that while normally they rarely argued, whenever they traveled they seemed to argue frequently. And it seemed to be over the most trivial of things that actually had little to do with the trip itself.

C. decided to investigate further and, amongst other things, asked her boyfriend what travelling meant to him, i.e., in the words that I am using here in this book, what world view did he hold about travel? His reply was that most of the travel that he had done was in the military where they lined up, only to have to wait and line up again and wait…you get the picture. So, when he traveled, he mentally prepared for it to be a tortuous experience. In his view, in an ideal world, he would arrive five minutes before the plane took off, be the last one on the plane, would walk down the jet-way, and the doors would close behind him! (This was in those halcyon, pre-9/11 days when it was actually some fun to travel.)

This answer gave her the clue she was looking for. Her experience was diametrically opposite. When she was young, she was to fly to see grandma, was taken to the airport, and by some misfortune, was left unattended at the airport – and the plane took off without her. She ran around the airport in a panic looking for her parents who had already left. So, her ideal travel dynamic was to arrive at the airport about three hours before the flight to ensure that everything was correct, her seat assignment was as it should be, and then be the first one to board the plane –that way she could be sure it wasn't going without her.

Their world views about travel were as different as you could get and, until explored, caused the unspoken angst between them, starting several hours before the trip.

For a fourth example, many years ago, I used to run creativity workshops. They would run for about four hours at the end of the day so would include the need to provide attendees with dinner. To start off the workshop, everyone would be sitting at the round tables where they would later be having their dinner. The dinners were very nice – white table cloths and everything! I wanted to start the workshop off by shaking the attendees out of their normal way of thinking. I would have roller ball pens at each place but would not have any paper on the tables. I would instruct the attendees that they were to take detailed notes for the next few minutes. There would always be one person who would wave their hand and ask for some paper to take the notes on. "Just write on the table cloth," I would nonchalantly reply.* There would always be a stunned silence, and then, normally in a timid voice, someone would say, "But I can't do that." My reply would always be, "Why not? I give you permission." ...Again silence, and then several people would say, "Because our mothers/fathers told us we couldn't." Even after I would reassure them that it was OK, that I had the permission from the hotel, there were people who couldn't physically bring themselves to write on the table, so deep is this world view.

Subsequently, when dinner was served, I would have arranged that it be served in "reverse sequence," i.e., dessert first then the entrée and finally, the salad. There were a relatively large number of people who actually couldn't and/or refused to eat their meal that way round! Where's the world view that says that salad has to come first?

I include this last story not by way of saying that you should go around writing things on the beautiful white table cloth of the next restaurant that you find yourself in (although the "eat dessert first" is not a bad idea), but rather to illustrate the profound impact that these, mostly invisible and unexplored, views can have on each of us.

On a slightly different tack, in his book, Nisbett [311] identified significant differences between the way that people from the Western Hemisphere think compared to those from Asia.**

I have described his experiment in more detail in the "Your Background Geography" section on page 248. From all of his fascinating findings, there are some important summarizations for our world views.

First, he found that Asian people, in general, have a more holistic view of the world around them and the situation that they are in than do Americans. He found Americans, when asked to describe a situation, were more apt to focus on themselves and/or the central player than were the Asians, who were more likely to describe the environment. The Asian population was far more able to describe the details of the environment than were the Americans in the study group.

Second, he found that Asians were better able to describe relationships between events. In addition, the Asian population was more likely to have confidence in what relationships they saw and were less likely to be influenced by their initial observation.

Third, the Americans in the study were more likely to want to control the situation around them and were less likely and less comfortable in adjusting to the situation. The Asians in the study had less need to control the situation around them and were more comfortable in making adjustments so that they could adapt to their environment.

All very interesting, but what has it got to do with our process here? Much. It says that your background will tend to determine for example:

➤ whether you look at the big picture and the world as a complex place over which you have little control and must adapt as the world changes or

---

* Please note that I checked with the restaurant or hotel and received approval beforehand.
** I offer here the same apologies to those people who are upset that I use the single term "Asian" as Nisbett did in his book. I do not intend to imply that all of the people that are covered by such a term are identical when they clearly are not. There is a myriad of distinctions. By using some generalizations, however, useful insights have been made.

➢ whether you see the world as a series of interconnecting parts that can be controlled, with you at the center

For most of us, in order to change for a better future, we need to understand how *our* world view effects everything that we do.

Understanding and fully grasping your own world view is an activity that, now you know about it, will probably take you the rest of your life. Beginning to understand it, however, can start now.

Take a look at the diagram below. It gives some sample categories of where our world view comes from. Most, if not all, of these areas will have had an impact on you at some time. To start with, identify those that you think have had the most impact on you and on others (identify what they are and the impact). The impact can be positive or negative – no need to judge that yet. Just attempt to identify what the impact has been. I have also included some examples of typical world views on the next couple of pages.

Once you have reflected on your world views and impacts, then review each to see whether there are thoughts that come to mind as to what you might want to take into the future to either add to, improve, or mitigate against that world view and its impacts.

The examples shown on the next page are just that: examples. You can probably think of many others. If you can't, then ask your spouse, close friend, children, etc. what they see you do frequently that puzzles them or what "sayings" do they always hear you use almost absentmindedly!

On the following page, I offer some examples of world views and their impact.

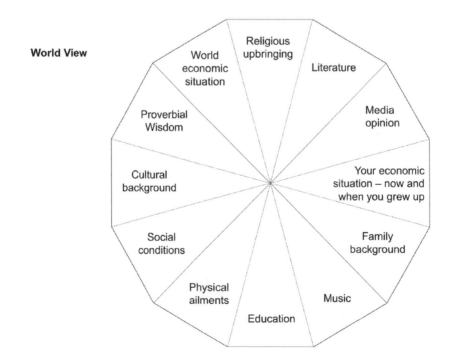

One particular aspect of our world view guides how we make decisions. When making decisions, selections, purchases, etc. we tend to look at our choices through one of two lenses: we tend to be either a "sufficer" or a "maximizer." We establish a list of criteria, either formally or mentally, that we will use in our decision-making or selection process.

Some people, once they have found a solution or product that meets their criteria, will simply opt for that one – sufficers. The solution meets what they need to accomplish, and so they can stop their search. On the other hand, there are people who will examine every possibility in order to maximize the return on their investment. They will want to find the very best solution or product and are called maximizers.

Here are some examples of some different world views and their possible impacts:

World View	A Sample Thought	A Possible Impact
Proverbial Wisdom	A bird in the hand is worth two in the bush.	You can act too soon and miss out on other possibilities.
World Economic Situation	The globalization trend is only a temporary fad.	You can be blindsided at a later date.
Religious Upbringing	Depends on the religion you were brought up in.	Can sometimes lead to religious intolerance.
Literature	Depends on what you read when you were growing up.	Can lead to growth mindset or fixed mindset
Media	What I hear on my preferred media channel is the correct way of looking at the world.	You can close your mind to looking at other viewpoints.
Your Economic Situation	Now...I am well off and can spend. Growing up...we were always poor, and so I must save.	Can spend no money on savings. You may miss out on better investment opportunities.
Family Background	I am the third in line in our family, and my two elders get the best of everything.	You may not stand up for yourself.
Music	Depends on what you listened to.	Can make you intolerant of other genres.
Education	I never got a college degree, and I did just fine.	Biased for or against people with education.
Physical Ailments	I have... [fill in the blank], and that means... [fill in the blank].	You might not fully pursue possibilities that arise.
Social Conditions	My spouse would never support me going back to college.	You might not fully pursue possibilities that arise.
Cultural Background	Growing up … [fill in the blank] means... [fill in the blank].	You restrict your thinking into a certain channel of possibilities.

Some more examples of world views; it was originally referred to as "Irrational Thoughts that Heighten the Feeling of Dread" [312]:

Something terrible will happen to me if I make a mistake.
There is a right and wrong way of doing things.
It is awful and horrible to be criticized.
I must be approved of all the time.
I must be competent, and I must be viewed as competent.
People in authority should never be challenged.
Life in the workplace must be fair and just.
I must be in control all of the time.
I must anticipate everything.
I must have things the way I want them.
Employees who are wrong should be punished.
I must have someone's shoulder to cry on.
I must feel perfect all of the time.
My worth as a person is exactly equated to my job performance.
I was promised a corporate rose garden.
It is too late for me to change, and if you expect it, I won't be able to handle it.
There is never enough (enough money, enough love, enough power, etc.)
I am not lovable.
I am not good enough.
I am not wanted.
To be successful in this world, I need to be masculine in my behavior.
If I earn more than my significant other, my relationship will be threatened.
If I don't reach too high, I can't fall too far.
If I acknowledge that I am good at something, I will be accused of boasting.
I will never get what I want in life.
If I go after what I want, others will see me as greedy.

Notes and References for "Understand Your Self: Your Tendencies":

[307] https://implicit.harvard.edu/implicit/

[308] Dvorsky, G. (n.d.). The 12 cognitive biases that prevent you from being rational. Academia.edu

[309] Duhigg, C. (2014). The Power of Habit: Why We Do What We Do in Life and Business. Random House Trade Paperbacks.

[310] A phrase that I learned from Dr. Evian Gordon

[311] Nisbett, R. E. (2004). The Geography of Thought: How Asians and Westerners Think Differently...and Why. Free Press.

[312] I accessed this sourced several years ago and now cannot find it. Please let me know if you know its origin!

Section C Part 3: Your Influencers

Cialdini [313] has identified six principles of what influence us. Some of these principles are closely related to facets of the 5 P's model, and others are related to the biases that we outlined earlier. In this section, I will outline Cialdini's six, together with some that might be more personal to you. The six from Cialdini are explained in more detail, together with examples, in Appendix B.

Section C Part 3a. Cialdini's Big Six

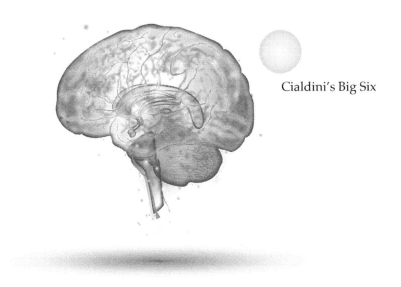

Cialdini's Big Six

The six are Reciprocation, Social Proof, Commitment and Consistency, Liking, Authority and Scarcity:

1. Reciprocation

Reciprocation recognizes that people feel indebted to those who do something for them or give them a gift. Even if the gift they are given is not something that they asked for or even voice a want for. This happens at a nonconscious level.

2. Social Proof

When people are uncertain about a course of action, they tend to look to those around them to guide their decisions and actions. They especially want to know what everyone else is doing – especially their peers.

3. Commitment and Consistency

People do not like to back out of deals. We're more likely to do something after we've agreed to it verbally or in writing. People strive for consistency in their commitments. They also prefer to follow pre-existing attitudes, values, and actions.

4. Liking

It has long been an adage in the sales field that, all other things being equal, people will do business with people they like. People prefer to say "yes" to those they know and like and are more likely to favor those who are physically attractive, similar to themselves, or who give them compliments. Philia or phobia: We are influenced in our choices by the things that we like or attracted to or things that we don't like or are put off by. These can range from cultural choices to accents.

5. Authority

People respect authority. They want to follow the lead of real experts. Business titles, impressive clothing, and even driving an expensive, high-performing automobile are proven factors in lending credibility to any individual.

6. Scarcity

Basically, the less there is of something, the more valuable it is. The more rare and uncommon a thing, the more people want it. A relatively recent and somewhat familiar example is urban campers waiting overnight to pounce on the latest iPhone.

Section C Part 3b. Other Influences

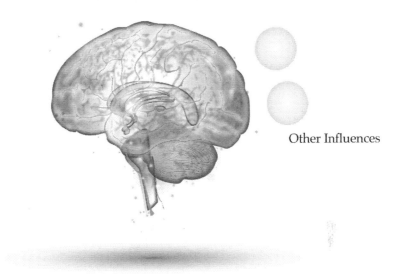

Other Influences

There are, however, other influences that are likely to be more specific to you.

We are all influenced by many other things, some consciously and some non-consciously. Here are some examples of things that might influence you:

1. Personal Memories

We are influenced to make decisions based upon past memories of how something of a similar nature worked out last time without thinking whether those conditions apply to the current situation or how this situation is similar or different to past occasions.

2. Beliefs, Values, Philosophies, Religion

We are always influenced by our long-standing internal views (see paradigms, world views, etc. from the previous section).

3. Prior Opinion or Knowledge

We are influenced by the knowledge or opinion that we have had of this situation in the past.

4. Intelligence

We are influenced by someone else's intelligence (as perceived by ourselves) or their lack of intelligence (again as perceived by ourselves). If we think someone is smart, we might always take their advice on face value rather than giving it due consideration. We might also be subject to the "halo" effect: if we think someone is good at one thing, we project that they are good at others too.

5. The Path of Least Resistance, Pain, or Risk

We tend to be influenced in our decisions by which is the easiest choice to make or pathway to take regardless as to whether it is in our own best interest or in the best interests of those around us.

6. Novelty

Some of us are influenced to try things that are new – they are attracted to new things, objects, and approaches and will adopt them just because they are new. Others are exactly the opposite and reject anything that is new. [314]

7. Necessity

We make decisions about whether we actually need to do something or not.

8. Urgency

We make decisions based upon whether we see them as urgent or not. In fact, we might leave out decision-making until things become urgent. (Is this a habit that you recognize in yourself?)

9. The Number of Choices Available

There is a body of research indicating that when we have too many choices, we become overwhelmed. In some cases, we plump for something at random, like the first one at hand. In other cases, we remove ourselves from the need to make the choice.

10. Familiarity and Comfort

We make decisions based on what we have done in the past and our familiarity or comfort with what has happened in the past. "It worked last time, so why wouldn't I do it again this time?"

11. Personal Connection or Rapport

Even though it may only be brief, we make decisions based upon a (possible fleeting) personal connection. How many of us go into a restaurant and ask the waitperson for their recommendation when, in fact, they know nothing about us?

12. Dream or Vision

We make a decision for against something based upon whether it fulfills or inhibits our ability to achieve a dream or vision.

13. Your Background Geography [315]

I brought this dynamic up under the section on world view and paradigms. I will expand on it here. As I mentioned, Nisbett compares the overall outlook on life between Asians and people of Western European descent. He offers a fascinating comparison between the "individual" orientation of the Western world vs. the "collective" orientation of the Eastern world and illustrates how this manifests itself.

He describes the different responses to the apparently straightforward request "Tell me about yourself."

> "North Americans will tell you about their personality traits ('friendly,' 'hardworking'), role categories ('teacher,' 'I work for a company that makes microchips'), and activities ('I go camping a lot'). Americans don't condition their self-descriptions much on context. The self-descriptions of Chinese, Japanese, and Koreans, on the other hand, very much depends on context. ('I am serious at work'; 'I am fun-loving with my friends.')"

The concept of context is expanded at a later stage in the book. On page 92, he describes an experiment that one of his students carried out. His student showed a number of animated underwater vignettes to students in Kyoto University and at the University of Michigan. I have decided to quote these paragraphs in their entirety as they describe it better than I ever could:

> "The scenes were all characterized by having one or more 'focal' fish, which were larger, brighter, and faster moving than anything else in the picture.

> Americans and Japanese made about an equal number of references to the focal fish, but the Japanese made more than 60 percent more references to background elements including the water, rocks, bubbles, and inert plants and animals. In addition, whereas Japanese and American participants made about equal number of references to movement involving active animals, the Japanese participants made almost twice as many references to relationships involving inert, background objects. Perhaps most tellingly, the very first sentence from the Japanese participants was likely to be one referring to the environment (e.g., 'It looked like a pond') whereas the first sentence from the Americans was three times as likely to be one referring to the focal fish (e.g., 'There was a big fish, maybe a trout, moving off to the left')."

So, this is nonconscious thought at the deepest level of world view. I do most of my work in Silicon Valley which has become massively inclusive in terms of Western and Eastern cultures. I have never heard a discussion, however, concerning the difference in fundamental, nonconscious thought patterns such as those described by Nisbett.

14. Influences from Other People

Finally, with regard to influencers, most of us have had a number of people who have been major influences in our lives. They could have been parents, uncles and aunts, close family friends, teachers, mentors, priests, etc. Their influence could have been positive or negative. What we do know is that their influence has an impact on who we are today and that reviewing their influence can be enlightening as to our view of ourselves.

For example, it might be useful at this point to do a "side-bar exercise." [‡]Take a sheet of paper and draw five columns. Now, think of 4, 5, or 6 people who have had a major influence on your life. These can be friends, parents, teachers, relatives, preachers, spouses, significant others, etc.

Write down each of their names on a separate line in column 1

---

‡ I learned this exercise many years ago from Jim Ewing – thanks Jim

For each of them write down:

> ➤ In column 2, the major influence or impact that they had on your life
> ➤ In column 3, a description of them as a person; this might include their job, their relationship to you, and some of why they had an impact
> ➤ In column 4, the positive characteristics or traits that you see or saw in them
> ➤ In column 5, the negative characteristics or traits that you see or saw in them

Once you have completed the exercise and filled out everything you can, review what you have written in the column of positive characteristics. What do you see in the way of patterns about these major influences? What words (or different words with similar meanings) do you see come up again and again? Use a highlighter, if necessary, to bring out the patterns.

Once you have identified these patterns in the positive traits column, repeat the same process with the negative traits column.

Typically, there is some relationship between the strengths (positive traits) and weaknesses (negative traits) we see in others and the strengths and weaknesses that we have, even though we may be blind to the connection.

On the strengths side of the balance sheet, when we see a strength in others it tends to come from one of two things. It is either:

> ➤ a strength that we have and comes from the viewpoint "You are just like me, therefore you must be a good person"
> ➤ a strength that we wish we had in ourselves, i.e., an area of opportunity for growth whether we have explicitly admitted it or not.

Take a look again at the strengths that you see in your major influencers, and see if there is any correlation with strengths you see in yourself or with attributes that you wish you had. Use the highlighter again, if necessary, to see the patterns. This is a great time to remind you of one thing – be honest with yourself here. There's no one to prove it to, no one to judge, and no one to take it away from you. Record what you notice together with any thoughts that this might bring up for what you want to take into the future.

On the weaknesses side, a similar process can be found. When we see a weakness in others, it tends to stem, again, from one of two areas:

> ➤ In the first instance, if you are strong in an area and the other people are weak, then it will come to your attention. The thinking goes something like this: "I'm good at this, and if only you were good at it, then you'd be just like me, and you'd be a good person too."
> ➤ On the other hand, we see weaknesses in others that are also weaknesses in ourselves. This time, the thinking goes like this: "I don't like this in you, and I don't like it in me either."

Take a look again at the weaknesses that you have noted in your major influencers, and see if there is any correlation to things that you notice about yourself. Again, be really honest.

If you feel like taking this exercise further, then you can always use the strengths and weaknesses that you have discovered in yourself as a basis of a conversation with key family and friends. You'll be amazed at what comes out of such conversations.

Which of the six Cialdini influences do you tend to be influenced by? Are these influences useful to you at this stage in your life? Which of the other, more personal, influences are you (knowingly) subject to? What other things influence you? Are these influences helpful? Who were the major influencers in your life? What impact are they still having?

Notes and References for "Understanding Your Self: Your Influencers":

[313] Cialdini, R. B. (2008). Influence: Science and Practice. Allyn and Bacon.

[314] Moore, G. (2014). Crossing the Chasm, 3rd Edition: Marketing and Selling Disruptive Products to Mainstream Customers (3rd ed.). HarperBusiness.

[315] Nisbett, R. E. (2004). The Geography of Thought: How Asians and Westerners Think Differently...and Why. Free Press.

Section C Part 4: Your Context

In this section, we will look at your past, where you are today, and where you want to be in the future. With this under your belt and with the information from the explorations about your brain and yourself, you will be able to develop a plan of action for moving forward.

Section C Part 4a. Your Past

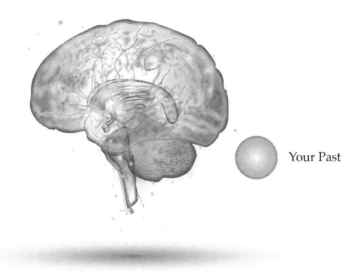

Your Past

Genetics

We are just starting to scrape the surface of how your genetics influences what you do and indeed, how what you do impacts your genes. For example, recent studies show that our abilities to successfully diet may, in some instances, be significantly driven by certain genes.

There has long been a debate about which is more important – nature or nurture? Well, according to Eric Turkheimer [316] in 2000, "The debate is over." According to Turkheimer, the impact of both nature and nurture can be summarized in terms of three laws:

First Law	*All human traits are heritable.*
Second Law	*The effect of being raised in the same family is smaller than the effect of genes.*
Third Law	*A substantial portion of the variation in complex human behavioral traits is not accounted for by the effects of genes or families.*

So, there you have it. Yes, no, or maybe. Seriously, what these laws say is what will seem to be intuitive to many of you…some of our behavior can be explained by our genes, some of it by how we were brought up, and some of it cannot be explained by either.

In 2015, a fourth law was suggested by Chabris et al [317] which states:
"A typical human behavioral trait is associated with very many genetic variants, each of which accounts for a very small percentage of the behavioral variability."

So, as we add to the laws we find, as we may have already come to expect when we are talking about the brain, "It's complicated."

At this stage, we can only say that genetics does play a role as does the way you were brought up, but neither of those factors explains everything.

Hopefully, as the science unfolds, we may know more about how all of this happens and its impact.

Your Personal Experiences

There is a large body of evidence that indicates that what happens to us in our childhood and adolescence casts a series of major shadows over the rest of our lives.

To pull all of the childhood and adolescent events that have had an impact on your life would probably take a long while. Absent that, take some time and recall those aspects of your upbringing that might cause you to react a certain way. Let's take a look at a few examples of the type of situation that might have caused an impact in your childhood:

➢ Growing up in a single parent family – for whatever reason
➢ Being an only child
➢ Being the eldest child
➢ Being the second eldest child
➢ Being the youngest child
➢ Being in an emotionally unstable household
➢ Being in an emotionally stable household
➢ Moving house frequently
➢ Never moving house
➢ Growing up rich/poor

➢ Being bullied
➢ Growing up in the country
➢ Growing up in the suburbs
➢ Growing up in the inner city
➢ Growing up in a highly religious household
➢ Growing up in an atheist or agnostic household
➢ Growing up with close relations who were in jail
➢ Growing up with an overbearing parent
➢ Growing up with absent parents (either physically or emotionally)

The list goes on. Any or all of these backgrounds can cause us to have different reactions to various threats or reward situations.

An example which arose recently was a mother reporting that her son was always getting into trouble at school. He was constantly called out by his teacher for acting up in class and was frequently sent to the school principal's office. Here's where the confusion came in.

Once he arrived at the principal's office, he became a different child: he became curious, well-behaved, and engaging. The principal was puzzled. On further questioning, it became clear that the boy was bored in class and acted out deliberately because he knew his reward would be to get attention from everyone and get involved with an interesting conversation with the principle who would answer all of his curiosity-based questions while he was sitting awaiting his "punishment." I wonder how this young man will behave when he is working for a manager at some time in the future, and he is bored with his job?

On a more personal note, when I was thirteen, in English class we were all asked to write a play for homework. At that time, I had never been to a play, and my only exposure to plays was reading Shakespeare out loud in a class of thirty boys, a dry and boring experience at the best of times for a thirteen-year-old. I had no idea where to start. I had, however, been around to a friend's house on several occasions, and they had a TV. So, I had seen some early TV shows. So, I based my play on what I had watched.

When my homework was reviewed in front of everyone in the class, my offering was ridiculed with the English master using me as an example of how not to write a play. I had changes of scenes every two or three lines. He pointed out how stupid that was, that that could never happen on a stage, and that I would never make a writer. He was correct. I didn't. I hated writing until I was in my mid-thirties when I realized how enjoyable it could be.

Life Cycles

The concept of life cycles was outlined in the Section C Part 2b entitled "Patterns of Behavior." If you did the exercise at that time, then there is no need to repeat it. If not, now would be a good time to do so.

But what else is going on for us over longer periods of our life? Decade to decade?

Frederic Hudson spent a good part of his life studying other people's lives and wrote several books on the subject. [318] [319] In *The Adult Years*, he gives titles to each of the decades of our adult lives as follows:

Twentysomething	*Breaking Out and Staking Out*
Thirtysomething	*Making It*
Fortysomething	*Taking Charge*
Fiftysomething	*Enjoying Life*
Sixtysomething	*Starting Over*
Seventysomething	*Living with Integrity*
Eightsomething	*Leaving a Legacy*
Ninetysomething	*Summing it UP*

He has us challenge a fundamental paradigm that we, at least we in the Western world, live by. He suggests that we have an underlying belief that our life will progress "up and to the right." By this he means that, if time is along the horizontal axis of a graph, and the quality of our life is on the vertical axis, then our belief is that our life will look like the first graph on the next page:

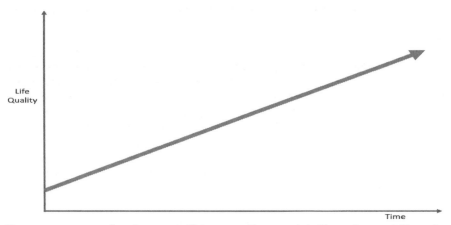

He goes on to say that in most of his research, people's lives do not follow that pattern or cycle. He suggests that our lives are more circular and that we repeat patterns…over and over again. More like this:

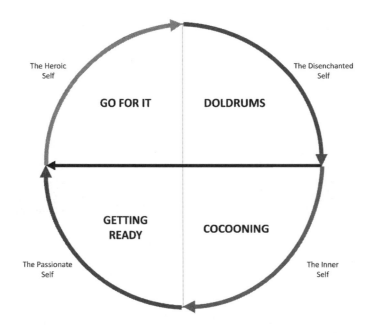

He suggests that our lives consist of chapters, and each chapter has four phases. We start with a dream or a vision, and we are all "gung ho" and ready to "Go for It" (the top left quadrant in the above diagram). Then, after some period of time, we reach a plateau: what we thought we were fascinated by, and attracted to, starts to wear thin. For some people, this plateau is because they have reached their dream or their work in that phase is done. We then enter into Phase II – the "Doldrums" (the top right quadrant in the above diagram).

After a while in the Doldrums, some of us make a slight change and start all over again, repeating the same thing (the left pointing arrow in the above diagram). Hudson calls this "restructuring the same chapter." This time round, it takes us a shorter time to reach the plateau, and we spend less time in the Doldrums. We might repeat this semicircular path a couple of times until we reach what Hudson refers to as "organismic disgust," i.e., we just can't take it anymore.

Then we really need to make a change. We dip below the midpoint and enter into the "Cocooning" phase (the bottom right quadrant in the above diagram). We step back from life, sometimes literally and physically and sometimes metaphorically. It is a time for reflection and healing. Then comes the turning point where we get a new sense of purpose and enter the next phase, "Getting Ready" (the bottom left quadrant in the above diagram). We again feel optimistic about the future, get creative, start to experiment, and are generally off and running again.

Hudson describes ten life skills required to successfully navigate these four phases. They bear repeating and I do so, verbatim, here:

Phase: Go for It.	Description: The Heroic Self
A **dream** or **vision** provides conviction, inspiration, and energy for constructing a life chapter. A **plan** schedules the dream with available resources and possibilities.	
Launching requires personal commitment, perseverance, and adaptations – and social and economic alignment.	
Plateauing sustains and deepens a successful functional life chapter.	
Phase: The Doldrums	**Description: The Disenchanted Self**
Managing the doldrums comes to terms with decline, negative emotions, and feeling trapped in an increasingly dysfunctional life chapter.	
Sorting things out results in a personal plan: what to keep, what to eliminate or change, what to add, and how to proceed into a revitalized life chapter.	
Ending a life chapter with dignity and care requires an ability to say farewell with gratitude and clarity, leaving you free to consider your next options. There are two possibilities at this point – restructuring the same chapter or making a life transition to a new chapter.	
Phase: Restructuring	
Restructuring, which conducts a mini-transition back into a refurbished life chapter, can be used to move across the center of the cycle if the life chapter can be improved with some specific changes. Restructuring is like minor surgery, with a strategic plan to make the life chapter work better – a new location, a new job, a new home, or a new partner. The same basic values and goals prevail, but the action steps, setting, and/or players in the drama are altered.	
Phase: Cocooning	**Description: The Inner Self**
Cocooning is the first activity of a life transition – turning inward to take stock. To find your own basic values and to disengage emotionally and mentally from the current life chapter. If the life chapter cannot be redeemed or if the optimal choice is to leave it in order to find a new and different one, the first step is to exit into a life transition where this cocooning skill is required. A life transition is like major surgery, usually resulting in personal development, new life options, and even transformation.	
Phase: Getting Ready	**Description: The Passionate Self**
Self-renewal follows from successful cocooning. It is the ability to be self-sustaining, producing confidence, energy, purpose, and hope. Self-renewal also involves a re-evaluation of core issues and beliefs.	

> **Experimenting**, the final and tenth skill of the cycle, engages you in being creative, learning, exploring, taking risk, and networking. When the self is ready to venture back into a life chapter, it takes on this skill.

So, consider where you are in the progression of your life cycle. Think whether you are on the track that is best for you at the moment. Consider whether there are any changes that you might want to be making. And consider how your Personal Threat Profile will help you or hinder you during the various phases and life skills required.

Recent Events

At any stage of our lives, recent events can cause us to go into a state that is different to that which we normally find ourselves in.

I was recently running a training workshop during which there was an optional debrief. One of the participants related that her Personal Threat Profile had changed over recent years. Several years ago, she would have placed the autonomy facet as her highest need. She had been laid off two years before, and it had taken her 18 months to find a new job. She and her kids had needed to leave their home. Her need for security now ranked far and ahead of all of the others.

On the other hand, if you had recently been through a major change at work, then it might be likely that you too would place security at the top of your list, even though that may not be your "normal" highest.

Are there any recent events in your life which will color how you respond to different threats and rewards?

Section C Part 4b. Your Future

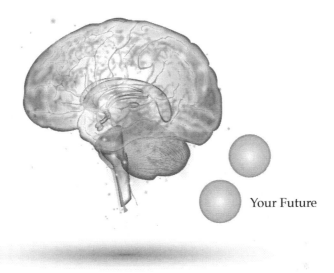

Your Future

Purpose, Vision, Passions and Dreams

Daniel Pink [320] identifies the three major motivators that drive us as autonomy, mastery, and purpose. He explains that the need for purpose has become ever important in the lives of both ends of the working population, i.e., the baby boomers at one end and Generation Y, millennials or echo boomers at the other. In his book *Start with Why*, [321] Simon Sinek makes a similar point. People want to get engaged with something that is bigger than them or bigger than the product that the company that they work for produces. We talked a little about this in the section on care and feeding of the brain – the need for a larger purpose in our lives.

The intent of this part of the book will differ for different people. For some, it will help them to capture the purpose that has been in their heart or their head for some time. For others, it will help them start to understand and develop their purpose.

For some people, their purpose on the planet became very clear to them early on in life, and hence, they were, and are, able to very easily line up their studies, pursuits, work, and energies behind that purpose and can pursue that purpose in everything they do. Their life's work is clear to them.

Not everyone, however, has that level of clarity. Having spent the past twenty-five years or so helping people think through what they want to with their lives, my suspicion is that there are many more of us who are not clear on our purpose than there are those who are clear. Most self-help books don't help either – they suggest that you find it – but don't offer a great deal of help in doing so. What if you can't identify or describe your purpose – or at least can't yet?

Sometimes our purpose, or some might define it as "calling," comes gradually. Some time back, I read an article in *Vanity Fair* magazine that talked about the work that Bono and Sir Bob Geldorf had done in pulling together a commitment from the G8 group to give $25 billion to Africa to overcome poverty. I sincerely doubt that when these two gentlemen were 21 years old, the concept of raising billions of dollars in this manner was in their sights. Maybe it was. For many of us, however, these things come to us gradually.

If you have a purpose that is clear to you, then great. Write it large and often. If you don't have one, then don't worry. It will become apparent at some stage in the future (maybe while you read this book and plan your journey but maybe not).

If you do not have or know your life's purpose, see whether the challenges below are useful in taking the first steps.

> ➤ Question: I don't know what my life's purpose is, but I have an inkling that it might be something to do with the following – and write down the thoughts that come to mind.

> ➤ Question: I don't know what my life's purpose is, but when I find it, it will most likely have some of the following attributes – and write down the thoughts that come to mind.

Some people state that they don't know what their purpose is, but they can state what their passion(s) is/are. *Webster's Dictionary* has many definitions of passion, and I am not going to quote them all – but here's one to go on with:

> *"A powerful emotion or appetite … and … boundless enthusiasm."*

My thesaurus adds:

> *"...fervor, ardor, obsession, infatuation, excitement, enthusiasm, zeal, craze, and delight."*

What I am looking for here are those things that, as someone once described it to me, "make your socks roll up and down!"

It doesn't matter what it is or how you describe it – it only has to mean something to you. So, as you complete the next thinking exercise just let the descriptions be those that are useful to you.

And don't forget that passions can be something that you just enjoy doing. For this exercise, it doesn't matter what they lead to, whether you'll ever make the news doing it, or whether you'll ever make money doing it. They are simply somethings that you want in your life going forward. If you want it, that's good enough.

I once taught a class where a colleague asked the class two key questions. The first was what job they were doing, and the second was what job did they think they would be doing in five years. People wrote down their answers and read them out one by one. My colleague then asked, "If I could guarantee you a million dollars a month for forever…now, what job would you be doing in five years?" Of the thirty people in the class, twenty-eight responded with a lot more enthusiasm, and I might add, with a different job. Asking yourself those questions might be one way that you can identify your passion. (Curiously enough, the two that had the same job in five years with or without the $1 million were both fashion designers!)

✗ Caution. Ensure that the passions that you are identifying and recording are those that are going to see you well into the future – what are those passions that you choose to pursue at this time?

✗ Caution. Ensure that they truly are your passions and that you are not living out someone else's dream!

✗ Caution. Ensure that they you do not equate them with talent. You can have a passion to do something and not be good at it.

To kick start your thinking, McLean and Hudson [322] summarized a list of passions as follows:

> ➤ Personal Mastery
> ➤ Achievement
> ➤ Intimacy
> ➤ Play & Creativity
> ➤ Search for Meaning
> ➤ Compassion & Contribution

Personally, I think there are many more passions at a much more granular level, but please make up your own.

Take some time and write down your passions.

Dreams? To some extent I am starting to split hairs at this point. I'm not sure we really know the difference between a desire and a passion or a passion and a dream. I include this extra category, however, for a specific reason. In the past when I have been working with people to help them chart out their future, some people have said something to the effect, "Well, I don't have a passion to travel – I mean, I wouldn't want to become a travel writer or anything like that, but I really want to go to Moscow someday – it's been a dream of mine for a long while."

So, it is time to capture those things that you would like to get into your future picture. They can be as straightforward as you want or as off the wall as you want. Your bucket list as it were.

So, what?

Why is all of this important? Why do we need to know our purpose, passions, and dreams to determine how we might react to certain threats or rewards?

In his books, [323] Bill Bridges talks about the losses that are associated with change. Let's take a look at a couple of examples.

If something happens at work that causes you to fear the loss of a dream, it is likely to impact the way you respond. If your brain perceives a cue that would act as a threat against your passions or your dreams, then that could trigger you.

On the other hand, if someone offers you an opportunity at work that they perceive as a reward, yet you do not see it as in line with your purpose, passion, or dream, or, worse yet, getting in the way of these things, then again, you will probably also have a threat response.

261

Your Values

Many years ago, when I was in my late twenties, I was asked to do an exercise and write down my personal values. I had never been asked such a question, and to be honest, didn't really know what the question meant. As the facilitator started to talk about some examples, I suddenly realized what a powerful question it really was. What were those things that I truly stood for? My father had been a policeman and one of the principles that had been drilled into us was that of honesty – it didn't matter what you had done or what the consequences were of owning up, be honest! So, honesty was clearly a value for me. As a policeman, he had also instilled a sense of being on time so that was a value – or was it? Was this simply his value, and I didn't care about it? I also had a passion for beautiful things so was beauty a value?

Hudson [324] suggests that there are "six abiding core values of adult life" as follows:

- ➢ A Sense of Self
- ➢ Achievement
- ➢ Intimacy
- ➢ Creativity and Play
- ➢ Search for Meaning
- ➢ Compassion and Contribution

You will notice a crossover between these and the 5 P's.

It took me a while to sort out my own value list, and I encourage you now, as the first part of becoming an expert on yourself, to take some time and sort out your own – or rather what values you want to hold on to as part of your future.

Some people can simply write down their values list. Others find it difficult to get started. If need be, and in order to spark your thinking, I have included a samples values list on the next page. If you use this list, you may find it useful to pick up a highlighter and while reading through, highlight those that immediately strike you as things that you want in the next chapter of your life.

✓ Caution. It is easy to read the list and highlight them all and start saying to yourself, "Yeah, that's important, yeah that's important, yeah that's important…" and so on. Resist the urge. Be discriminatory. If you have more than 12 to 20, it might be easier to go back through the list and be honest with yourself – what are the ones that are truly the most important to you as you move forward? Imagine someone sitting on your shoulder asking you this question – truly important?

✓ Caution. It is easy to delude yourself into thinking that a certain value "should be important to me, therefore, I'll highlight it." If it truly isn't important to you at this stage in your life, be honest with yourself – and move along. By the way, you are the only one reading the book. ☺

✓ Caution. And this is the opposite of the one above – if something truly is important to you, but you're not paying attention to it today, then highlight it.

Once again, we can ask the question "So, what?"

Again, if something happens at work that causes you to experience an "attack" on your values, it is likely to impact the way you respond. If your brain perceives a cue that would act as a threat against your values, then that could trigger you.

Acceptance	Accountability	Achievement	Adaptability	Administration
Advancement	Adventure	Aesthetics	Affect	Affection
Alignment	Art	Assertion	Authority	Awe
Balance	Beauty	Being Liked	Being Myself	Being Supportive
Belonging	Care	Celebration	Collaboration	Comfort
Communication	Community	Competence	Competitiveness	Competition
Confidence	Congruence	Construction	Contemplation	Control
Cooperation	Coordination	Cosmic purpose	Courtesy	Craft
Creativity	Curiosity	Decisiveness	Design	Detachment
Dexterity	Directedness	Discernment	Discipline	Discovery
Diversity	Duty	Dwelling	Ecology	Economic Security
Education	Efficiency	Empathy	Endurance	Entrepreneur
Equality	Equilibrium	Ethics	Evaluation	Expansion
Expressiveness	Faith	Fame	Family	Family Life
Fantasy	Fate	Fidelity	Flexibility	Focus
Food	Freedom	Friendship	Function	Generosity
Growth	Happiness	Harmony	Healing	Health
Helpfulness	Honesty	Honor	Hope	Hospitality
Human Dignity	Human Rights	Humor	Ideation	Image
Independence	Initiation	Information	Innovation	Insight
Integration	Integrity	Intellectual	Interdependence	Intimacy
Involvement	Joy	Justice	Knowledge	Labor
Law and Order	Leisure	Liberation	Life	Limitation
Listening	Love	Loyalty	Meaning	Meditation
Membership	Mission	Moderation	Morality	Nature
Nurture	Obedience	Obligation	Order	Originality
Ownership	Patience	Patriotism	Personal Issues	Physical Affection
Physical Pleasure	Pioneerism	Planning	Play	Pleasure
Possessions	Presence	Preservation	Prestige	Productivity
Profit	Progress	Property	Prophecy	Propriety
Power	Purpose	Rationality	Rebellion	Recreation
Recognition	Relaxation	Research	Respect	Responsibility
Rights	Risk taking	Ritual	Rules	Safety

Salvation	Science	Search	Security	Self-Actualization
Self-assertion	Self-Competence	Self-Confidence	Self-Development	Self-Discipline
Self-Esteem	Self-Interest	Self-Preservation	Self-Respect	Self-Worth
Sensory Pleasure	Service	Sexuality	Sharing	Shelter
Simplicity	Social Concern	Solitude	Spiritual	Stability
Status	Stimulation	Success	Survival	Synergy
Technology	Tradition	Transcendence	Trust	Truth
Uniformity	Unity	Vision	Vocation	Warmth
Wealth	Wholeness	Wisdom	Work	Workmanship

Your Environment

The environment that envelops you will also have an impact on your actions and reactions on a daily, hourly, and possibly, moment to moment basis. The role or roles that you play, your living situation, how you spend your free time, your commute, the challenges you face…the list goes on. All of these things will impact the way in which you respond to the threats and rewards that your daily life will throw at you. Here's a partial list of the things to take into consideration:

> Your personal frame of mind
> Your relationship with significant others
> Your family situation
> Your friendships
> Your social situation
> Your community contribution
> Your hobbies and leisure time activities
> Your professional situation and contribution, i.e., your work and career
> Your house and living situation
> Your political leanings and those of the people that you engage with
> Your economic and financial situation
> Your sense of the enormity of the impact of climate change
> Your health – mental, emotional, and physical
> Your view of and use of technology
> Your spirituality
> Your sense of personal growth

This is not intended to be a complete list but a pointer to the type of things that you might consider when thinking about your own environment and what is working, what is not, and what you might want to change.

If I might add some spice to your thinking, George Vaillant [325] participated in what I believe is (or was) the longest running study of aging in the world. I believe it started off by being called the Grant Study and later became the Harvard Study on Aging. The results of the study are fascinating. The study started in 1937 and consisted of several hundred subjects who were followed from the time they left college until they were in their eighties and nineties. They participated in a biennial written survey and numerous face to face interviews over that time. The researchers were looking for the fundamental principles that make for a successful life. The participants finished their working lives in a very wide range of situations ranging from the proverbial drunk under the bridge through to very successful business people.

The learnings from the study? Here are some of them (from the books with some additions):

- That everyone has challenges: Success comes from recognizing that they are challenges, putting them in perspective, dealing with them, and then moving on, leaving the challenges behind rather than dwelling on them.
- It is not the bad things that happen that doom us; it is the good people who happen to us, at any age, that facilitate an enjoyable old age.
- Healing relationships are facilitated by a capacity for gratitude, for forgiveness, and for taking people inside.
- A good marriage at 50 predicted positive aging at 80. Surprisingly, low cholesterol levels did not.
- Alcohol abuse – unrelated to unhappy childhood – constantly predicted unsuccessful aging.
- Learning to play and create after retirement and learning to gain younger friends as we lose older ones add more to life's enjoyment than retirement income.
- Objective good health was less important than subjective good health. (George explains this as meaning that it is all right to be ill as long as you don't feel sick.)

Section C Part 4c. Your Present

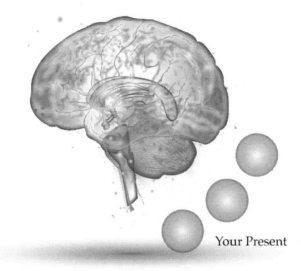

Your Present

The previous sections regarding your context have looked at the past and the future. This section will look at who you are today. It will address your strengths and weaknesses, some of the characteristics that you bring to bear on every situation, and the way that you are currently looking at your life. Let's get started.

Strengths and Weaknesses

There are a number of ways of identifying these. You probably know most of them anyway. Most of us do. Simply writing two columns on a sheet of paper is the easiest way.

Another way of getting at them is the "influence" exercise that I outlined in a previous section. That will identify some of the more hidden ones and is worth doing if you haven't done so already.

Another method is to ask your friends and family. While this can sometimes be a painful exercise, and although in some cases they may not be willing to be fully candid with you, it is a quick way of learning a lot about yourself. This approach, however, can be very difficult for some of our brains. Depending on your Personal Threat Profile, it can feel very threatening to hear your weaknesses from other people whom you hold near and dear. If, for example, your need to feel equal or more important than others is very high, this may not be the best tack for you. Or if your need to be right is very high, again it may not be the best way for you to learn.

Over the past several decades, there has been significant growth in the Positive Psychology Movement. One outcome of this has been the rise of the Strengths Movement, best illustrated by the Gallup Organization and one of its alumni, Marcus Buckingham. One of Buckingham's books [326] has become somewhat of a best-seller; you can buy the book and get access to an online assessment of your strengths. Buckingham categorizes 34 strengths; the book describes all 34, and the assessment identifies your top 5. The general strategy of the Strengths approach is twofold:

➢ That if you play to your strengths in life, then you'll increase your chance of being successful.
➢ If you focus on your weaknesses, then you are wasting your time because you will never become really good at them.

There are at least two schools of thought on this approach. The first school of thought supports the idea that focusing on your strengths is a good idea. The opposite school of thought says that it is not a good idea. The second school suggests that to become a more well-rounded person, you need to leverage your strengths but mitigate against your weaknesses. One example of this opposite school of thought is offered by Robert Kaiser. [327] Here are some of the downsides of only focusing on strengths (from Kaiser's book with some additions):

➢ They can become overused – if the only tool you have is a hammer, everything looks like a nail.
➢ They can continue to be used when they are no longer needed in the situation.
➢ They become flaws when the situation requires a different skill set.
➢ They can be useful – until the situation changes.
➢ What is seen as a strength in one culture can be seen as a weakness in another.
➢ Mastering the art of leadership requires learning to do some things that don't come naturally.
➢ A focus on strengths can promote stagnation and inhibit learning and development.
➢ Strengths can become weaknesses through overuse and over reliance.

Peter Drucker was a proponent of the strengths-based approach – with a caveat. "Most people think they know what they are good at; they are usually wrong."

Research shows that, if we're not very good at something, we tend to overrate our abilities, and if we are really good at something, we tend to underrate our abilities. The Dunning-Kruger effect rears its ugly head again!

Intelligence

A discussion of strengths and weaknesses would not be complete without some discourse on intelligence. I think most people are aware of and understand the concept of IQ. And many people are still under a couple of illusions about IQ. First, that it is a good way of measuring intelligence. Second, that is the only way of measuring Intelligence. Let's dig a little deeper.

The concept of IQ was introduced in the early 1900s, and it became widely adopted as a standard measure of intelligence. Until the 1980s, that is, when the concept of a single way of measuring intelligence started to get challenged, particularly by Howard Gardner. [328] Gardner introduced the concept of multiple intelligences. Over time, he has identified nine separate intelligences namely:

➢ mathematical-logical
➢ verbal-linguistic
➢ musical-rhythmic
➢ bodily-kinesthetic
➢ interpersonal

267

- ➤ intrapersonal
- ➤ visual-spatial
- ➤ naturalist
- ➤ existential

As a small caution, Gardner's work has met with some debate and criticism since he first introduced it, although my assessment is that we can all get significant value out of recognizing different intelligences.

Since the time of the introduction of multiple intelligences, Daniel Goleman has introduced the concepts of emotional intelligence [329] and social intelligence, [330] David Livermore, the concept of cultural intelligence, [331] and Esther Perel, the concept of erotic intelligence. [332] There may be others that have been introduced, and who knows what other intelligences might be introduced in the near future? The point here is that when we are reviewing our strengths or weaknesses with regard to intelligence, then all of these different intelligences need to become part of our consideration.

So, finding out what your real strengths are, where your areas of weaknesses are, and where things might tend to go wrong (or, in the field of management, where you might tend to get derailed) is an important step.

The Players on Your Team

Have you ever had to answer a survey or a questionnaire that gives you a range of answers with the instructions "Pick which is most like you"? You sit for a moment or two and the true answer that you want to respond with is "It depends."

It depends on a number of things. It might depend on how you feel at that moment. It might depend on the time of day that you are thinking about. It might depend on what has just happened to you.

We are not people who have a single cohesive personality. This is one of the reasons why I have developed a healthy skepticism for personality assessments. Very rarely do people fit neatly into one personality label or type. We all tend to exhibit different characteristics at different times. In fact, many of us display different characters on a regular and predictable basis, depending on what is going on. I call these different characters the different "players" on your team.

Let's step back for a moment and consider Carl Jung. Jung believed that we were driven by both our conscious thoughts and our nonconscious thoughts. He divided the nonconscious into our personal nonconscious and the collective nonconscious. He identified a number of commonly accepted archetypes.

They were/are:

The Innocent	The Lover
The Orphan/Regular Guy or Gal	The Creator
The Hero	The Jester
The Caregiver	The Sage
The Explorer	The Magician
The outlaw	The Ruler

You can find these explained in more detail in Appendix C Part 3. Most of us have aspects of many of these archetypes. Some people have all of them. See if you can identify yours.

It is easier for some people to take one hundred points and allocate them across the twelve, based upon how much of that character shows up in their daily lives.

So, that was Jung's approach. He introduced us to the concept of multiple characters without it being considered as an illness or that something was wrong with us. That was a great step forward but not enough for some like Assagioli. In the spirit of Jung, he suggested that we had these multiple characters, but they were not restricted to Jung's twelve archetypes. Assagioli developed a therapeutic approach based on multiple personalities which he called psychosynthesis which he discusses in his book *Psychosynthesis* [333] – for me, this is a somewhat arcane and unapproachable book, so be warned. He called the multiple characters "subpersonalities."

He suggested that we could identify our subpersonalities, and, in doing so, we could heal ourselves so that we could synthesize the subpersonalities into a meaningful, harmonized whole rather than allowing the separate personalities to play out on their own, possibly clashing with each other.

He went further to suggest that what holds these subpersonalities together is the "self" and the self does so through the act of will. He describes this in his book, *The Act of Will*. Again, for me, this is a somewhat difficult book. [334] Assagioli's approach, however, is well explained by Piero Ferrucci in his summary. [335]

In more recent times, Rita Carter [336] has taken this subpersonality approach and integrated it with the Five Factor Inventory I mentioned at the beginning of the second part of this book. In addition, in her descriptions, she has overlaid it with our more recent knowledge of the brain, to come up with an approach which she calls "multiplicity."

Carter identifies six functional categories and multiple characteristics within those categories. Her brief descriptions might be useful to assist you in identifying your own.

You will see some overlap with Jung's archetypes but not a total one-to-one mapping.

Whichever of these three approaches you use, it is very useful to identify, recognize, and honor all of your subpersonalities, whether you like them or not. It is most often when a subpersonality is neglected or becomes overbearing or just no longer useful, it gets us into trouble.

I have used this "multiple characters" or "the players on your team" approach many times in coaching sessions. It often helps clients understand the multiple, and sometimes conflicting, parts of themselves and helps explain the "It depends" syndrome that I mentioned earlier. And it can be used to take explicit approaches to different situations.

Defenders	Protect and guard us against threats, both real and imagined.	
	The Guardian	Watches out and alerts us to danger. Driven by our limbic system.
	The Worrier	Worries unnecessarily about things that could go wrong – inventing many of them – all the time.
	The Pleaser	Ensures that we stay on the good side of people – safe from anger and dislike.
	The Fighter	Hits out against threats – first.
Controllers	Drive and steer our behavior.	
	The Wise Friend	Grown-up, sensible voice – driven by the prefrontal cortex.
	The Driver	Gets us going and keeps us going.
	The Organizer	Puts things in place and gives us order in our lives.
Punishers	Defenders and controllers whose energy has become misdirected.	
	The Critic	Constantly monitors us and others – and points out where we (and they) have failed.
	The Bully	Probably a Fighter who hits out without cause.
	The Martyr	Probably was a Pleaser – now sacrifices our own ambitions and aims.
Role Players	Subpersonalities created for a particular situation or purpose.	
	The Success	Keeps up appearances – especially where failure is not an option.
	The Professional	Similar to the Driver but addresses the job at hand, most frequently, work.
	The Boss	Attempts to control others and the situation at all times.
	The Clown	Amuses others – and often does so in order to draw attention to themselves.
Relics	Old subpersonalities that no longer have a useful function.	
	The Abandoned Child	Lives out past emotional episodes.
	The Mule	Stubborn and uncooperative for no justifiable reason.
Creatives	Where our new ideas, aims, and visions come from.	
	The Artist	Sees things that need to be made and works out how to make them happen.
	The Dreamer	Thinks about how things could be but lacks the Artist's follow through.

Let me give an example of its use. Many years ago, I was working with a client, ME, who was a VP of Sales. She was a well-dressed, highly successful, put together woman who, in most aspects of her life, was on top of things. Except with her ex-husband. Although well-off, he would constantly fail to pay alimony and child support, and she had to go back to court on many occasions. While in court, all of the past emotions and feelings that she would have for him would arise, she would feel sorry for him, and would let him off. Then feel bad about it afterwards.

We identified her various subpersonalities. There were, of course, some obvious ones: wife, mother, daughter, church-goer, do-gooder, sympathetic ear, and successful sales person. Then there were some that were a little less obvious: rebel, sensual flirt, and risk-taker. She gave them all names. I asked her who showed up as the VP of Sales. She described this very crisp, no-nonsense person who was a fair but demanding boss. I asked her which of the subpersonalities best represented the VP of Sales? Her reply, "None of the above. She's another one altogether. I am going to call her Miss Strictly Business." As we examined her court visits, she realized that the wife, do-gooder, and sympathetic ear were the characters that showed up in the courtroom.

It got her nowhere. She determined that as a strategy, at the next court visit she made, the only personality she was going to take into the room was the Miss Strictly Business character. She knew how to do it but had never used those characteristics outside of the VP setting. That next court visit, she got exactly what she wanted.

If you elect to take this approach, I suggest that you take a sheet of paper and draw on it a number of circles, as shown below. I show twelve here, but any reasonably large number will work.

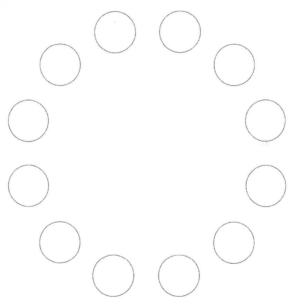

Then fill out each of the circles with a name, description, or character type that is applicable to the subpersonality that you have identified. Once you have done this, review each with the same type of detail as Jung's archetypes, i.e., what is/are their:

> Motto(s):
> Core desire(s):
> Goal(s):
> Greatest fear(s):
> Strengths:
> Weakness:
> Strategy/Strategies:
> Talent(s):

This process will provide you with some more insight into "the players on your team."

Once you have identified them all, take a look at the following:

> ➢ Are there cases two or more of the characters join together to make powerful allies?
> ➢ Are there cases where there is inner conflict between two or more of the characters.
> ➢ Which of the characters gets to make most of your decisions – and under what conditions?
> ➢ Which of the characters contributes most in your life?
> ➢ Which of the characters would you like to see more of as you move forward?
> ➢ Which of the characters would you like to see less of as you move forward?

Here are some of the typical characters that my past clients have discovered in themselves:

> ➢ A friendly parent
> ➢ A harsh parent
> ➢ A loving spouse/partner
> ➢ An indifferent or cold spouse/partner
> ➢ A happy child
> ➢ An unhappy child
> ➢ A playful child
> ➢ A sexually repressed spouse/partner
> ➢ A judge
> ➢ A flirt
> ➢ A lazy self

If you want to go into this area in more detail, you could take one of the personality/character profiles that I mentioned earlier and answer the profile as if you were one of the subpersonalities. You are less likely to find yourself answering "It depends" and more likely to get a rich description of that subpersonality.

Your Current Outlook

If you are wanting to make a change, then what is happening to you right now plays an important role. If there's a lot going on, for example, then sometimes it's not the best time to throw in yet another change. Sometimes it's exactly the opposite. Nothing could be worse than piling something else on. It will depend on your personal thirst for change and your overall Personal Threat Profile. It might also depend on your current Personal Threat Context, especially with regard to what degree of control and choice you believe you have.

Also, important to note when making changes is that they need to be broken down into manageable steps. The brain ultimately experiences change as a threat. Smaller changes mean smaller threats and hence can be managed more successfully by the PFC. Over time, as change is successful, the brain will tolerate larger steps for change.

So, the first thing to look at is your current situation. For you, make a decision on whether you want to add another thing in to the mix right now. Consider where you are in the Hudson life cycle. Where are you and what comes next? Boredom?

Cocooning? Consider the strengths that you have. Which strengths will help you through a change? Consider the subpersonalities that you have. Which can you bring to bear on the change? Maybe there's some smaller changes that you can make in advance of some bigger ones.

The next thing to consider are your current goals. What is already on your plate to get done? Immediate, short-term, medium-term and long-term goals. If you choose to make a change, which of these goals will no longer be necessary and/or will disappear? How much spare time will you have to devote to working on the change? (It does take extra work. ☺)

Your current attitude needs to be taken into consideration. If you are feeling positive about life in general, then that can be a perfect time to consider what you want to move to next. If you are not feeling so positive, then step back for a moment. Will the change improve your attitude or make it worse? What about the extra effort involved? Attempting a change with the wrong attitude not only makes it more difficult, but it increases the chance of failure. That makes this change unsuccessful but anchors something negative about change in your mind. On the other side of the coin, if you are feeling low, then maybe, as the old saying goes, "A change will do you good."

Finally, what is your current stress level? As you will have read earlier, adding yet more stress into an already stressful life can have dire consequences. Take a look back at the stressor list. Even things like "revision of personal habits," "change in sleeping habits," and "change in eating habits" all add some, if not a huge, amount of stress.

Notes and References for "Understanding Your Self: Your Context":

[316] Turkheimer, E. (2000). Three Laws of Behavior Genetics and What They Mean. Current Directions in Psychological Science, 9(5), 160–164.

[317] Chabris, C. F., Lee, J. J., Cesarini, D., Benjamin, D. J., & Laibson, D. I. (2015). The Fourth Law of Behavior Genetics. *Current Directions in Psychological Science*, *24*(4), 304–312. http://doi.org/10.1177/0963721415580430

[318] Hudson, F. (1999). The Adult Years: Mastering the Art of Self-Renewal. Jossey-Bass.

[319] McLean, P. D., & Hudson, F. M. (2011). LifeLaunch: A Passionate Guide to the Rest of Your Life (5 ed.). The Hudson Institute Press.

[320] Pink, D. (2011). Drive. Riverhead Books.

[321] Sinek, S. (2011). Start With Why: How Leaders Inspire Everyone to Take Action. Portfolio.

[322] McLean, P. D., & Hudson, F. M. (2011). LifeLaunch: A Passionate Guide to the Rest of Your Life (5 ed.). The Hudson Institute Press.

[323] Bridges, W. (1992). Surviving Corporate Transition (3rd ed.). William Bridges and Associates.

[324] Hudson, F. (1999). The Adult Years: Mastering the Art of Self-Renewal. Jossey-Bass.

[325] Vaillant, G. (1977). Adaptation to Life (1st ed.). Little, Brown.

[326] Buckingham, M., & Clifton, D. O. (2001). Now, Discover Your Strengths (1st ed.). Gallup Press.

[327] Kaiser, R. B. (2009). The Perils of Accentuating the Positive. Hogan Press (March 4, 2009).

[328] Gardner, H. (2006). Multiple Intelligences: New Horizons in Theory and Practice. Basic Books.

[329] Goleman, D. (2005). Emotional Intelligence (10 ed.). Bantam Books.

[330] Goleman, D. (2006). Social Intelligence: The New Science of Human Relationships. Bantam.

[331] Livermore, D. (2009). Cultural Intelligence: Improving Your CQ to Engage Our Multicultural World (Youth, Family, and Culture). Baker Academic.

[332] Perel, E. (2017). Mating in Captivity: Unlocking Erotic Intelligence. Harper Paperbacks.

[333] Assagioli, R. (1971). Psychosynthesis: A Manual of Principles and Techniques. Viking Compass.

[334] Assagioli, R. (1977). The Act of Will. Penguin Books.

[335] Ferrucci, P. (2009). What We May Be: Techniques for Psychological and Spiritual Growth Through Psychosynthesis. TarcherPerigee.

[336] Rita Carter, 2008, Multiplicity

Summary

It was ten years ago that I first discovered that we have brains. Of course, I am joking, but that was the time when I decided to focus my attention on our brains and how they impact what we do on a moment by moment basis. Since then, I have read hundreds of books and thousands of papers. And I am constantly amazed at the new discoveries that are being made on a weekly basis, if not daily. The more I have learned, the more I have realized that we are still only just scratching the surface.

I started my investigative journey thinking, like I believe most people do, that my brain was under my control. I assumed that my will, if you like, was what was driving the whole show. It has been a humbling experience to learn I am really not in the driver's seat and that my brain has a mind of its own!

Here are a few thoughts from my own personal list of surprises:

- 99% of the activity of the brain is occurring at a nonconscious level.
- I knew that we were all biased but to learn that even when we learn about our biases it is tough do anything about them.
- The large number of biases that we can be subject to.
- We often behave irrationally – for a whole variety of reasons.
- Social or emotional pain is handled in the brain in a very similar way to physical pain or the threat of physical pain.
- There are so many untruths and myths circulating about the brain.
- The degree to which chronic stress is bad for us … both our bodies and our brains.
- The large number of things that can act as triggers to put us under stress.
- The large number of things that influence our brains (and hence our thinking) that we are not consciously aware of … anchoring numbers in our brains, for example.
- The complexity of interactions between the brain and other parts of our bodies … the brain and the gut, for example.
- The interactions between our different senses that influence taste.

I wonder what your own list of surprises covers?

Let me take a moment and review where we've been for the last two hundred pages or so. At the very highest level, obviously, I have given you a few models of how to look at your brain and how to look at your "Self." That may have set in motion some thoughts on how you might want to change a few things. Maybe. Maybe not.

Here's what we covered about the brain:

- What the brain is made of.
- The Five Brain Principles (One purpose, two modes, three layers, four processes, and five driving forces).
- The Five Driving Forces (Protection, Participation, Prediction, Purpose, and Pleasure).
- The Five Brain Dynamics (Our biases, irrationality, stress, resisting change, and the fact that we are driven by internal rhythms).
- The many myths about the brain.
- How to keep your brain healthy.

And here's what we covered about the "Self," i.e., YOU!

> That you can take a deeper look at yourself, what you are driven by, and how you might react and behave by using some simple profiles.
> You can identify some of your tendencies by looking at your habits, biases, patterns, triggers, and the world view that you hold.
> You can examine how the general influences that we all have and your specific influences and influencers affect you.
> Looking at your context, you can help explain why you are driven (or not) to do certain things and resist others, i.e., what has happened in your past, where you want to be in the future, and what is going on in your world right now.

In order to pull all of this together and apply it to the various challenges and changes that you will inevitably face, you will need a healthy brain. The research suggests that you can best do this by:

> Identifying what your stress drivers are by using the Personal Threat Profile.
> Identifying your current Personal Threat Context.
> Ensuring that you have a good, healthy diet.
> Exercising appropriately.
> Using deep breathing as a way of ameliorating your reaction to stress.
> Getting an appropriate amount of sleep.
> Associating with the appropriate people.
> Having a healthy relationship with a significant other.
> Having a spiritual life which works for you.
> Holding a future-oriented, positive and growth-oriented attitude.
> Creating a positive and supportive social life, i.e., family and friends.
> Being mindful and practicing a meditation regime that works for you.
> Listening to music or playing an instrument.
> Using brain training exercises.
> Being careful about your use of technology.
> Increasing your education and engaging in intellectual pursuits.
> Being ethical and moral, surrounding yourself with similar people, and engaging in business and political practices that support those values.

In the early part of the book, I cited a song from Pink Floyd. Maybe it would be appropriate to finish by leveraging another line from the song:

> "The time is gone. The song is over.
> Thought I'd something more to say."

There is so much more to say…which is why I wanted to tell you about the next book(s).

If you are interested in some help in taking what you have just learned and applying it at work and at home, there are two more books in progress. I described these briefly at the very beginning – they are *A Field Guide to Using Your Brain at Work* and *A Field Guide to Using Your Brain at Home*. The current structure of the first one is shown below, and the outline of the second is shown after that.

Lastly, thank you for spending time reading the book. I appreciate it.

A Field Guide to Using Your Brain at Work

A. Your Brain on its Own
1. Find Out Who You Are
2. Personal Change
3. Focus, Attention, and Willpower
4. Stress Mastery & Resilience
5. Time and Energy Management
6. Self-awareness
7. Decision-Making
8. Personal Innovation/Insight
9. Presence
10. Mindfulness
11. Happiness

B. Your Brain with Another Person
1. Find Out Who They Are
2. Change Facilitation
3. Bias and the Nonconscious Brain
4. Communicating
5. Trust
6. Performance Management
7. Delegation
8. Coaching
9. Recruiting
10. Influencing & Negotiation
11. Encouraging Innovation in Others
12. Handling Conflict
13. Collaboration
14. Motivation
15. Selling

C. Your Brain with Several Other People (i.e., a Team)
1. Find Out Who They Are
2. Changing the Team and its Direction
3. Innovation and Brain-Storming in the Team
4. Diversity & Inclusion
5. Developing High-Performing Teams and Psychological Safety
6. Team Process
7. Facilitating the Team and Meeting Management
8. Visioning and Team Direction

D. Your Brain in an Organization
1. Find Out Who They Are, Why They are There, and What They Stand For
2. Change Management
3. Values/Culture/Diversity
4. Engagement
5. Visioning
6. Creating a Culture of Innovation
7. Predicting Change, the VUCA Environment, and Wicked Problems

A Field Guide to Using Your Brain at Home

A. Your Brain on its Own
B. Your Brain with Your Partner
C. Your Brain in the Family
D. Your Brain in the Community

Understand Your Brain:
For a Change

Appendices

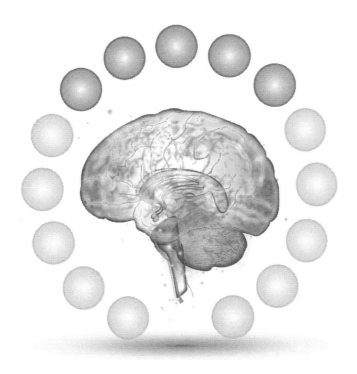

Appendices

Appendix A: Biases
Appendix B: Influences
Appendix C: Some Items in More Detail

Appendix A: Biases

In this Appendix, I have collected a number of biases that I have discovered delivering workshops over the years.

The first set of biases, social biases, are those that have arisen from asking the simple question, "What are you biased about?" (78 currently identified)

The second set, cognitive biases, are those downloaded from the *Wikipedia* website. (189 currently identified)

The third set, which I am currently calling neurodiversity biases, are those biases that seem to arise as a result of how our brains and personalities influence our decisions. (54 currently identified)

That brings our current total to over 320. I am convinced that there are many more in each category. I also am convinced that these categories are porous, i.e., some biases may be part of two or more categories. Please send me any that you discover.

Part 1: Social Biases

These have arisen from various workshops that I have delivered over the past several years. They came from asking the simple question, "What do you notice that you are biased about?"

Accent	We attribute certain characteristics to accents (national, regional, and local).
Age	Ageism is rampant (young and old).
Asexuality	People who are not interested in sexual relations – in any direction.
Attractiveness	More attractive people tend to earn more.
Bigger	In the western part of the world, bigger is often considered as better – and we, generally, have this bias.
Blindness	We tend to shy away from people who are blind.
Body Art	Tattoos make a powerful statement.
Body Type	Shape of one's body can influence how people perceive your ability.
Car	The car (or other vehicle you drive) has an impact at first sight.
Career Women	For or against? Expectations?
Career/Job	What do you do? – one of the first questions asked in the Western world.
Chest/Breast Size	For men *and* women.
Child Status	Bias for/against having/not having children; being a single parent.
Clear Skin	See complexion.
Club Memberships	What club you belong to can be important to some.
Complexion	Judgments about current (or past) facial complexion issues.
Country/State/City of Origin	Where are you from?
Deafness	One of the silent disabilities.
Diet	Keto, vegan, vegetarian. This has an impact for some, for or against.
Dress	The dress code that one wears – jeans and T-shirt influence.
Education Level	For or against people with higher or lower education.
Ethnicity	No need to explain this one.
Facial Hair	For or against – "All the execs are clean shaven."
Facial Jewelry	Can put some people off.
Facial Stigma	Something on someone's face impacts our impression of that person.
Facial Measurements	Distance between the nose and mouth and the nose and chin.

Favorite Sports	Favorite sport, e.g., hunting. People can be strongly for or against.
Favorite Teams	Team allegiance can be very strong and biasing.
Fragrance	Men and women.
Gender	No need to explain this one.
Geography	Where you come from impacts what people think of you. For example, British.
Geography of Thought	Where you come from impacts how you think. East vs. West, legal structure, etc. We have a tendency, in the West, to focus on the "big fish."
Good Looks (For and Against)	We attribute good looks with other abilities – or not.
Grammar	The use of grammatically incorrect sentences can influence the listener.
Gum Chewing	If someone is chewing gum, what assumptions do you make?
Gun Ownership/Control Advocacy	For or against.
Hair Color	Can have influence, especially on first impressions.
Hair Sheen	Lustrous gets more attention because it indicates good health.
Hair Style	Biases against short hair on women and long hair or ponytails on men.
Height	Taller people tend to have better jobs and higher wages.
Income	For or against people with higher or lower incomes.
Inconsiderate	If someone is inconsiderate, what do you interpret about that person?
Introverted or Extroverted	Often depends on your own temperament.
Language	The use of language can be striking.
Lips	Fuller lips tend to get more attention.
Loudness	Often depends on your own temperament.
Marital Status	Bias for or against married, single, or divorced.
Military	Must be good if you were with the military.
Muscularity	Body fitness.
Neighborhood	Exactly which part?
Past Firms/Organizations	"Correct" firms or organizations to have worked for, e.g., consulting, military.
Political Party	No need to explain.
Pregnancy	Pregnant women – for or against?
Pupil Size	Women to men.
Race	No need to explain this one.

Renter or Owner	If you rent or own your own house – particularly associated with age and country.
Scent	Powerful scent – can be positive or negative.
School/University Attended	Some colleges are acceptable and others no – or what if no college?
Sexual Orientation	No need to explain this one.
Skin Color	No need to explain this one.
Smoking	For or against.
Social class	For or against – in either direction.
Socio-economic status	Assumptions regarding someone who is higher or lower in socioeconomic status.
Sports enthusiasm	Can't visit on Monday – football's on.
Spectrum	How do we view people who are on the spectrum?
Stay-at-Home Moms/Dads	For or against.
Stupidity/ Senselessness	When someone or some system seems senseless.
Style	Different personality styles will attract or detract.
Symmetry	Symmetry of features and their relation to health.
Up and to the Right	We have a tendency to think that "success" is up and to the right.
Visible disability	How do we respond to someone who is visibly disabled?
Vocabulary	The ability to be able to speak well and have a wide vocabulary.
Voice	Women, in general, are attracted to lower voices. Men, in general, are attracted to higher voices.
Waist-to-Hip Ratio	0.7
Wearing (or Not) Make-up	For or against.
Wearing Glasses	Seen as more serious when wearing glasses (especially women).
Weight	Often see a bias against people with weight issues and tend to make assumptions.
Women's Marital Surname	Married males seen as more feminine, less masculine, and less powerful when the female keeps her own name.

Part 2: Cognitive Biases (Decision-making, Belief, and Behavioral Biases)

These were downloaded from Wikipedia on July 2, 2018, and were translated from the English spelling to the American. They may have changed slightly since then. Wikipedia divides them into three groups:

1. Decision-making, belief, and behavioral biases
2. Attributional biases
3. Memory errors and biases

Ambiguity Effect	The tendency to avoid options for which missing information makes the probability seem "unknown."
Anchoring or Focalism	The tendency to rely too heavily, or "anchor," on one trait or piece of information when making decisions (usually the first piece of information acquired on that subject).
Anthropocentric Thinking	The tendency to use human analogies as a basis for reasoning about other, less familiar, biological phenomena.
Anthropomorphism or Personification	The tendency to characterize animals, objects, and abstract concepts as possessing humanlike traits, emotions, and intentions.
Attentional Bias	The tendency of our perception to be affected by our recurring thoughts.
Automation Bias	The tendency to depend excessively on automated systems which can lead to erroneous automated information, overriding correct decisions.
Availability Heuristic	The tendency to overestimate the likelihood of events with greater "availability" in memory which can be influenced by how recent the memories are or how unusual or emotionally charged they may be.
Availability Cascade	A self-reinforcing process in which a collective belief gains more and more plausibility through its increasing repetition in public discourse (or "repeat something long enough and it will become true").
Backfire Effect	The reaction to disconfirming evidence by strengthening one's previous beliefs.
Bandwagon Effect	The tendency to do (or believe) things because many other people do (or believe) the same. Related to groupthink and herd behavior.
Base Rate Fallacy or Base Rate Neglect	The tendency to ignore base rate information (generic, general information) and focus on specific information (information only pertaining to a certain case).
Belief Bias	An effect where someone's evaluation of the logical strength of an argument is biased by the believability of the conclusion.
Ben Franklin Effect	A person who has performed a favor for someone is more likely to do another favor for that person than they would be if they had received a favor from that person.
Berkson's Paradox	The tendency to misinterpret statistical experiments involving conditional probabilities.

Bias Blind Spot	The tendency to see oneself as less biased than other people or to be able to identify more cognitive biases in others than in oneself.
Bystander Effect	The tendency to think that others will act in an emergency situation.
Cheerleader Effect	The tendency for people to appear more attractive in a group than in isolation.
Choice-Supportive Bias	The tendency to remember one's choices as better than they actually were.
Clustering Illusion	The tendency to overestimate the importance of small runs, streaks, or clusters in large samples of random data (that is, seeing phantom patterns).
Confirmation Bias	The tendency to search for, interpret, focus on, and remember information in a way that confirms one's preconceptions.
Congruence Bias	The tendency to test hypotheses exclusively through direct testing instead of testing possible alternative hypotheses.
Conjunction Fallacy	The tendency to assume that specific conditions are more probable than general ones.
Conservatism (Belief Revision	The tendency to revise one's belief insufficiently when presented with new evidence.
Continued Influence Effect	The tendency to believe previously learned misinformation even after it has been corrected. Misinformation can still influence inferences one generates after a correction has occurred.
Contrast Effect	The enhancement or reduction of a certain stimulus's perception when compared with a recently observed, contrasting object.
Courtesy Bias	The tendency to give an opinion that is more socially correct than one's true opinion so as to avoid offending anyone.
Curse of Knowledge	When better-informed people find it extremely difficult to think about problems from the perspective of lesser-informed people.
Declinism	The predisposition to view the past favorably (rosy retrospection) and future negatively.
Decoy Effect	Preferences for either option A or B change in favor of option B when option C is presented, which is completely dominated by option B (inferior in all respects) and partially dominated by option A.
Default Effect	When given a choice between several options, the tendency to favor the default one.
Denomination Effect	The tendency to spend more money when it is denominated in small amounts (e.g., coins) rather than large amounts (e.g., bills).
Disposition Effect	The tendency to sell an asset that has accumulated in value and resist selling an asset that has declined in value.
Distinction Bias	The tendency to view two options as more dissimilar when evaluating them simultaneously than when evaluating them separately.
Dunning–Kruger Effect	The tendency for unskilled individuals to overestimate their own ability and the tendency for experts to underestimate their own ability.

Duration Neglect	The neglect of the duration of an episode in determining its value.
Empathy Gap	The tendency to underestimate the influence or strength of feelings, in either oneself or others.
Endowment Effect	The tendency for people to demand much more to give up an object than they would be willing to pay to acquire it.
Exaggerated Expectation	Based on the estimates, real-world evidence turns out to be less extreme than our expectations (conditionally inverse of the conservatism bias).
Experimenter's or Expectation Bias	The tendency for experimenters to believe, certify, and publish data that agree with their expectations for the outcome of an experiment, and to disbelieve, discard, or downgrade the corresponding weightings for data that appear to conflict with those expectations.
Focusing Effect	The tendency to place too much importance on one aspect of an event.
Forer Effect or Barnum Effect	The observation that individuals will give high accuracy ratings to descriptions of their personality that supposedly are tailored specifically for them but are in fact vague and general enough to apply to a wide range of people. This effect can provide a partial explanation for the widespread acceptance of some beliefs and practices, such as astrology, fortune telling, graphology, and some types of personality tests.
Framing Effect	Drawing different conclusions from the same information, depending on how that information is presented
Frequency Illusion	The illusion in which a word, a name, or other thing that has recently come to one's attention suddenly seems to appear with improbable frequency shortly afterwards. This illusion is sometimes referred to as the Baader-Meinhof phenomenon.
Functional Fixedness	Limits a person to using an object only in the way it is traditionally used.
Gambler's Fallacy	The tendency to think that future probabilities are altered by past events when in reality they are unchanged. The fallacy arises from an erroneous conceptualization of the law of large numbers. For example, "I've flipped heads with this coin five times consecutively, so the chance of tails coming out on the sixth flip is much greater than heads."
Hard-Easy Effect	Based on a specific level of task difficulty, the confidence in judgments is too conservative and not extreme enough.
Hindsight Bias	Sometimes called the "I knew it all along" effect, the tendency to see past events as being predictable at the time those events happened.
Hostile Attribution Bias	The "hostile attribution bias" is the tendency to interpret others' behaviors as having hostile intent, even when the behavior is ambiguous or benign.
Hot-Hand Fallacy	The "hot hand fallacy" (also known as the "hot hand phenomenon" or "hot hand") is the fallacious belief that a person who has experienced success with a random event has a greater chance of further success in additional attempts.

Hyperbolic Discounting	Discounting is the tendency for people to have a stronger preference for more immediate payoffs relative to later payoffs. Hyperbolic discounting leads to choices that are inconsistent over time – people make choices today that their future selves would prefer not to have made, despite using the same reasoning. Also known as current moment bias, present-bias, and related to dynamic inconsistency. A good example of this: a study showed that when making food choices for the coming week, 74% of participants chose fruit, whereas when the food choice was for the current day, 70% chose chocolate.
Identifiable Victim Effect	The tendency to respond more strongly to a single identified person at risk than to a large group of people at risk.
IKEA Effect	The tendency for people to place a disproportionately high value on objects that they partially assembled themselves, such as furniture from IKEA, regardless of the quality of the end results.
Illusion of Control	The tendency to overestimate one's degree of influence over other external events.
Illusion of Validity	Belief that our judgments are accurate, especially when available information is consistent or inter-correlated.
Illusory Correlation	Inaccurately perceiving a relationship between two unrelated events.
Illusory Truth Effect	A tendency to believe that a statement is true if it is easier to process or if it has been stated multiple times, regardless of its actual veracity. These are specific cases of truthiness.
Impact Bias	The tendency to overestimate the length or the intensity of the impact of future feeling states.
Information Bias	The tendency to seek information even when it cannot affect action.
Insensitivity to Sample Size	The tendency to under expect variation in small samples.
Irrational Escalation	The phenomenon where people justify increased investment in a decision based on the cumulative prior investment, despite new evidence suggesting that the decision was probably wrong. Also known as the sunk cost fallacy.
Law of the Instrument	An overreliance on a familiar tool or methods, ignoring or undervaluing alternative approaches. "If all you have is a hammer, everything looks like a nail."
Less-is-Better Effect	The tendency to prefer a smaller set to a larger set judged separately but not jointly.
Look-Elsewhere Effect	An apparently statistically significant observation may have actually arisen by chance because of the size of the parameter space to be searched.
Loss Aversion	The disutility of giving up an object is greater than the utility associated with acquiring it.
Mere Exposure Effect	The tendency to express undue liking for things merely because of familiarity with them.
Money Illusion	The tendency to concentrate on the nominal value (face value) of money rather than its value in terms of purchasing power.

Moral Credential Effect	The tendency of a track record of non-prejudice to increase subsequent prejudice.
Negativity Bias or Negativity Effect	Psychological phenomenon by which humans have a greater recall of unpleasant memories compared with positive memories.
Neglect of Probability	The tendency to completely disregard probability when making a decision under uncertainty.
Normalcy Bias	The refusal to plan for, or react to, a disaster which has never happened before.
Not Invented Here	Aversion to contact with or use of products, research, standards, or knowledge developed outside of a group. Related to IKEA effect.
Observer-Expectancy Effect	When a researcher expects a given result and therefore unconsciously manipulates an experiment or misinterprets data in order to find it (see also subject-expectancy effect).
Omission Bias	The tendency to judge harmful actions as worse, or less moral, than equally harmful omissions (inactions).
Optimism Bias	The tendency to be over-optimistic, overestimating favorable and pleasing outcomes (see also wishful thinking, valence effect, positive outcome bias).
Ostrich Effect	Ignoring an obvious (negative) situation.
Outcome Bias	The tendency to judge a decision by its eventual outcome instead of based on the quality of the decision at the time it was made.
Overconfidence Effect	Excessive confidence in one's own answers to questions. For example, for certain types of questions, answers that people rate as "99% certain" turn out to be wrong 40% of the time.
Pareidolia	A vague and random stimulus (often an image or sound) is perceived as significant, e.g., seeing images of animals or faces in clouds, the man in the moon, and hearing nonexistent hidden messages on records played in reverse.
Pessimism Bias	The tendency for some people, especially those suffering from depression, to overestimate the likelihood of negative things happening to them.
Placebo Effect	The belief that a medication works – even if merely a placebo.
Planning Fallacy	The tendency to underestimate task-completion times.
Post-Purchase Rationalization	The tendency to persuade oneself through rational argument that a purchase was of good value.
Pro-innovation Bias	The tendency to have an excessive optimism towards an invention or innovation's usefulness throughout society, while often failing to identify its limitations and weaknesses.
Projection Bias	The tendency to overestimate how much our future selves share one's current preferences, thoughts, and values, thus leading to suboptimal choices.
Pseudo Certainty Effect	The tendency to make risk-averse choices if the expected outcome is positive, but make risk-seeking choices to avoid negative outcomes.

Reactance	The urge to do the opposite of what someone wants you to do out of a need to resist a perceived attempt to constrain your freedom of choice (see also reverse psychology).
Reactive Devaluation	Devaluing proposals only because they purportedly originated with an adversary.
Recency Illusion	The illusion that a word or language usage is a recent innovation when it is in fact long-established (see also frequency illusion).
Regressive Bias	A certain state of mind wherein high values and high likelihoods are overestimated while low values and low likelihoods are underestimated.
Restraint Bias	The tendency to overestimate one's ability to show restraint in the face of temptation.
Rhyme as Reason Effect	Rhyming statements are perceived as more truthful. A famous example being used in the O.J Simpson trial with the defense's use of the phrase, "If the gloves don't fit, then you must acquit."
Risk Compensation / Peltzman Effect	The tendency to take greater risks when perceived safety increases.
Selection Bias	The tendency to notice something more when something causes us to be more aware of it, such as when we buy a car, we tend to notice similar cars more often than we did before. They are not suddenly more common, we just are noticing them more. Also called the observational selection bias.
Selective Perception	The tendency for expectations to affect perception.
Semmelweis Reflex	The tendency to reject new evidence that contradicts a paradigm.
Sexual Over Perception Bias/Sexual Under Perception Bias	The tendency to over/underestimate sexual interest of another person in oneself.
Social Comparison Bias	The tendency, when making decisions, to favor potential candidates who don't compete with one's own particular strengths.
Social Desirability Bias	The tendency to over report socially desirable characteristics or behaviors in oneself and underreport socially undesirable characteristics or behaviors.
Status Quo Bias	The tendency to like things to stay relatively the same.
Stereotyping	Expecting a member of a group to have certain characteristics without having actual information about that individual.
Subadditivity Effect	The tendency to judge probability of the whole to be less than the probabilities of the parts.
Subjective Validation	Perception that something is true if a subject's belief demands it to be true. Also assigns perceived connections between coincidences.
Surrogation	Losing sight of the strategic construct that a measure is intended to represent and subsequently acting as though the measure is the construct of interest.

Survivorship Bias	Concentrating on the people or things that "survived" some process and inadvertently overlooking those that didn't because of their lack of visibility.
Time-Saving Bias	Underestimations of the time that could be saved (or lost) when increasing (or decreasing) from a relatively low speed and overestimations of the time that could be saved (or lost) when increasing (or decreasing) from a relatively high speed.
Third-person Effect	Belief that mass communicated media messages have a greater effect on others than on themselves.
Parkinson's Law of Triviality	The tendency to give disproportionate weight to trivial issues. Also known as bike-shedding, this bias explains why an organization may avoid specialized or complex subjects, such as the design of a nuclear reactor, and instead focus on something easy to grasp or something rewarding to the average participant, such as the design of an adjacent bike shed.
Unit Bias	The tendency to want to finish a given unit of a task or an item. Strong effects on the consumption of food in particular.
Weber–Fechner Law	Difficulty in comparing small differences in large quantities.
Well-Travelled Road Effect	Underestimation of the duration taken to traverse oft-traveled routes and overestimation of the duration taken to traverse less familiar routes.
"Women Are Wonderful" Effect	A tendency to associate more positive attributes with women than with men.
Zero-Risk Bias	Preference for reducing a small risk to zero over a greater reduction in a larger risk.
Zero-Sum Bias	A bias whereby a situation is incorrectly perceived to be like a zero-sum game (i.e., one person gains at the expense of another).

Part 3: Cognitive Biases (Attributional Biases)

Actor-Observer Bias	The tendency for explanations of other individuals' behaviors to overemphasize the influence of their personality and underemphasize the influence of their situation (see also fundamental attribution error), and for explanations of one's own behaviors to do the opposite (that is, to overemphasize the influence of our situation and underemphasize the influence of our own personality).
Authority Bias	The tendency to attribute greater accuracy to the opinion of an authority figure (unrelated to its content) and be more influenced by that opinion.
Defensive Attribution Hypothesis	Attributing more blame to a harm-doer as the outcome becomes more severe or as personal or situational similarity to the victim increases.
Egocentric Bias	Occurs when people claim more responsibility for themselves for the results of a joint action than an outside observer would credit them with.
Extrinsic Incentives Bias	An exception to the fundamental attribution error, when people view others as having (situational) extrinsic motivations and (dispositional) intrinsic motivations for oneself.
False Consensus Effect	The tendency for people to overestimate the degree to which others agree with them.
Forer Effect (aka Barnum Effect)	The tendency to give high accuracy ratings to descriptions of their personality that supposedly are tailored specifically for them but are in fact vague and general enough to apply to a wide range of people. For example, horoscopes.
Fundamental Attribution Error	The tendency for people to overemphasize personality-based explanations for behaviors observed in others while underemphasizing the role and power of situational influences on the same behavior.
Group Attribution Error	The biased belief that the characteristics of an individual group member are reflective of the group as a whole or the tendency to assume that group decision outcomes reflect the preferences of group members even when information is available that clearly suggests otherwise.
Halo Effect	The tendency for a person's positive or negative traits to "spill over" from one personality area to another in others' perceptions of them (see also physical attractiveness stereotype).
Illusion of Asymmetric Insight	People perceive their knowledge of their peers to surpass their peers' knowledge of them.
Illusion of External Agency	When people view self-generated preferences as instead being caused by insightful, effective, and benevolent agents.
Illusion of Transparency	People overestimate others' ability to know them, and they also overestimate their ability to know others.
Illusory Superiority	Overestimating one's desirable qualities and underestimating undesirable qualities relative to other

	people. (Also known as the "Lake Wobegon effect," "better-than-average effect," or "superiority bias.")
In-Group Bias	The tendency for people to give preferential treatment to others they perceive to be members of their own groups.
Just-World Hypothesis	The tendency for people to want to believe that the world is fundamentally just, causing them to rationalize an otherwise inexplicable injustice as deserved by the victim(s).
Moral Luck	The tendency for people to ascribe greater or lesser moral standing based on the outcome of an event.
Naïve Cynicism	Expecting more egocentric bias in others than in oneself.
Naïve Realism	The belief that we see reality as it really is – objectively and without bias, that the facts are plain for all to see, that rational people will agree with us, and that those who don't are either uninformed, lazy, irrational, or biased.
Outgroup Homogeneity Bias	Individuals see members of their own group as being relatively more varied than members of other groups.
Self-Serving Bias	The tendency to claim more responsibility for successes than failures. It may also manifest itself as a tendency for people to evaluate ambiguous information in a way beneficial to their interests.
Shared Information Bias	Known as the tendency for group members to spend more time and energy discussing information that all members are already familiar with (i.e., shared information) and less time and energy discussing information that only some members are aware of (i.e., unshared information).
Sociability Bias of Language	The disproportionally higher representation of words related to social interactions in comparison to words related to physical or mental aspects of behavior in most languages. This bias attributed to nature of language as a tool facilitating human interactions. When verbal descriptors of human behavior are used as a source of information, sociability bias of such descriptors emerges in factor-analytic studies as a factor related to prosocial behavior (for example, of extraversion factor in the Big Five Personality Traits).
System Justification	The tendency to defend and bolster the status quo. Existing social, economic, and political arrangements tend to be preferred and alternatives disparaged, sometimes even at the expense of individual and collective self-interest. (See also status quo bias.)
Trait Ascription Bias	The tendency for people to view themselves as relatively variable in terms of personality, behavior, and mood while viewing others as much more predictable.
Ultimate Attribution Error	Similar to the fundamental attribution error, in this error a person is likely to make an internal attribution to an entire group instead of the individuals within the group.
Worse-Than-Average Effect	A tendency to believe ourselves to be worse than others at tasks which are difficult.

Part 4: Cognitive Biases (Memory Errors and Biases)

Bizarreness Effect	Bizarre material is better remembered than common material.
Choice-Supportive Bias	In a self-justifying manner, retroactively ascribing one's choices to be more informed than they were when they were made.
Change Bias	After an investment of effort in producing change, remembering one's past performance as more difficult than it actually was.
Childhood Amnesia	The retention of few memories from before the age of four.
Conservatism or Regressive Bias	Tendency to remember high values and high likelihoods/probabilities/frequencies as lower than they actually were and low ones as higher than they actually were. Based on the evidence, memories are not extreme enough.
Consistency Bias	Incorrectly remembering one's past attitudes and behavior as resembling present attitudes and behavior.
Context Effect	That cognition and memory are dependent on context, such that out of context memories are more difficult to retrieve than in-context memories (e.g., recall time and accuracy for a work-related memory will be lower at home and vice versa).
Cross-Race Effect	The tendency for people of one race to have difficulty identifying members of a race other than their own.
Cryptomnesia	A form of misattribution where a memory is mistaken for imagination because there is no subjective experience of it being a memory.
Egocentric Bias	Recalling the past in a self-serving manner, e.g., remembering one's exam grades as being better than they were or remembering a caught fish as bigger than it really was.
Fading Affect Bias	A bias in which the emotion associated with unpleasant memories fades more quickly than the emotion associated with positive events.
False Memory	A form of misattribution where imagination is mistaken for a memory.
Generation Effect (Self-Generation Effect)	Self-generated information is remembered best. For instance, people are better able to recall memories of statements that they have generated than similar statements generated by others.
Google Effect	The tendency to forget information that can be found readily online by using Internet search engines.
Hindsight Bias	The inclination to see past events as being more predictable than they actually were; also called the "I-knew-it-all-along" effect.
Humor Effect	Humorous items are more easily remembered than non-humorous ones, which might be explained by the

	distinctiveness of humor, the increased cognitive processing time to understand the humor, or the emotional arousal caused by the humor.
Illusion of Truth Effect	People are more likely to identify as true statements those they have previously heard (even if they cannot consciously remember having heard them), regardless of the actual validity of the statement. In other words, a person is more likely to believe a familiar statement than an unfamiliar one.
Illusory Correlation	Inaccurately remembering a relationship between two events.
Lag Effect	The phenomenon whereby learning is greater when studying is spread out over time, as opposed to studying the same amount of time in a single session. See also spacing effect.
Leveling and Sharpening	Memory distortions introduced by the loss of details in a recollection over time, often concurrent with sharpening or selective recollection of certain details that take on exaggerated significance in relation to the details or aspects of the experience lost through leveling. Both biases may be reinforced over time and by repeated recollection or retelling of a memory.
Levels-of-Processing Effect	Different methods of encoding information into memory have different levels of effectiveness.
List-Length Effect	A smaller percentage of items are remembered in a longer list, but as the length of the list increases, the absolute number of items remembered increases as well. For example, consider a list of 30 items ("L30") and a list of 100 items ("L100"). An individual may remember 15 items from L30, or 50%, whereas the individual may remember 40 items from L100, or 40%. Although the percent of L30 items remembered (50%) is greater than the percent of L100 (40%), more L100 items (40) are remembered than L30 items (15).
Misinformation Effect	Memory becomes less accurate because of interference from post-event information.
Modality Effect	That memory recall is higher for the last items of a list when the list items were received via speech than when they were received through writing.
Mood-Congruent Memory Bias	The improved recall of information congruent with one's current mood.
Next-in-Line Effect	People taking turns speaking in a group tend to have diminished recall for the words of others who spoke immediately before them.
Part-List Cueing Effect	Being shown some items from a list and later retrieving one item causes it to become harder to retrieve the other items.
Peak-End Rule	People seem to perceive not the sum of an experience but the average of how it was at its peak (e.g., pleasant or unpleasant) and how it ended.
Persistence	The unwanted recurrence of memories of a traumatic event.

Picture Superiority Effect	The notion that concepts that are learned by viewing pictures are more easily and frequently recalled than are concepts that are learned by viewing their written word form counterparts.
Positivity Effect (Socioemotional Selectivity Theory)	That older adults favor positive over negative information in their memories.
Primacy effect, Recency Effect & Serial Position Effect	That items near the end of a sequence are the easiest to recall, followed by the items at the beginning of a sequence; items in the middle are the least likely to be remembered.
Processing Difficulty Effect	Information that takes longer to read and is thought about more (processed with more difficulty) is more easily remembered.
Reminiscence Bump	The recalling of more personal events from adolescence and early adulthood than personal events from other lifetime periods.
Rosy Retrospection	The remembering of the past as having been better than it really was.
Self-Relevance Effect	Memories relating to the self are better recalled than similar information relating to others.
Source Confusion	Confusing episodic memories with other information, creating distorted memories.
Spacing Effect	That information is better recalled if exposure to it is repeated over a long span of time rather than a short one.
Spotlight Effect	The tendency to overestimate the amount that other people notice your appearance or behavior.
Stereotypical Bias	Memory distorted towards stereotypes (e.g., racial or gender).
Suffix Effect	Diminishment of the recency effect because a sound item is appended to the list that the subject is not required to recall.
Suggestibility	A form of misattribution where ideas suggested by a questioner are mistaken for memory.
Telescoping Effect	The tendency to displace recent events backward in time and remote events forward in time so that recent events appear more remote and remote events, more recent.
Testing Effect	The fact that you more easily remember information you have read by rewriting it instead of rereading it.
Tip of the Tongue Phenomenon	When a subject is able to recall parts of an item, or related information, but is frustratingly unable to recall the whole item. This is thought to be an instance of "blocking" where multiple similar memories are being recalled and interfere with each other.
Travis Syndrome	Overestimating the significance of the present. It is related to the enlightenment idea of progress and chronological snobbery with possibly an appeal to novelty logical fallacy being part of the bias.

Verbatim Effect	The "gist" of what someone has said is better remembered than the verbatim wording This is because memories are representations not exact copies.
von Restorff Effect	An item that sticks out is more likely to be remembered than other items.
Zeigarnik Effect	That uncompleted or interrupted tasks are remembered better than completed ones.

Part 3: Neurodiversity Biases

This is a draft version of work under development at the moment. As I have studied biases over the past twenty years or so, the ones that have been identified in the first two parts of this Appendix are often addressed in training programs.

The biases that might arise from different behavioral characteristics, personality characteristics, or brain strengths are less frequently addressed. They deserve more attention, hence their inclusion here. Once again, I invite comment and contribution to this list.

The ones that I have selected are simply some more common representatives. I am sure there are others that could have been included.

FFI Factors	Openness to Experience	
	Conscientiousness	
	Extraversion/Introversion	
	Agreeableness	
	Neuroticism	
Personality Factors	Social Styles	
Threat Profile	Protection	
	Participation	
	Prediction	
	Purpose	
	Pleasure	
Brain Factors	Perception	Recognition and interpretation of sensory stimuli (smell, touch, hearing, etc.).
	Sustained Attention	Ability to sustain concentration on a particular object, action, or thought, and ability to manage competing demands in our environment.
	Controlled Attention	Ability to sustain concentration on a particular object, action, or thought, and not get distracted by our own thoughts.
	Working Memory	Be able to hold in memory all of the information required to deal

		effectively with the problem at hand (limited storage capacity.
	Recall Memory	Be able to recall the information associated with the content and context of the problem at hand (unlimited storage capacity).
	Processing Speed	Speed of processing other functions.
	Motor Coordination	Ability to mobilize our muscles and bodies and ability to manipulate objects.
	Inhibition	Planned and non-impulsive in decision-making and reactions and the ability to withstand internally driven urges.
	Flexibility	The capacity for quickly switching to the appropriate mental mode.
	Executive Function	Abilities that enable goal-oriented behavior, such as the ability to plan and execute against a goal.
	Theory of Mind	Insight into other people's inner world, their plans, their likes, and their dislikes.
	Anticipation	Prediction based on pattern recognition.
	Problem-Solving	Defining the problem in the right way to then generate solutions and pick the right one.
	Decision-Making	The ability to make decisions based on problem-solving and incomplete information.
	Identifying Emotions	The ability to tune into face and body cues to effectively interpret other people's natural intentions and authenticity.
	Emotion Self-Regulation	The ability to have insight into their own nonconscious biases and factor that awareness into their decisions and actions.
	Language Ability	Skills allowing us to generate sounds into words and generate verbal output.

	Visual and Spatial Processing	Ability to process incoming visual stimuli, to understand spatial relationship between objects, and to visualize images and scenarios.
	Sequencing	The ability to break down complex actions into manageable units and prioritize them in the right order.
BRISC Components*	Stress Level	To have insight into what stresses them and be in control or have mastery over their stress.
	Anxiety Level	The ability to not react out of fear, to not exaggerate threats, and to adapt to threats.
	Mood Level	The ability to be in control of their moods and be upbeat most of the time.
DASS Components**	Positivity-Negativity Bias	Put threat or potential threat into context, encouraging new ideas in themselves and others – a positive influence and having positive contagion.
	Resilience	The ability to bounce back very quickly from setbacks and obstacles and maintain their course of action in spite of those setbacks.
	Social Capacity	The ability to have high connections with others and to magnify and leverage those connections.
Multiple Intelligences	Naturalist*	Understanding living things and reading and relating to nature.
	Musical	Discerning sounds, their pitch, tone, rhythm, and timbre.
	Logical-Mathematical	Quantifying things, making hypotheses, and proving them.
	Existential	Tackling the questions of why we live and why we die.
	Interpersonal	Sensing people's feelings and motives.

---

* Brief Risk-Resilience Index for Screening
** Depression, anxiety, and stress scale
* Descriptions from Mark Vital, https://blog.adioma.com/9-types-of-intelligence-infographic/, downloaded July 6, 2018.

	Bodily-Kinesthetic	Coordinating your mind with your body.
	Linguistic	Finding the right words to express what you mean.
	Intra-Personal	Understanding yourself, what you feel, and what you want.
	Spatial	Visualizing the world in 3D.
Team Membership**	Resource Investigator	Outgoing, enthusiastic, explores opportunities, and develops contacts.
	Team Worker	Co-operative, perceptive, and diplomatic. Listens and averts friction.
	Coordinator	Mature, confident, identifies talent, and clarifies goals.
	Plant	Creative, imaginative, free-thinking, generates ideas, and solves difficult problems.
	Monitor-Evaluator	Sober, strategic, and discerning. Sees all options and judges accurately.
	Specialist	Single-minded, self-starting, and dedicated. They provide specialist knowledge and skills.
	Shaper	Challenging, dynamic, thrives on pressure. Has the drive and courage to overcome obstacles.
	Implementer	Practical, reliable, efficient. Turns ideas into actions and organizes work that needs to be done.
	Completer-Finisher	Painstaking, conscientious, anxious. Searches out errors. Polishes and perfects.

** Downloaded from http://www.belbin.com/about/belbin-team-roles/. I have only used the positive descriptions here.

Appendix B: Influences

Cialdini, who I have mentioned many times, has spent a good deal of his professional career studying influence. Here are the six principles of influence that he has identified:

Principle #1: Reciprocation

Reciprocation recognizes the fact that people feel indebted to those who do something for them or give them a gift. This indebtedness is felt even if the gift they are given is not something that they asked for or even want. And it happens at a nonconscious level.

Cialdini says: *"The implication is you have to go first. Give something: give information, give free samples, give a positive experience to people, and they will want to give you something in return."*

Two examples will serve to illustrate this principle:

Example 1 – Tips

When I use this example in workshops, people are blown away. In advance of telling them about the influence, we ask them what influences the amount of tip they give at a restaurant. The answers are typically the quality of the food, the service from the wait staff, and the ambience of the overall dining experience. I then show them the following data.

Behavioral Scientist David Strohmetz examined the impact of the wait staff leaving a gift (a piece of candy for each diner) on the same plate as the bill at the end of a meal in a restaurant.

Results:

Condition	Increase in tip
A single piece of candy left on the plate	3.3%
Two pieces of candy left on the plate	14.1%
A single piece of candy, followed by a return to the table with an extra piece	23%

Example 2 – Sticky Notes

Social scientist Randy Garner published a 2005 experiment that tested whether sticky notes could persuade people to respond to a marketing survey. He sent one-third of the surveys with a hand-written sticky note requesting completion, one-third with a blank sticky note, and one-third without a sticky note. The results:

Condition	Response Rate
Hand-written note	69%
Blank sticky note:	43%
No sticky note	34%

"[The principle of reciprocation] was born out in the fact that not only did those who received the hand-written note have twice as much compliance, the quality of the answers they gave was significantly better," Cialdini says.

The reciprocation principle explains why free samples can be so effective. People who receive a free, unexpected gift are more likely to listen to a product's features, donate to a cause, or tip a waitress more money. The gifts do not have to be expensive or even material; information and favors can work.

It seems that there are three factors at work:

> What is given is seen by the recipient as significant; two candies (or sweets), although not requested, significantly increased the tip percentage.
> It was unexpected.
> It was personalized.

So, what does all of this mean to you?

The impact of this at work for leaders, managers, and team members is huge. Give first. Make it significant (which does not necessarily mean costly – simply use the "currency" of the individual). Make it personalized.

Also understand that you are subject to the same nonconscious influence from those around you.

Principle #2: Social Proof

When people are uncertain about a course of action, they tend to look to those around them to guide their decisions and actions. The brain wants predictability, and it will look for it amongst a social group. People especially want to know what everyone else is doing – especially their peers.

"Laugh tracks on comedy shows exist for this very reason," Cialdini says.

I will use four examples to illustrate this principle:

Example 1 – Reuse of Towels in a Hotel:

Cialdini and a team of colleagues ran an experiment to see which types of signs would most encourage Arizona hotel visitors to reuse towels. They tested four types of signs with the following results:

Sign	Re-use %
Cited environmental reasons to encourage visitors to reuse their towels	38%
Said the hotel would donate a portion of end-of-year laundry savings to an environmental cause	36%
Said the hotel had already given a donation and asked: "Will you please join us?"	46%
Said the majority of guests reused their towels at least once during their stay	48%

When guests found out that most people who stayed in the same hotel reused their towels, they were more likely to comply with the request.

"What's most interesting to me," Cialdini says, "is that the most effective strategy was entirely costless to the hotel. But I've never seen it used by any hotel room in any city."

Example 2 – Copying Others Who We Feel Are Like Us:

Goldstein and Cialdini (2007) published a paper showing how if we have a "merged identity" with another person or group, then we will tend to take on their attributes and behavior, i.e., we non-consciously copy them.

Example 3 – Facebook's "Like" Function:

Facebook, knowingly or not, has leveraged our tendency to like the things that others like.

Example 4 – Technology Adoption:

Geoffrey Moore, in his book *Crossing the Chasm*, demonstrates an adoption curve covering five adoption stages; in any given stage people are far more likely to listen to other people or other references that are in their same stage.

So, what does all of this mean to you?

Testimonials from satisfied customers show your target audience that people who are similar to them have enjoyed your product or service. They'll be more likely to become customers themselves.

A similar principle applies to television commercials that say, "If our lines are busy, please call again," instead of saying, "Operators are standing by." The first response implies that other people like your offer so much that the phone lines are busy, which may persuade others to act similarly, whereas the second implies that no-one is calling, and the operators are hanging around.

Principle #3: Commitment and Consistency

People do not like to back out of deals. We're more likely to do something after we've agreed to it verbally or in writing, Cialdini says. People strive for consistency in their commitments. They also prefer to follow pre-existing attitudes, values, and actions.

In 1987, social scientist Anthony Greenwald approached potential voters on election day eve to ask whether they would vote and to provide reasons why or why not. 100% said they would vote.

Condition	Voting %
Asked whether they would vote	86.7%
Not asked whether they would vote	61.5%

Those who publicly committed to voting on the previous day proved significantly more likely to actually vote. People want to be both consistent and true to their word.

Getting customers or co-workers to publicly commit to something makes them more likely to follow through with an action or a purchase.

Getting people to answer "yes" makes them more powerfully committed to an action, Cialdini says. For instance, don't tell people, "Please call if you have to cancel." Asking, "Will you please call if you have to cancel?" gets customers to say yes and measurably increases their response rates.

Research has shown that in the retail environment, purchasers are less likely to cancel their purchases if they fill out the forms themselves rather than have salesperson do so.

It also seems that the older we get, the more we value consistency. And that may make it harder for older people to make a change. Stephanie Brown et al (2007) found that "We conclude that, because of a heightened motive for emotional harmony, older individuals are especially likely to prefer consistent activities, cognitions, and people...as avoiding emotional disruption becomes a more salient motivation with increasing age."

So, what does all of this mean to you?

Ask your team members if they'll support your next initiative, and say why. If you are holding a meeting and you really require someone's presence, be sure to ask them if the meeting date and time suits them. Ask them if there's anything specific that they would like addressed at the meeting?

What about the issue of change? What if you are asking someone or a group to do something different. Introduce large changes in small increments. Once someone has committed to a small change, they are more likely to act consistently as bigger changes in the same direction are introduced.

The general use of this principle can be very powerful. Making public statements about a position, goal, or commitment can be very powerful in terms of goal accomplishment. So, using this in a team setting for monthly goal setting can help to get things moving. On the other hand, public statements can make people more rigid about their demands. If, for example, you are working on trying to gain agreement on an overall approach or working to mediate a situation, once people have made their position public, they are more likely to want to act in accordance with their public statement. Getting people's positions, thoughts, and demands in private makes it more likely that they can change their mind as the process moves along.

Principle # 4: Liking

It has long been an adage in the sales field that, all other things being equal, people will do business with people they like. Cialdini's work supports that adage. "People prefer to say 'yes' to those they know and like," Cialdini says. People are also more likely to favor those who are physically attractive, similar to themselves, or who give them compliments.

Something as "random" as having the same name as your prospects can increase your chances of making a sale.

In 2005, Randy Garner mailed out surveys to strangers with a request to return them. The request was signed by a person whose name was either similar or dissimilar to the recipient's. For example, Robert James might receive a survey request from the similarly-named Bob Ames.

Request Signed By	Response %
Similar sounding names	56%
Dissimilar sounding names	30%

It seems that this "liking" reaction is in response to very subtle similarities, the name example cited above being just one. The same birth dates seem to have a similar effect.

In our workshops, we will have people divide into pairs or threes and take a few moments to find out what they have in common. First of all, it always amazes us that people inevitably find something in common. Then they report, anecdotally, that not only do they like the person, but immediately their level of trust for that individual has gone up as well as their perception of that person's intelligence and competency. "You are just like me so you must be a great person" seems to be the underlying subtext.

Sometimes we try this exercise by asking people about which breed or breeds of dogs they own.

So, what does all of this mean to you?

Coaches, HR, and learning & development people have been suggesting to managers for many years that their teams will be more engaged, more productive, and more efficient if they like them as bosses and managers. This influence seems to confirm that advice.

Get closer to your team. Understand the people who are responsible for your success, whether they are people who work for you, your team members, your clients, or your vendors. And yes, even you, boss. The more you can find and point out genuine similarities (don't make them up), the greater the chance of them taking a liking to you.

I should, however, point out that simply finding out similarities will not overcome other fatal flaws that you might have. ☺

Principle #5: Authority

People respect authority. They want to follow the lead of real experts. Business titles, impressive clothing, and even driving an expensive, high-performing automobile are proven factors in lending credibility to any individual.

Giving the appearance of authority actually increases the likelihood that others will comply with requests – even if their authority is illegitimate.

There are two discussions that I want to present in support of the principle of authority, one of them being the now infamous Milgram experiment:

Example 1 – Milgram Experiment:

Stanley Milgram, psychologist, Yale University, conducted a 1974 experiment where ordinary people were asked to shock "victims" when they answered questions incorrectly. Those in charge were dressed in white lab coats to give the appearance of high authority. The participants were told that the shocks they gave increased fifteen volts in intensity each time the person answered incorrectly. In fact, the shocks were completely imaginary. Respondents were acting. As participants continued to shock their victims, the respondents feigned increasing discomfort until they let out agonized screams and demanded to be released. Astoundingly, about two-thirds of participants ignored these cries of pain and inflicted the full dose of 450 volts.

"According to Milgram, the real culprit in the experiments was the [participants'] inability to defy the wishes of the boss, the lab-coated researcher who urged and, if necessary, directed them to perform their duties, despite the emotional and physical mayhem they were causing."

The participants in Milgram's study were males from a range of age, occupation, and education levels. Later research concluded that the subjects' sex was irrelevant to their willingness to shock the victim.

Example 2 – Some Excerpts from the Changing Minds Website:

If a policeman came up to you in the street and told you to move out of the street as there was a parade starting, would you go? What if the policeman said you fitted the description of someone who was wanted for burglary and that you should go with them to clear this up, would you go?

In fact, most people would obey unquestioningly, which is a fact well known by confidence tricksters. We see the uniform and never dream to question the possibility that the policeman may not, in fact, be a policeman.

The double bind of authority is that not only are we compelled to obey it, but we are not even permitted to challenge it. This makes it a very powerful persuasion principle.

How do we know when someone else is in a position of authority? Other than known people like parents, managers, and policemen, here are some deliberate or accidental approaches set up to remind us of who is in charge.

> Uniforms are very overt symbols of authority. They show membership of and allegiance to specific groups. Mostly, we associate uniforms with police and military forces. We also stretch the authority acceptance to water inspectors, security guards, postmen, and more. Doctors in white coats are another example, often used by pharmaceutical and political ads.

> We assume that if someone is wealthy, then they are successful, and if they are more successful than us, then they must somehow be superior to us. We tend to ascribe extra abilities to people who have made it rich even though they may have had little to do with their own success.

> Symbols of power are used to attract people (join my gang, and I'll protect you) or bully people (join my gang, or I'll hurt you). Symbols can include weapons, wealth, and the trappings of a recognized position.

> Leaders and senior members of organizations all use symbols to remind other people of their positional power, from stripes on a sergeant's arm to the size of an executive office.

- A taller, stronger person could hurt us, and our evolutionary programming tells us to generally play it safe. We will thus tend to yield to such people even though our social rules protect us from physical harm in most situations.

- It is a fact that more top jobs in companies are taken by taller people. Taller men and taller women are seen by most of us as being more authoritative. There is also a reciprocal effect: we will perceive people in authority to be taller than they really are.

- If you act like you're in charge, many people will not challenge you. You will be protected by the double bind whereby they feel unable to challenge you just in case you are in charge.

This nonconscious compliance with authority is maybe not universal; people with high need for autonomy (e.g., teenagers, rebels, this author) tend to react against authority.

So, what does all of this mean to you?

When people are uncertain, they look outside themselves for information to guide their decisions. Given the incredible influence of authority figures, it would be wise to incorporate testimonials from legitimate, recognized authorities to help persuade prospects to respond or make purchases.

Borrow the symbols of authority that already exist. Dress to your audience and their expectations. Talk like you are in charge. Ensure that you present your credentials

Principle #6: Scarcity

In fundamental economic theory, scarcity relates to supply and demand. Basically, the less there is of something, the more valuable it is. The more rare and uncommon a thing, the more people want it. Familiar examples are frenzies over the latest holiday toy or urban campers waiting overnight to pounce on the latest iPhone.

Study after study shows that items and opportunities are seen to be more valuable as they become less available. The tendency to be more sensitive to possible losses than to possible gains is one of the best-supported findings in social science.

The power of "loss language" has been demonstrated many times. Half of a group of California home owners were told that if they fully insulated their homes, they would save a certain amount of money each day. The other half were told that if they failed to insulate, they would lose that amount each day. Significantly more people insulated their homes when exposed to the loss language.

So, what does all of this mean to you?

As in all of the above cases, there are two sides to this coin. On the one hand, you can use this scarcity principle to gain influence over others. On the other, you can be affected by it too without being consciously aware of the fact.

It has been shown that potential losses figure far more heavily in managers' decision-making than potential gains. Also remember that exclusive information is more persuasive than widely available information.

In any case, if your product or service is genuinely unique, be sure to emphasize its unique qualities to increase the perception of its scarcity.

Appendix C: Some Items in More Detail

Part 1: Some More Brain Myths

Myth	Truth
We need a full brain to function effectively.	Some people who've had one brain hemisphere surgically removed in childhood due to illness can function reasonably well in adulthood.
Modern humans have larger brains than Neanderthals.	Neanderthals' brains were probably slightly larger than ours.
Areas of activation on brain scans mean that brain regions are becoming more active.	Areas of activation on brain scans sometimes mean that some brain regions are inhibiting other regions.
"Alpha consciousness" is associated with states of relaxation.	There's no evidence that boosting the brain's alpha waves increases relaxation; moreover, some people who aren't relaxed, such as children with attention deficit/hyperactivity disorder, have high levels of alpha waves.
Blind people have especially well-developed senses of hearing and touch.	There's little evidence that the blind have superior abilities in other senses, including hearing, touch, or smell.
Blind people can detect obstacles at a distance by sensing heat and pressure on their foreheads.	There's no evidence for this claim.
A coma is a state of deep sleep.	People in comas are not asleep.
We can "awaken" people from comas by playing their favorite songs.	There's no scientific evidence that people can be brought out of comas by presenting them with their favorite songs or other familiar stimuli.
Biofeedback is a uniquely effective means of reducing tension.	Most studies indicate that biofeedback is no more effective than relaxation for reducing anxiety.
Humans have an invisible "body energy" that can cause psychological problems when blocked.	There's no scientific evidence for invisible energy fields in or around the human body.
Alcohol kills brain cells.	Alcohol appears not to kill brain cells themselves, although it can damage neuronal "dendrites," which are portals that bring messages into neurons.
Alcohol's primary effect is stimulating the brain.	Alcohol is primarily a depressant and is typically a stimulant only at low doses.
Alcohol enhances sexual arousal.	Alcohol tends to inhibit sexual arousal and performance, especially at high doses.

Alcohol promotes sleep.	Although alcohol typically results in falling asleep more quickly, it usually suppresses deep sleep, often producing awakenings later in the night.
Alcohol warms the body.	Although drinking alcohol in cold temperatures can make us feel warmer, it actually results in a loss of body heat and therefore cools the body.
It's easier to get drunk at high altitudes, such as while flying in an airplane.	Studies show that higher altitudes don't result in greater intoxication.
Impaired judgment after drinking occurs only after obvious signs of intoxication.	Impaired judgment can occur well before drunkenness is apparent.
Drinking coffee is a good way to sober up after heavy drinking.	Drinking coffee won't help with a hangover; it just turns us into a "wide awake drunk."
A cold shower or exercise is a good way to sober up after heavy drinking.	Same as the above explanation – they turn us into a "wide awake drunk."
Switching among different types of alcohol is more likely to lead to drunkenness than sticking to one type of alcohol.	The total amount – not the type – of alcohol predicts the risk of intoxication.
One can't become an alcoholic by drinking beer only.	Not true.
There's good evidence that people who smoke marijuana for many years end up apathetic.	The evidence for "amotivational syndrome" is mixed, largely in part because heavy marijuana smokers frequently use other drugs.
Most people with a brain injury look and act disabled.	Most people with a brain injury appear normal and act normally aside from subtle deficits on neuropsychological tests.
Following a head injury, the best prescription is rest.	Following a head injury, the best prescription is a gradual return to activity.
A head injury can't produce brain damage unless the person is knocked unconscious.	Brain damage that's detectable on neurological and neuropsychological tests can occur even with no loss of consciousness.
Prefrontal lobotomies (more popularly called "lobotomies") turn people into human "vegetables."	Most people who've received lobotomies are far from "vegetables," although they are typically apathetic.
Most colorblind people see the world in black and white.	Almost all colorblind people can see at least some colors. "Monochromats" who see the world in black and white, comprise only about 0.005% of the population.
Dogs see the world in black and white.	Dogs have red-green color blindness but can perceive a number of colors, including blue and yellow.

Consuming ice cream or other cold substances too quickly causes pain in our brains.	"Brain freeze" is caused by a constriction of blood vessels in the roof of the mouth, followed by an expansion of these vessels, triggering pain.
Magnets, like those embedded in shoe insoles, can reduce pain.	Controlled studies reveal that such magnets are useless for pain reduction.

Part 2: Rosenberg Self-Esteem Scale (RSE)

Author: Morris Rosenberg

The purpose of the 10 item RSE scale is to measure self-esteem. Originally, the scale was designed to measure the self-esteem of high school students. However, since its development, the scale has been used with a variety of groups, including adults, with norms available for many of those groups.

Please record the appropriate answer for each item, depending on whether you strongly agree, agree, disagree, or strongly disagree with it.

1 = Strongly agree
2 = Agree
3 = Disagree
4 = Strongly disagree

_____ 1. On the whole, I am satisfied with myself.

_____ 2. At times, I think I am no good at all.

_____ 3. I feel that I have a number of good qualities.

_____ 4. I am able to do things as well as most other people.

_____ 5. I feel I do not have much to be proud of.

_____ 6. I certainly feel useless at times.

_____ 7. I feel that I'm a person of worth.

_____ 8. I wish I could have more respect for myself.

_____ 9. All in all, I am inclined to think that I am a failure.

_____ 10. I take a positive attitude toward myself.

Calculating Scores:

#1, 2, 4, 6, and 7:

Strongly agree	= 3
Agree	= 2
Disagree	= 1
Strongly disagree	= 0

#3, 5, 8, 9, and 10:

Strongly agree	= 0
Agree	= 1
Disagree	= 2
Strongly disagree	= 3

Scale Range: 0 to 30

Normal Range of Scores: 15 to 25
Low Self-esteem: 0 to 15

Part 3: Jung's Archetypes

1. **The Innocent** – Also known as: Utopian, traditionalist, naive, mystic, saint, romantic, dreamer.
Motto: Free to be you and me.
Core desire: To get to paradise
Goal: To be happy
Greatest fear: To be punished for doing something bad or wrong
Strategy: To do things right
Weakness: Boring for all their naive innocence
Talent: Faith and optimism

2. **The Orphan/Regular Guy or Gal** – Also known as: the good old boy, everyman, the person next door, the realist, the working stiff, the solid citizen, the good neighbor, the silent majority.
Motto: All men and women are created equal.
Core desire: Connecting with others
Goal: To belong
Greatest fear: To be left out or to stand out from the crowd
Strategy: Develop ordinary solid virtues, be down to earth, the common touch
Weakness: Losing one's own self in an effort to blend in or for the sake of superficial relationships
Talent: Realism, empathy, lack of pretense

3. **The Hero** – Also known as: the warrior, crusader, rescuer, superhero, the soldier, dragon slayer, the winner, and the team player.
Motto: Where there's a will, there's a way.
Core desire: To prove one's worth through courageous acts
Goal: Expert mastery in a way that improves the world
Greatest fear: Weakness, vulnerability, being a "chicken"
Strategy: To be as strong and competent as possible
Weakness: Arrogance, always needing another battle to fight
Talent: Competence and courage

4. **The Caregiver** – Also known as: the saint, altruist, parent, helper, supporter.
Motto: Love your neighbor as yourself.
Core desire: To protect and care for others
Goal: To help others
Greatest fear: Selfishness and ingratitude
Strategy: Doing things for others
Weakness: Martyrdom and being exploited
Talent: Compassion, generosity

5. **The Explorer** – Also known as: the seeker, iconoclast, wanderer, individualist, pilgrim.
Motto: Don't fence me in.
Core desire: The freedom to find out who you are through exploring the world
Goal: To experience a better, more authentic, more fulfilling life
Biggest fear: Getting trapped, conformity, and inner emptiness
Strategy: Journey, seeking out and experiencing new things, escape from boredom
Weakness: Aimless wandering, becoming a misfit
Talent: Autonomy, ambition, being true to one's soul

6. **The Outlaw** – Also known as: the rebel, revolutionary, wild man, the misfit, or iconoclast.

Motto:	Rules are made to be broken.
Core desire:	Revenge or revolution
Goal:	To overturn what isn't working
Greatest fear:	To be powerless or ineffectual
Strategy:	Disrupt, destroy, or shock
Weakness:	Crossing over to the dark side, crime
Talent:	Outrageousness, radical freedom

7. **The Lover** – Also known as: the partner, friend, intimate, enthusiast, sensualist, spouse, team-builder.

Motto:	You're the only one.
Core desire:	Intimacy and experience
Goal:	Being in a relationship with the people, work, and surroundings they love
Greatest fear:	Being alone, a wallflower, unwanted, unloved
Strategy:	To become more and more physically and emotionally attractive
Weakness:	Outward-directed desire to please others at a risk of losing own identity
Talent:	Passion, gratitude, appreciation, and commitment

8. **The Creator** – Also known as: the artist, inventor, innovator, musician, writer, or dreamer.

Motto:	If you can imagine it, it can be done.
Core desire:	To create things of enduring value
Goal:	To realize a vision
Greatest fear:	Mediocre vision or execution
Strategy:	Develop artistic control and skill
Task:	To create culture, express own vision
Weakness:	Perfectionism, bad solutions
Talent:	Creativity and imagination

9. **The Jester** – Also known as: the fool, trickster, joker, practical joker, or comedian.

Motto:	You only live once.
Core desire:	To live in the moment with full enjoyment
Goal:	To have a great time and lighten up the world
Greatest fear:	Being bored or boring others
Strategy:	Play, make jokes, be funny
Weakness:	Frivolity, wasting time
Talent:	Joy

10. **The Sage** – Also known as: the expert, scholar, detective, advisor, thinker, philosopher, academic, researcher, thinker, planner, professional, mentor, teacher, contemplative.

Motto:	The truth will set you free.
Core desire:	To find the truth
Goal:	To use intelligence and analysis to understand the world
Biggest fear:	Being duped, being misled, or ignorance
Strategy:	Seeking out information and knowledge; self-reflection and understanding thought
Weakness:	Can study details forever and never act
Talent:	Wisdom, intelligence

11. **The Magician** – Also known as: the visionary, catalyst, inventor, charismatic leader, shaman, healer, medicine man.

Motto:	I make things happen.
Core desire:	Understanding the fundamental laws of the universe
Goal:	To make dreams come true
Greatest fear:	Unintended negative consequences
Strategy:	Develop a vision and live by it
Weakness:	Becoming manipulative
Talent:	Finding win-win solutions

12. **The Ruler** – Also known as: the boss, leader, aristocrat, king, queen, politician, role model, manager, or administrator.

Motto:	Power isn't everything, it's the only thing.
Core desire:	Control
Goal:	Create a prosperous, successful family or community
Strategy:	Exercise power
Greatest fear:	Chaos, being overthrown
Weakness:	Being authoritarian, unable to delegate
Talent:	Responsibility, leadership

Part 4: Belbin Team Roles

The nine behavioral clusters are:

Role	Description	Strengths and Weaknesses	Don't be surprised to find that...
Resource Investigator	Uses his/her inquisitive nature to find ideas to bring back to the team.	Outgoing, enthusiastic. Explores opportunities and develops contacts. Might be over-optimistic and can lose interest once the initial enthusiasm has passed.	He/she might forget to follow up on a lead.
Team-worker	Helps the team to gel, using his/her versatility to identify the work required and complete it on behalf of the team.	Cooperative, perceptive, and diplomatic. Listens and averts friction. Can be indecisive in crunch situations and tends to avoid confrontation.	He/she might be hesitant to make unpopular decisions.
Coordinator	Needed to focus on the team's objectives, draw out team members, and delegate work appropriately.	Mature, confident, identifies talent. Clarifies goals. Can be seen as manipulative and might offload his/her own share of the work.	He/she might over-delegate, leaving themselves little work to do.
Plant	Tends to be highly creative and is good at solving problems in unconventional ways.	Creative, imaginative, free-thinking, generates ideas, and solves difficult problems. Might ignore incidentals and may be too preoccupied to communicate effectively.	He/she could be absent-minded or forgetful.
Monitor Evaluator	Provides a logical eye, making impartial judgements where required, and weighs up the team's options in a dispassionate way.	Sober, strategic, and discerning. Sees all options and judges accurately. Sometimes lacks the drive and ability to inspire others and can be overly critical.	He/she could be slow to come to decisions.
Specialist	Brings in-depth knowledge of a key area to the team.	Single-minded, self-starting, and dedicated. He/she provides specialist knowledge and skills. Tends to contribute on a narrow front and can dwell on the technicalities.	He/she overloads you with information.
Shaper	Provides the necessary drive to ensure that the team keeps moving and	Challenging, dynamic, thrives on pressure. Has the drive and courage to overcome obstacles.	He/she could risk becoming aggressive and bad-humored in

	does not lose focus or momentum.	Can be prone to provocation and may sometimes offend people's feelings.	his/her attempts to get things done.
Implementer	Needed to plan a workable strategy and carry it out as efficiently as possible.	Practical, reliable, efficient. Turns ideas into actions and organizes work that needs to be done. Can be a bit inflexible and slow to respond to new possibilities.	He/she might be slow to relinquish his/her plans in favor of positive changes.
Completer-Finisher	Most effectively used at the end of tasks to polish and scrutinize the work for errors, subjecting it to the highest standards of quality control.	Painstaking, conscientious, anxious. Searches out errors. Polishes and perfects. Can be inclined to worry unduly and can be reluctant to delegate.	He/she could be accused of taking their perfectionism to extremes.

Index

Go For It, 256-257
- *see Hudson Life Cycle*
Gratification
- Instant gratification, 69, **127**
- Sensual gratification, 69, **127**
Grassi 8 Factor Model, 210-211
Growing older, 186-188
Growth mindset, 118, **172**, 241

H
Habits, 4, 36, 37, 40, 46, 50, 51-53, 62, 88, 132, 142, 148, 159, 215, 227, **229-231**, 235, 248, 273, 276
Harmony, 69, **110**, 205, 206, 263
Healthiness
- Physical health, 82-83
- Mental health, 82-83
- Emotional health, 82-84
- Spiritual health, 82-84

I
IQ, **147-148**, 160, 267
Influences, 54, 86, 109, 119, 148, 153, 154, **247-251**
Imposter syndrome, 96-97
Information handling, 29
In-group, **86-88**, 91, 108, 109, 169, 228
- In-group bias, 228
Inquiry
- In relation to the Advocacy/Inquiry Matrix, 211-212
- In relation to the TAPS Model, 228
Intelligence, 28, 89, **149**, 178, 183, 223, 224, **247**, 267-268
Intelligences, 110, **267-268**
Interoception, 147
Introvert, 51, 59, 87, **215**
Irrational/irrationality, 50, **54-57**, 90, 102, 106, 148, 227, 229, 242, 275

J
Jung's archetypes, 268-272

L
Layers of the brain, **66**, 141
- *see reptilian brain*
- *see mammalian brain*
- *see rational brain*
Leader, 3, **5-7**, 8, 9, 10, 11, 19, 20, 88, 90, 94, 99, 105, **220-224**, 267
- Extraordinary leader, 221-223
Leadership circle, 223-224
Leadership style, 220-224
Left brain, **26**, 141-142
Life cycles, **232-234**, 255-258
Hudson Life Cycle, **255-258**, 272
Liking (social media),86, 184, 245, **246**
Limbic system, **39-40**, 44, 46, 62, 66, 98, 269
- *see mammalian brain*
Limitations of brain research, 12-13
Love, 69, 81, 102, 124, 129, 143, **164-167**, 170-171, 174, 242, 263
- Love in men, 143
- Love in women, 143

M
Male brain, 143-144
Mammalian brain, 39-40
- *see limbic system*
Meditation, 89, 154-155, 169, **174-177**, 187, 188, 263, 276
Mediterranean diet (and the brain), 159
Memory, 15, 16, 42, 60, 66, 114, 141, 143, **146**, 150, 158, 160, 171, 172, 175, 178, 182, 187
Meninges, 144
- *see pain*
Mental health, 16, 39, **82-84**, 148, 153, 168-169, 173
Mind, 7, 8, **12**, 52, 53, 72, 80, 89, 110, 125, 144, 146, 165, 168, 169, 175, 185, 228, 237, 240, 241, 264, 273, 275,
Mindfulness, 89, **174-177**, 276, 277
Mindset, 71, 118, 142, 170, **171-172**, 241
- *see fixed mindset*
- *see growth mindset*
Modes, 16, 33, **36-38**, 275
- *see nonconscious mode*

see conscious mode
Morality, 165, **188-190**, 263
    see ethics
Multiplicity, 269
Multi-tasking, 16, **144-145**
(The) Mule, 270
    see subpersonalities
Music (and the brain), 7, 1222, 161, 164, **177-180**, 241, 267, 276
Myths about the brain, 13, 108, **139-150,** 275

N
Negativity, 64, 131, 156, **171**, 228
Negativity bias, 64, 131, **228**
Neocortex, **39-40**, 44, 66
    see rational brain
Neural networks, **27-28**, 29, 35, 37, 40, 43, 106, 140, 141, 150, 161, 165, 174, 184
-     Visual networks, 29
    see synapse
    see neurotransmitters
Neurodiversity bias, **51**, 227
Neuron, 11, **26-27**, 27-28, 29, 60, 93, 100, 140, 142, 144, 159, 176, 227
-     Structure of a neuron, 26-27
Neuroplasticity, **29**, 142
Neuroscience, 3, 5, 6, 7, **10-12**, 19, 27, 28, 72, 76, 113, 139, 142, 148, 150, 159, 170, 180
Neurotheology, 169-170
Neuroticism, 188, **215**
Neurotransmitters, **27**, 28, 166, 167
Nonconscious mode, 33, **36-38**
Normalization, 132

O
Openness, 75, 119, **214-215**

P
Pain, **33**, 40, 43, 75, 89, 96, 123, 143, 144, 147, 175, 176, 181, 216, 228, 248, 266, 275
-     Physical pain, 33, 43, 75, **144**, 275
-     Social pain, 33, 43, **89**

Participation, 33, 49, 66, 68, 69, 70, 71, 78, 81, **85-97**, 109, 117, 205, 218, 275
Passion/Passionate, 69, 118, **123-124**, 164, 179, 257, 259-261, 262
Passive Social Media Use, 183
Past, 42, 71, 72, 79, 211, 216, 229, 235, 247, 248, **253-258**, 276
Patterns, 37, 51, 63, 97, 116, 132, 144, 145, 180, 201, **232-234**, 249, 250, 255, 256, 276
Perfectionism, 68, 97, **103-104**, 221
Personal Threat Context, **130-132**, 207
Personal Threat Profile, 62, 72, 73, 81, 130, 132, 163, **205-206**, 207, 217, 231, 235, 236, 258, 266, 272, 276
Physical health, **82-83**, 166
Pleasure, 33, 40, 44, 49, 66, 69, 95, 96, 117, 123, **126-129**, 147, 167, 180, 216, 218, 228, 263, 264, 275
Positive stress response, 173
Positivity, **131**, 153, **170-172**, 182
Prediction, 16, 33, 39, 44, 49, 61, 66, 68-69, 70, 78, 93, 96, **98-116**, 117, 180, 205, 218, 275
Prefrontal cortex, 25, **44-46**, 60, 62, 74, 77, 80, 85, 98, 109, 110, 140, 145, 165, 169, 176, 177, 231, 269, 272
Present, 175, 216, **266-273**
Processes of the brain, 2, 8, 33, **41-47**, 107, 142, 158, 16, 175, 177, 180, 186, 187, 189, 275
-     Diagram of the processes of the brain, 42, 45
(The) Professional, 270
    see subpersonalities
Proprioception, 147
Protection, 33, 49, 66, 68, 69, 70, 71, **74-84**, 117, 205, 275
Psychological safety, **75**, 125, 218
(One) Purpose, 33, 40
    see Five Brain Principles

R
Recent events, 258
Reciprocation, **57**, 245
Reptilian brain, **39-40**, 46, 66
Rest, **16**, 25, 38, 83, **140-141**, 157

69350084R00202

Made in the USA
Columbia, SC
15 August 2019